COSMOPOLITAN
A-Z of Sex

COSMOPOLITAN
A-Z of Sex

The Ultimate Reference Book

EMILY HAYES

ROBSON BOOKS

First published in Great Britain in 2004 by Robson Books, The Chrysalis Building, Bramley Road, London, W10 6SP

An imprint of **Chrysalis** Books Group plc

British Library Cataloguing in Publication Data
A catalogue record for this title is available from the British Library.

ISBN 1 86105 663 X

Typeset by SX Composing DTP, Rayleigh, Essex
Printed and bound by Clays Ltd, Bungay, Suffolk NR35 1ED

Introduction

At *Cosmopolitan* we've always been dedicated to making your sex life the best it can possibly be, and, for the first time in our 30-year history, we've packed all that erotic info and advice – plus much, much more – into just one book. Over the next 346 pages, you'll find enough tips, tricks and tantalising techniques to make you and your partner sigh, moan and gasp with pleasure.

From awesome arousal techniques to Zen-sational zip tricks, this sexy guide is guaranteed to expand your horizontal horizons. Packed with more than a thousand new and exciting sex techniques, all arranged in handy alphabetical order, this is the definitive raunchy reference book.

But wait, we hear you pant: so much info, so little time. Want to know the best way to use this book? Whether you're sexily single or cosily coupled up, you have two simple choices. First you could look up the specific area of your sex life that needs a little lust injection: the entries should be pretty logical. If you don't know where to start, try going back to basics: even the how-they-work sections such as **penis**, **vagina**, **arousal** and **masturbation** are packed with naughty tips and tricks ranging from the basic to the bed-shaking. Most entries are cross-referenced, too, so, once you get started, this book will take you and your sex life in all sorts of new and exciting directions.

If you're feeling adventurous, the second approach is just to open this book at random and see what catches your eye. If you dare, close your eyes and point to the page, then act out whatever sex tip your finger lands next to (there should be something exciting to do pretty much on every page). Alternatively, try reading out that passage to your lover: just hearing those sexy suggestions can be arousing in itself and – bonus – you'll both be learning something at the same time.

And, if you fancy reading this book from cover to cover, do so: we're sure you'll find something new to try. Great sex is about fun and confidence both in and out of the bedroom (see **outdoor sex** if you're bored with your boudoir). We're not promising to magic a liberal sprinkling of sexual confidence out of thin air but, with a few flirty facts, saucy sex secrets and those oh-so-intimate details of other people's sex lives, you'll be well on your way to sex goddess (or god) status. And, although this book is written with a female reader in mind (it is from *Cosmo* after all), there's tons of info and tips for him too (just leave it hanging around and we're sure he'll pick it up).

From sex therapists and agony aunts to lap dancers and call girls, we've consulted sex experts the world over (not to mention those real-life couples – you know who you are!). They've been happy to share their intimate secrets just so *you* get to have better sex. How generous!

Sex is fun, free and can be fabulous, and the more you know about it, the better it'll become. Keep this book by your bed and let it become your bedroom bible. Sex is never perfect but, with knowledge at your fingertips, it can be pretty damn hot. Read on and enjoy.

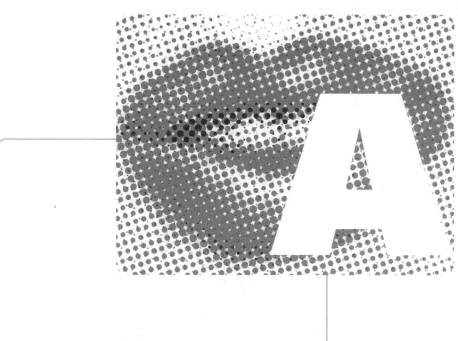

ABANDON
See also: body confidence, quickies

Dictionary definition: Desert, give up altogether, freedom from inhibitions.

Cosmo definition: To go utterly wild in the bedroom, fling your inhibitions out of the window (along with your clothes, prejudices, restrictions and all forms of conventional, uptight behaviour) and live in the moment, focusing purely on your pleasure and his.

Sex goddess status is all about wild abandon, so what are you waiting for?

Wild Abandon: How To Get It

1) Stop thinking about how you look and start focusing on how you *feel*. The more you focus on outward sensations, the less inhibited you'll become.

2) Think about each of your senses in turn. Start with sight: drink in the bits of your man's body you love with your eyes; watch where he places his hands on your body. Next, focus on touch – the feel of his fingertips, the sensation of his mouth on yours. Listen to his breathing and yours (it gets faster and

stronger near orgasm). Smell his body and hair. Each sense will intensify the more you focus on it.

3) A couple of glasses of alcohol can help you relax but a whole bottle (or two) will dull your senses and make it harder for you (and him) to climax. We're talking *wild* abandon here not abandon-all-sense-of-shame-after-three-too-many.

4) Focus on different parts of your body in turn: your nipples, the muscles in your calves and thighs if you're on top, the arching of your back, the feeling of him inside you. It makes you aware of the whole of your body, not just your obvious erogenous zones.

5) Be spontaneous. Don't keep sex just for Saturday nights in the bedroom. Ambush your man for a quickie as soon as he walks through the door, get naughty in the car on the way to your mother-in-law's or play footsie under the table at your best friend's wedding. Anything goes so long as you keep surprising each other.

'For me going wild in the bedroom is an emotional thing: you don't have to scream, you just have to be so involved that you forget the outside world.'
Rachel, 27, call centre manager

ABSTINENCE

Reasons to Abstain from Sex

1) The longer you hold out, the sexier it'll be when you do get together again.

2) Introducing a 'no-penetration' rule for a week or a month makes you more creative with your foreplay techniques.

3) For men, the longer he goes between ejaculations, the bigger the bang will be.

4) For women, the longer you delay your climax during each sex session, the bigger the bang will be.

Reasons Not to Abstain from Sex

1) The more sex you're getting, the more you'll want, so actually having regular sex (even if it's in the form of masturbation) naturally ups your libido levels.

2) Over time, if you really have no sexual contact, your sexual

responses learn to shut down. Like an athlete, you need to keep your sex muscles (both the physical and the mental ones) constantly in training.

3) Sex is cheaper than a massage and relieves more stress.

4) It'll be painful to continue reading this book if you intend to do nothing with all this information. Go and buy a nice cosy Aga saga instead.

Cosmo's Chastity Commandments

If you're reading this book, chances are you're not really the abstaining type but you can have fun playing with the idea of a self-imposed sex 'ban'. Here's how:

Commandment 1: Thou shalt take a vow of chastity

Pretend you're a vestal virgin who has taken a lifelong vow of chastity. It's your partner's job to awaken your sexuality and teach you the pleasures of the flesh.

Commandment 2: Thou shalt confess thy sins

Pretend to confess your sex sins to your partner. Start each statement with 'Forgive me for I have sinned. Today I thought about . . .' Then describe any sexy thoughts you've had. Use this technique to reveal your fantasies. Take turns being the confessor so you get to hear his sexy secrets, too.

Commandment 3: Thou shalt not touch one another

You can touch yourself and he can touch himself but you're not allowed to touch each other. Try commanding your partner where and how to touch himself. It creates sizzling tension.

ADRENALINE
See also: arousal, hormones

Adrenaline is released when you're frightened, excited or under stress – it's also released when you're highly aroused. It primes your body for fight-or-flight by heightening your awareness of your environment, increasing your heart rate and making your nerve endings tingle. Upping your adrenaline levels by putting yourself in a stressful or slightly scary situation can be just the libido lifter you need.

SEX FACT: *Couples who watch a horror movie are more likely to spend the night together than couples who watch any other type of film. Get* **The Ring** *on video now.*

Up your adrenaline levels by . . .

- Going to a theme park on your first date – the buzz you get from the scary rides will make you feel sexier.
- Having sex in a semi-public place – the fear of getting caught causes adrenaline to course round your veins.
- If you trust your partner, getting him to tie you up or blindfold you. The 'fear' of what he'll do next is all part of the fun.
- Taking up a challenging new activity together that makes you face your fears, such as rock climbing or abseiling. You'll be so pumped up by the sense of achievement that your body will be crying out for some more intimate physical attention.

SEX FACT: *People who go through traumatic events such as getting stuck in a lift together often have sexual feelings towards each other because of the raised adrenaline levels in their system due to the trauma.*

AFTERPLAY
See also: zzzzzz

Make the most of that post-sex moment with these tips:

'I love the way our bodies are so hot and her face looks all flushed after sex. I like to put my hand on her chest and feel her pulse racing – it reminds me of how physical we've just been.'
Jeremy, 33, personal trainer

Get Body to Body
The more body contact you get after sex the better. Being face to face with your legs entwined can be incredibly intimate, or try the spoons position (on your sides with him snuggled behind you). Use the palm of your hand to stroke each other: post-orgasm, your skin should feel extra-sensitive.

Say 'Thank You'

While you're this close, make a point of complimenting each other on the part of your sex session you enjoyed the most. Forget analytical detail, just say something simple, like 'That thing you do with your tongue against my thighs is amazing.' A compliment will boost both your rosy glows and you'll be able to store the I-loved-that information for next time.

Cosmo tip:
Never use the afterglow to analyse your relationship, criticise his (or your) sexual performance, confess a secret or ask an important question. Your judgement won't be clear.

Get Physical

Start a pillow fight or tickle him into submission. Nonsexual physical activity in the bedroom can be extremely arousing, so by the time you've finished it may be time for Round Two.

SEX FACT *Female sexual responses take longer to calm down if you haven't had an orgasm. Try getting yours in first or ask him for manual or oral sex after penetration if you want to get to sleep quickly.*

AIDS
See under: sexually transmitted infections

Acquired immune deficiency syndrome, caused by the human immunodeficiency virus (HIV).

ALCOHOL
See also: drugs

A few glasses can loosen your inhibitions in the bedroom and make you a little more adventurous. Great. But be warned: too much alcohol can have an adverse effect on your sex life.

'We tend to be more experimental when we're both drunk – we've done it in the garden and in front of the window with all the lights on after big nights out, which is fun, but I do find it harder to climax after drinking.'
Kerry, 25, hairdresser

Too much alcohol can:

- Dull your sexual responses, making it harder for you to climax.
- Make you feel bloated and sleepy.
- Cause him to have the notorious 'brewer's droop' i.e. not be able to maintain an erection.
- Dehydrate you all over, including your vaginal secretions, which can make sex painful.
- Make you take unnecessary risks or go further than you'd like to go.
- Impair your judgement over things like using a condom.

ANAL SEX
See also: bottom, G-spot – male, spanking

The Anatomical Stuff
Anal stimulation is a turn-on for him because . . .
- his prostate gland (the male G-spot) can be felt about 4 cm (1½ inches) up the back passage towards the front wall. This can feel extremely pleasurable (to some men) when stimulated with a finger, penis or sex toy.

SEX FACT: *If a man enjoys anal stimulation it does not mean that he's gay: having sensitive nerve endings tickled is not the same thing as fancying other men.*

Anal sex is a turn-on for you because . . .
- the vagina and rectum are in very close contact, so penetration via the back door can indirectly stimulate the sensitive vaginal nerve endings.

'For me, anal sex is way better than vaginal sex, it just turns me on more. I've had to ditch some boyfriends who weren't into it because I find it difficult to climax any other way now.'
Clara, 32, conference organiser

Anal sex is a turn-on for both of you because . . .
- the anal area and first third of the back passage is packed with highly sensitive nerve endings.
- your anal sphincter muscles contract during orgasm, anyway, so

direct stimulation here can feel good.

- it's often perceived as extra-naughty, forbidden or dirty (which can also be a major turn-off).

'I tried it once but it was so painful we had to stop. No way will I be doing that again.'
Lisa, 22, cabin crew

Some people love it, some hate it, some couples are just curious and do it once, others go for it on a regular basis. Here's all the anal info you need:

Rules of engagement

1. Talk things through before you try any form of anal stimulation (even if you've done it before with a previous partner). Anal sex takes trust and communication and should not be entered into lightly.

2. Take things s-l-o-w-l-y. Anal sex can be painful for women (and men) if your partner just shoves in his thing in one thrust.

3. Use lots of lube. Unlike the vagina, the anus has no natural lubricant, so make sure he's slathered in a sexy lubricant, and top it up frequently.

4. Always use a condom. Delicate anal tissue can tear easily, making you more vulnerable to sexually transmitted infections. Avoid condoms that contain the spermicide nonoxynol-9 (N-9), now thought to increase the risk of HIV transmission via anal and vaginal intercourse.

5. Never put anything (toy, finger, penis) that's been in the anus back into the vagina without washing it first. It can cause infections.

SAFETY INFO: Never try any sex act for the first time if you're drunk or on drugs: you need to have as much control as you can over your body if you want to try something new.

Anal Sex: Your Beginner's Go-for-it Guide

Step 1: Start by getting each other highly aroused. Like regular penetrative sex, lots of foreplay makes the whole experience more pleasurable.

Step 2: Get him to play around your anal area with his fingers to see how you like the sensations, gently and slowly inserting a finger. Get used to how this feels. He can try gently pushing it in and out or moving it in small circular motions. (Chances are, if you're considering anal intercourse, you already find anal stimulation pretty arousing. If you don't, forget going any further right now!)

Step 3: Whatever position you choose, make sure you take things literally one centimetre at a time. Popular positions are entry with you on your hands and knees or with him sitting while you lower yourself on to him. Any position used for vaginal intercourse can be adapted for anal.

Step 4: With a highly lubricated penis, get him to push himself in one centimetre, then stop while you get used to the feeling. Next, try another centimetre, and so on. Talk about how you're feeling. Pausing should relax you and help you feel in control. Don't hold your breath, as this causes your sphincter muscles to tighten.

SAFETY INFO: If anything hurts, stop! Never force yourself to do anything that causes you pain, shame or embarrassment.

Step 5: Once he's inside you, stay still until you feel totally comfortable (this can take 30 seconds or more). Next, move your hips back and forth slowly on to him while you get used to the sensation. Once you're used to how it feels, he can thrust into you as well.

Step 6: Experiment with different positions and sensations. The partner being penetrated should always have control over the speed and depth of thrusting.

Step 7: Once you've both finished, make sure he pulls out just as slowly as he went in. Gently does it all the way . . .

SEX FACT: *The anus has two sphincter muscles, one on the outside that you can voluntarily control (hence being able to control your bowel movements) and one on the inside that contracts involuntarily when anything is near it. This is why you need to be totally relaxed (and learn to relax this second muscle) in order to have comfortable anal sex.*

More Anal Play: For Girls (and Boys) who Don't Necessarily Want to Go All the Way

Don't fancy the whole anal-intercourse bit? There's plenty of fun to be had (for you and him) without going all the way.

Finger fun

Practise on yourself first to get used to the sensations. Then either direct your partner to what you like or try it on him. Start with a highly lubricated finger and draw small circles around the anal area. Next, gently try inserting a finger. Once the finger's in, relax for a few seconds: it may feel strange at first as you feel the anal sphincters contracting. Deep breathing will help you relax. Next, experiment with different movements – try circles and gently thrusting in and out. Point your finger towards the front of the body (rather than towards the tailbone) to stimulate the G-spot in women and the prostate gland (the male G-spot) in men. Experimenting with anal play during oral sex and vaginal intercourse can be fun for both of you.

'I love it when my girlfriend sticks her finger up my bottom when we make love: it makes my climax so much more intense!'
Ray, 34, distribution manager

Kiss my butt

Kissing, licking, sucking and tonguing (known as rimming) the anal area can be arousing. Some people concentrate on stimulating the nerves around the anal opening; others insert a firm tongue inside. Do whatever feels good.

SAFETY INFO: Any mouth-to-anal contact can cause the transmission of hepatitis, so either both have a sexual health check or use a dental dam (a square of latex) or a cut-up condom over the area for protection.

Toy joy

Dildos and vibrators can be used to stimulate the anal area (but remember to use a condom or wash them thoroughly before using them in or around the vagina). Try pressing a vibrator against your perineum or his (the sensitive patch of skin between the vagina/penis and the anus). Edge it closer and closer to the anus, concentrating on the sensitive tissue in this area. The same rules apply for anal penetration with a toy as they do with his penis: take things slowly, stop if it hurts and use lots of lube.

⚠ *SAFETY INFO: Always use toys designed for anal play that have a flared base. Involuntary movements of the anal sphincter can cause non-flared toys to be sucked up inside you, which may need to be removed surgically.*

More toy joy

- Butt plugs are short solid dildos designed specifically for anal play. They come in all shapes and sizes. Some vibrate, others don't (and they're safe because they have a flared base).
- Anal beads are a solid string of beads that are inserted into the anus and pulled out slowly at the point of orgasm, heightening arousal.
- Dildos with suckers at the base can be stuck to a table or wall for you to lean back onto.

Sex-toy websites have loads of info about how to choose the right anal toys for you, so read as much as you can before you decide what you'd like.

SEX FACT: *According to the National Survey of Attitudes and Lifestyle 11.3 per cent of women who replied had had anal sex in the year 2000 compared with 6.5 per cent in 1990.*

APHRODISIACS
See also: food, yohimbe

Dictionary definition: Any substance that arouses sexual desire.
***Cosmo* definition:** Any food, drink, lotion or potion that makes you want to ravish each other as passionately as possible.

Food that makes you feel and act sexy has been around for centuries. Some substances have been scientifically proven to have an effect on your genitals, while others are simply made sexy by the way you eat them. Anything that arouses your desire or his can be considered an aphrodisiac: think Ben & Jerry's slowly licked off a long spoon or a martini olive popped into a heavily lipsticked mouth and pulled out again before being crunched between perfect teeth. Have fun discovering your own sexy treats.

SEX FACT: *One of the world's earliest aphrodisiacs involved boiling goat's testicles in milk: testicles contain the sex hormone testosterone, now used as a drug treatment to increase libido levels in both men and women.*

If you want to stick to the classics, here's a list of the most common arousal enhancing substances:

Asparagus

Fresh green spears smothered in butter and then sucked, licked and eaten. Do you really need any more explanation than that? (The downside is that they do make your pee, sperm and bits smell odd – you have been warned!)

Apples, pears and cherries

The original forbidden fruit contains all the sexy connotations that surround the Garden of Eden. Fruit also contains vitamins A and B, which are needed in the production of sex hormones.

'I don't eat red meat very often but sometimes I have a massive craving for a big juicy rare steak. I always feel really sexy afterwards and feel like I could make love for hours: weird!'
Julian, 29, bathroom fitter

Bananas

High in potassium and vitamin B, which increase sex drive, phallic in shape and full of energy-boosting natural sugars, bananas are the perfect pre-sex snack. Try eating one while maintaining eye contact with your lover without making it sexual. Pretty tricky.

Chocolate

Contains caffeine and other stimulants that make you feel alert and more 'switched on' plus feel-good chemicals similar to those released by the brain after sex, exercise or extreme pleasure. Chocolate also seductively melts at body temperature. Yummy!

Oats

Thought to raise testosterone levels, hence the phrase 'sowing his wild oats'. (Porridge for breakfast also gives you slow-burn carbohydrates that'll keep you going for longer no matter what you're up to.)

Oysters

Packed with zinc (a libido-lifting and healthy-sperm-generating mineral) oyster shells are said to represent the female vulva and eating them is supposed to resemble 'eating' a woman.

Supplements, Lotions and Potions

An array of spices, herbal supplements, homeopathic prescriptions and alternative remedies are marketed as aphrodisiacs. Common examples include ginkgo biloba, ginseng, liquorice, fenugreek and any supplements high in vitamins A, E and B. Although many of these products claim to work (and have many adoring fans), there's little concrete scientific evidence to support their effectiveness other than simply enhancing good health in general. Always check with your doctor before taking any supplements, as they may interfere with the effectiveness of prescription drugs, including the contraceptive pill. Many creams and lotions sold in sex shops claim to 'keep you harder, longer!'. They may be fun to try, but don't count on amazing results.

Cosmo tip:
Compliments during sex are one of life's best aphrodisiacs. They have no side effects and are guaranteed to work every time.

AROUSAL

See also: orgasm, penis, vagina

Want to know what happens to your brain, body and bits when you're with someone you find sexually irresistible?

It's also handy to discover *his* body–brain connection and find out how – and why – it differs from yours. Here's all the info you need:

The Basic Stages

Male and female arousal cycles follow the same basic pattern:

1) **Arousal** a.k.a. 'Oooh, yes, please . . .'; 'Hmm, kissing nice . . .'; 'Naked? I think so!'
2) **Plateau** a.k.a. 'Yes – touch me there' . . . 'and there . . .'; 'keeping going . . .'; 'ummm!'
3) **Orgasm** a.k.a. 'Ooh – left a bit . . .'; 'Yes . . .'; 'Yes! Yes . . .'; 'YES! YES! YES!'
4) **Resolution** a.k.a. You: 'Ahhh! Cuddle, please . . .'; him: 'Zzzzzzzzzzzz . . .'

Before going into the details, there are some crucial differences between men and women that are worth bearing in mind (men, please pay careful attention here):

MEN	WOMEN
can gain an erection within seconds of receiving any form of sexual attention and are ready to go! go! go!	take much longer to become aroused. That's why God invented foreplay.
have an obvious tent-pole-shaped signal that they're ready and waiting.	aren't so easy to read: although we become lubricated when turned on this should *not* be taken as a sign that we're ready for said tent pole.
need time to recover between sex sessions: around 15 minutes in younger men and up to 24 hours in older men.	need no time at all between orgasms to recover. Like the Duracell bunny, we can go and go again!

The Details: Arousal for Him

Stage 1: Instant desire
Anything sexually alluring can trigger this first stage: a brush past someone he finds attractive on the bus; your dirty laugh; the way

your bottom wobbles when you brush your teeth. His brain sends neurological signals down his spinal cord straight to his genitals. This increases the blood flow to his penis, causing an erection. His heart rate rises and testicles tighten.

What you can do: Men respond strongly to visual stimulation. He'll pick up on basic preening gestures so fiddle with your hair, or run your finger across your mouth or along your collarbone.

Stage 2: Turn-on central
This covers everything up until the moment of orgasm: he'll be experiencing intense sexual arousal and a desperate need to be touched in all the right places. His breathing and heart rate become faster; his nipples harden and his penis gets even bigger when stimulated directly. The head darkens in colour and some liquid (pre-ejaculatory fluid) will be secreted.

What you can do: Don't head for his genitals straightaway. Intensify his pleasure by running your hands across his chest, down his inner thighs and around his abdomen. Next, run a flat hand from his balls all the way up his shaft to his belly and down again. Finally build up a firm stroke.

Stage 3: Blast off!
By now, he's at the stage of 'ejaculatory inevitability': he's going to come and nothing will stop him. He's likely to increase the speed and depth of thrusting if you're having penetrative sex, his legs and feet tense (watch his toes for clues!). His prostate gland (inside him, under his bladder) emits fluid into the urethra (the channel that links the bladder to the outside world), causing a feeling of fullness. His balls rise up towards his body and muscles contract rhythmically in his penis and anus. Semen is then propelled out of the urethral opening (at the tip of his penis), with contractions every 0.8 seconds.

SEX FACT *Men actually ejaculate a few seconds after they feel the muscular contractions of orgasm because semen has a little way to travel before it shoots out.*

What you can do: When you feel him about to climax try mirroring his movements: tense your own body and pulse in time with him. Alternatively, try massaging his perineum, the flat patch of skin between his balls and his anus, in time with his contractions.

Stage 4: Total shutdown

His heart rate and breathing gradually return to normal. His penis shrinks to 50 per cent of its erect size (it takes around 20 minutes for it to return to its flaccid state), his balls drop down again and he enters into a deep state of relaxation.

What you can do: Don't be offended if he falls straight to sleep – it's not you, it's his body's natural response. His penis, like your clitoris after climax, will be extremely sensitive, so handle it with care.

The Details: Arousal for You

Stage 1: Slow burn sexy

Like him, all your sexual responses start in your brain. Your brain sends neurological messages down your spine, causing sexual responses all over your body. Your nipples harden, your skin feels sensitive and your breath quickens. Gradually, blood flows to your genitals, causing your clitoris and vaginal lips to feel fuller and larger. Natural lubricants start to flow from inside the vagina.

What he can do: The more non-genital foreplay he does the better. Passionate kissing is intimate and arousing: the longer you stay at first base, the more exciting it'll feel when you move on.

Stage 2: The excitement plateau

At this stage, your vagina darkens in colour and your body is stimulated all over. Your temperature rises, your skin becomes flushed and your muscles tense. The head of the clitoris becomes erect and the inside of your vagina expands, making more room for him inside you. Just before orgasm, your clitoris may retreat inside the clitoral hood, particularly during penetrative sex, so it's protected from his hard thrusting.

What he can do: To encourage your whole body to respond sexually, get him to try massaging your clitoris with one hand while stroking a not-so-obvious erogenous zone with the other. Next time you're stimulated in these areas your brain remembers the clitoral stimulation you had last time and connects the two feelings.

Stage 3: Yes! Yes! Yes!
Your heart rate, breathing and lubrication peak, your body may shudder and you may feel twitches in your abdomen and buttocks. The lower third of your vagina becomes congested with blood. At the point of orgasm, you'll feel muscular contractions in the floor of the pelvis, uterus and vaginal area at 0.8-second intervals (the same rate as his orgasmic contractions). Your clitoris retreats under its hood, your pupils dilate and you may feel disconnected from your body. You'll feel waves of pleasure around your clitoris, vagina and anus.

What he can do: Women want different things at orgasm. Some want him to carry on doing exactly what he's doing (i.e. carry on clitoral or vaginal stimulation); others want to be held, kissed or cuddled. Some remain completely still. As your clitoris may feel sensitive at this point, stimulation of your vaginal lips may feel nicer.

SEX FACT *After orgasm your lips (the ones on your face) stay fuller and redder than usual for around 20 minutes.*

Stage 4: Satisfaction
Orgasm usually lasts around 15–20 seconds. Afterwards your genitals gradually return to their normal size and colour. Your breathing slows and your muscles relax. Lubrication stops and within five to ten minutes the swelling of the vagina goes down. This whole process can take longer if you haven't climaxed.

What he can do: To make sure you really enjoy this stage he can try stroking your secondary erogenous zones (the ones you discovered in Stage Two). At the point of orgasm, women release the hormone oxytocin, which is also released during breastfeeding and is thought to help mother and baby bond. This is why women love bonding activities like cuddling after sex.

A-SPOT
See also: G-spot, U-spot

The What-Is-It? Bit
Technically known as the anterior fornix erogenous zone, it's a patch of super-sensitive skin about two thirds of the way up from the vaginal entrance on the front wall of the vagina. It was discovered by scientists researching alternative methods of pain reduction for women with spinal injuries. It's quite hard to reach with your fingers but may be easier to hit with a vibrator or during deep penetration. It's also known as the vaginal cul-de-sac, presumably because it's near the end of the vaginal canal with nowhere else to go.

The Science Bit
It's thought that hitting the A-spot increases vaginal lubrication, which can make sex feel wetter and therefore better. It also explains why many women get a whole load of pleasure from very deep penetration. Previous scientific research, claiming that nerve endings were concentrated only around the first third of the vagina, couldn't really explain the deep-penetration thing, and although the first third *is* the most sensitive, it's nice to know there's a secret little spot right inside that feels good, too.

> **Cosmo tip:**
> Try clenching your abdominal and PC muscles (the ones you use when you pee) just as he starts thrusting, and he's more likely to hit the spot.

The Find-it Bit
Any position involving deep penetration will hit this spot.
- Try any rear-entry position (his entering you from behind) for deep penetration.
- During the missionary position, try bending your legs back towards your chest. This shortens the vaginal canal, so penetration feels deeper.
- Try any position where you're sitting or squatting over him, e.g. with him sitting on a chair and you sitting over him, or with him lying flat on the floor or bed while you either kneel or squat.

The Caution Bit

If he penetrates too deeply you can find that his penis knocks against your cervix (the solid area at the top of the vaginal canal) which can feel uncomfortable or lead to inflammation or cystitis.

> **Cosmo tip:**
> Although sexy-spot discovery can be part of great sex, it's not the be-all and end-all. If it feels great, pay it attention. If you can't find it, try something else – simple as . . .

Astro-Hotspots
See also: erogenous zones

According to astrologers, each star sign is ruled by a different part of the body. By focusing on this area, you'll be zoning in on the erogenous zone that's most closely connected to your personality or his. Next time you ask him his star sign, let him know you have more than a quick personality analysis in mind . . .

> **Cosmo tip:**
> Never ask a man what his star sign is on a first date. In general, men consider anything astro far too girlie (until you pay attention to his astro-hotspot that is . . .).

Star Sign	Astro-Erogenous Zone
Aries (20 March–19 April)	Face and head
Taurus (20 April–20 May)	Throat and neck
Gemini (21 May–20 June)	Hands, arms and shoulders
Cancer (21 June–22 July)	Breasts/chest
Leo (23 July–22 August)	Heart and hair
Virgo (23 August–22 September)	Midriff/stomach
Libra (23 September–22 October)	Lower back and buttocks
Scorpio (23 October–21 November)	Genitals
Sagittarius (22 November–21 December)	Hips and thighs
Capricorn (22 December–19 January)	Knees and joints
Aquarius (20 January–18 February)	Shins, ankles and calves
Pisces (19 February–19 March)	Feet

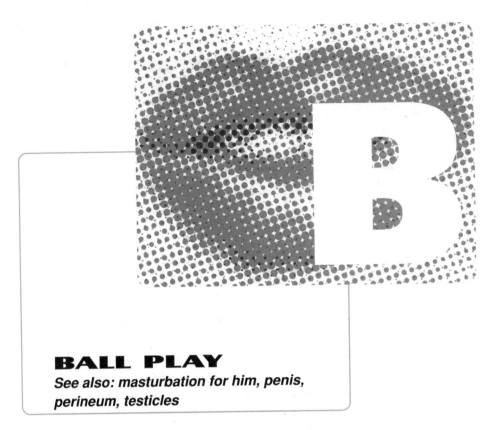

BALL PLAY
*See also: masturbation for him, penis,
perineum, testicles*

What do women really know about testicles?

1) They're extremely sensitive and we shouldn't go anywhere
   near them with our knees, high heels (unless that's his thing,
   obviously), any sharp objects or threatening movements.
2) Men often play with them while pretending to search for old
   tissues in very deep pockets.
3) They're situated at the base of a much more popular sex
   organ that tends to hog all the action.
4) They deserve more attention that we normally give them.

SEX FACT: *It's normal for one ball to be bigger than the other –
they're like feet, hands and ears: no two are identical.*

Ball Play: Your Training Schedule

Stoke his fire
When he has an erection, stroke a flat hand all the way down his

penis, over his balls and on to his inner thighs, then slowly move it back up again. The sensation will be most intense around the tip of his penis but by continuing the stroke you'll get him used to the different levels of arousal in each area.

The tug boat

For a more erotic, urgent sensation, place one hand firmly around his shaft and cup his balls with the other. As you move one hand up his shaft, gently pull his balls downwards with the other. When you move your shaft hand downwards, release his balls. Keep up a regular rhythm to build up the friction. Just before men ejaculate, their testicles are naturally pulled upwards, in towards their bodies, so the tug technique is ideal if you want to delay his climax.

Ridge rider

Lying with your elbows between his legs, study his testicles closely. You'll find a little ridge that goes up the middle of the scrotal sac dividing the two ball bags. This is his most sensitive spot. Try massaging it gently with the pads of your fingers or running your tongue along the ridge from the bottom, where his balls meet his perineum (the sensitive patch of skin between his anus and his testicles) right across to the base of his penis. Flick this area with your tongue while using your hands on his shaft, or massage it while you give him oral sex.

> **Cosmo tip:**
> Always handle his balls with care. Like your breasts, they're more sensitive at different times depending on the temperature, how aroused he is and how long ago he had sex.

Ring-a-ding-ding

With your thumb and forefinger, delicately form a ring around the top of his balls where they're attached to his body and squeeze downwards until they form a firm ball: you're trapping the blood here so they'll feel extra-sensitive. Stroke, massage or even tap this globe gently with your other hand.

Suck 'em and see

While you're down there (particularly as a warm-up for oral sex) lick and kiss his balls, then gently draw them, one at a time, into your mouth. Move them around, slowly swirling your tongue over each one. The heat and wetness of your mouth feels particularly erotic when accompanied by hand action elsewhere.

'I love it when a girl plays with my balls while she's giving me oral sex: it feels like she's really into me and is confident with what she's doing.'
Martin, 28, electrical engineer

Ball-Perfect Positions
These sex positions give you maximum access to his balls:

The reverse cowgirl
Sit on top of him facing his feet: you get direct access to his balls as he thrusts in and out of you. Try gently lifting them with one hand and letting them fall into the other, then repeat this action (like doing doggy paddle over the top of them).

The kneeling dog
You kneel in front of him while he kneels on the bed and enters you from behind. Reach through your legs and cup his balls in your hands while he thrusts. Alternatively, if he's thrusting hard, feel his balls slapping against your bottom.

Sexy spoons
Both lie on your sides with him behind you. Bend one knee forward and raise the other over his thigh so he can penetrate you. Reach through his legs to stroke his inner thighs and balls.

SEX FACT: *Men with larger testicles are more likely to be unfaithful: they produce more sperm and are therefore biologically programmed to sow more oats.*

BDSM
See also: bondage, fantasy, role-play, spanking

Know your lingo: BDSM is a collective name for sexual games or practices that include *bondage and discipline* (B/D or B&D), *domination and submission* (D/S or D&S), and *sadomasochism* (S/M or S&M). All these games involve playing with the idea of power and control in a sexual context and can be as heavy (think dungeons, dominatrix and full-on flagellation) or as light (think fluffy handcuffs, silk blindfolds or simply holding your man's wrists down while you have sex) as you like. SM (or S&M) play is sadomasochistic sex play in which one partner (the 'S' part) enjoys inflicting pain on the other partner (the 'M' part), who enjoys that pain. *Sub-dom* play is similar to S&M but is to do with control rather than pain: the sub(missive) partner submits to the control of the dom(inant) partner.

BDSM sex play is about consensual power play where both partners get something from the experience. It does not mean physical or emotional abuse. It can often involve acting out fantasies, dressing up and playing out roles where the balance of power is unequal (think doctor and patient, master and slave, teacher and naughty pupil) and can be fun and liberating if you're both into it.

BEDROOM TO BOUDOIR
See also: lighting

Transform your bedroom into the ultimate lust palace with these sensual tips:

1) Sight for phwoar! eyes
Bedrooms should be for sex and sleeping. No desks. No telly. No dirty laundry. Clearing your clutter will allow your sexual energy to flow freely.

2) Touch-sensitive
Think texture and touch: silky sheets that feel great against your

Cosmo tip:
Transforming your bedroom into ready-for-sex boudoir can be arousing in itself. Think of it as pre-foreplay. Take pleasure in touching the items you'll be rolling around on later and drinking in the atmosphere: it all adds to your arousal.

body, deep-pile carpets or rugs (they don't call it 'shag pile' for nothing), fluffy cushions and fur throws.

3) Smell sweet

Smell is one of the most evocative and sexual senses: the smell of a lover's perfume can instantly transport you back to your last lust encounter. Forget air fresheners: they always smell too synthetic. Think sensual scented candles, intense incense or even a few sprays of your favourite scent.

4) Sound sexy

Think about the type of music you want to set the mood. Keep the volume low. Set the CD player on repeat so you don't have to break the mood to change the tunes.

5) Carnal colours

Colour can have a huge effect on mood: red is passionate and intense, blue (the nation's favourite bedroom colour) is cool and calming, so great for sleep but not so good for sex. A blue or white bedroom may need to be warmed up with some clever lighting: try coloured tealight holders in red and orange for a warm sexy glow. (See **lighting** for more info).

Dream Themes

A few simple props can transform your bedroom into the ideal fantasy location, ready for you to act out your wildest dreams.

Bedouin bliss

Try draping long saris or sheer pieces of fabric from the middle of the ceiling (ideally over the bed) to the edges of the wall and then down. Coloured muslin is cheap and can just be pinned to the ceiling.

Touch of the Orient

Red lacquer accessories, incense, paper lanterns and sumptuous oriental bed linen (again, preferably red) will create an intense eastern feel: perfect for geisha girl role play.

> ⋮ **Delightful dungeons**
> Sheets of black plastic against the walls and taped to the floor,
> red bulbs in the lamps and dark, dangerous bed linen will all give
> a dungeon-like feel.

BLINDFOLDS
See also: bondage

Restricting one sense will heighten all the others and, by being blindfolded in bed, you're putting yourself entirely at the mercy of your partner. This loss of control can feel very sexy. Here's how to make the most of an erotic eye mask:

Stripping for the Blind

Blindfold your man and sit him, fully clothed, in the middle of your bed. Start by whispering in his ear exactly which piece of clothing you'll remove first. Once you've removed it, stroke it gently against his face and describe to him how sensual the fabric feels. Keep talking dirty to him until you've taken off all your clothes. Once you're naked, start touching yourself in front of him, describing exactly what you're doing. Pull his hands over your body so he can mirror your movements. Finally, remove his clothes slowly and seductively, and make love while he still can't see you: use lots of sensual body strokes, as his sense of touch will be extremely acute.

Dinner à *Deux*

Again, blindfold your man and set before him a selection of sensual treats. Think of food with different tastes, smells and textures: strawberries, crackers, celery, cucumber, grapes and chocolate all work well. Start by seductively describing the food without using its name. Let him smell it, eat some yourself then kiss him. Lightly rub or tap the food across his body and lick it off. Let him dip his fingers in it and

'I felt a bit scared the first time Georgia produced a blindfold, but, when you can't see, every other sense feels amazing: oral sex is my favourite – it's so intense.'
Nathan, 28, management consultant

rub it across *your* body. Finish by feeding him a teeny taste. He has to guess what's on the menu.

Fantasy Fun

Try sharing your wildest fantasies with your lover while he's blind-folded. Make your description as visual as possible. His imagination will run wild. Try touching him in time with your story. If it's about being tied up, tie his hands as you're talking. If it's about being worshipped by a sexy stranger, run his hands across your body. Think about props and sound effects: the sound of a champagne cork popping can be a sexy surprise; the buzz of a sex toy could be anything you want it to be. Halfway through the story, get him to describe exactly what *he's* seeing: it'll take the fantasy in a new direction and give you a clue to what goes on in his sexual imagination.

Cosmo tip:
If he can't see what you're doing it can sometimes be incredibly liberating for you, allowing you to do or say things you'd normally find embarrassing if he were watching. Make the most of it and really let yourself go.

BLOW JOB
See under: oral sex for him

If you're blowing rather than sucking, licking or kissing, he's probably not as happy as you think he is . . .

BODY CONFIDENCE
See also: confidence, lighting

Boost your body confidence by:
1. Remembering that in bed you're so much more than just your body shape.
2. Picking out three things you love about you body – focusing on your good points helps you psychologically minimise your bad ones.

3. Complimenting your partner on his body (he's bound to do the same for you).

4. Having an image role model who is a similar shape to you: see how she dresses to make the most of her assets; watch how she moves and soak up the pride she has in her body.

5. Pampering yourself: have a great haircut, treat yourself to a fake tan, get a pedicure then show off the new supercharged you in the bedroom.

Positions for Total Body Confidence

Use these positions to show off your best bits and make the best of the bits you're not so fond of:

> **Cosmo tip:**
> Exercise will boost your self-esteem *and* your body image. It also sends the same feel-good chemicals racing round your body that you get at orgasm.

To draw attention to your generous breasts:

- Have sex with your hands tied or handcuffed over your head. This lifts and tightens your breasts, and also makes your nipples more sensitive.

To proudly display your J-Lo curves:

- Do it doggy style – put your *derrière* in the air as if you just don't care. When you're on all fours, your bottom will look firmer because the muscles and skin are stretched taut.

For a flatter stomach:

- Go for the straightforward missionary position with your back slightly arched and your hands above your head.

To slim chunky thighs:

- Lie back and stretch out your legs as far back over your head as they can go. He then penetrates you from the front. This flexes your hamstrings, disguises cellulite and can be very comfy.

To lengthen legs:

- High heels with stockings and suspenders create an illusion of length. Fishnets are great for making skinny legs look more shapely, but go for plain stockings if you don't need extra bulk. Wearing heels forces your weight forward, so you naturally hold your stomach in and your breasts up and out, arching your back in a sensual feminine way.

BODY LANGUAGE
See under: flirting

Find out how to make your body work for you and what his is saying about him.

BONDAGE
See also: BDSM, blindfolds, fantasy, role-play, spanking

Dictionary definition: serfdom, slavery, subjection to constraint.
***Cosmo*'s definition:** The tie-me-up tango: a range of pleasurable advanced sex techniques for bad girls and boys only.

Tie-me-up techniques don't need to involve pain – the sheer sensation of being restrained sends adrenaline pumping round your body creating toe-tingling arousal.

Bondage Rules
- Discuss your fantasies and set your boundaries before you start to play. Never go further than either of you wants.
- Have a code word that means 'stop'. Use a neutral word like 'leaf' rather than 'no', 'don't' or 'stop', which can often mean the opposite when you're role-playing.
- Never leave each other tied up or in any way restrict your breathing.
- Don't try bondage games for the first time when you've had too much to drink. The point is to *play with the idea* of control rather than to lose it completely.
- Trust is essential – sex games can build intimacy in your relationship but not if you're scared to death.

Bondage for Beginners: Your Go-For-It Guide

What you'll need: Four silk scarves, a long feather (a peacock feather is ideal).

1) Decide who's going to dominate (do the tying up) and who's going to submit (be tied). Hot tip: taking turns will fuel your sexual fire and you'll discover which role you like better.

2) Tie your naked lover's wrists to the bedposts, firmly but not too tightly (don't do anything that restricts the blood flow or that you won't be able to undo). Tie his ankles in the same way to opposite bedposts. (If you don't have bedposts, try tying his wrists or ankles together: it has a similar effect.)

SEX FACT: *Being dominated is the most common fantasy requested by men who call sex phone lines.*

3) Get into your dominant role and warn him to stay passive. If he moves a muscle, he'll be punished.

4) Tease him with the feather, stroking it up and down his whole body. Staying away from his obvious erogenous zones will drive him wild.

5) Use your lips to nibble, kiss and lick your way oh-so-slowly from his toes upwards, stopping just short of his penis. If he begs you to go further (which he will) stop and start the whole process all over again.

6) If (and when) you decide to get naked, sit over one of his legs and rub your clitoris along it, working your way up to his penis – but never touching it – then going back down again.

7) Finally, lower yourself on to him for penetration. Don't let him climax until *you're* ready. You're the one in control – this time!

8) Make him beg for more – get him to ask you, very nicely, to continue (and we know what'll happen if he doesn't say the magic word . . .) Start again from Step Three, leaving him tied and completely at your mercy.

Cosmo tip:
Being tied up allows you to surrender all control. All you have to do is lie back and receive pleasure. The dominant partner should also become aroused by the feelings of being in control of your pleasure.

9) Although many men love to be dominated, don't forget your fun too. As a reward for being such a good boy, let him tie you up in a similar way and tease, tickle and tempt you to the edge.

Advanced Bondage Games for Really Bad Girls

Get into character

Many role-play scenarios involve partnerships where the balance of power is unequal, and getting into a dominant role can make it easier to exert the control you need to. Think about the roles you commonly take in your sexual fantasies for clues as to what 'character' you might like to play in the bedroom. See **role-play** and **dressing up** for more naughty tips.

'I imagine I'm a prisoner in my head and I desperately need to get away, struggling against my [fake] chains. When my "prison guard" decides to give me pleasure rather than pain, it's incredibly erotic!'
Faith, 29, nurse

Dress the part

Think tactile, think spiky, think downright dirty: anything tight and leather (or latex) will help you feel the part. Spike heels are great for giving you height (to tower over him) and power (threaten to use them as a weapon!). Chokers give the impression of restraints while full-red lips make you look in control. Even threatening to 'get the shoes out' can arouse him if he was at your mercy the last time you wore them.

Cosmo tip:
If full-on bondage feels too much at first you don't have to go the whole way. Just holding down someone's wrists while you're having sex on top and ordering them not to move can be arousing.

Go shopping

There are hundreds of bondage accessories for sale in sex shops and over the Internet, from handcuffs and restraints to bondage videos and whole pieces of 'dungeon furniture'. Professional cuffs and restraints are often safer than handmade ties that can be hard to undo and could cause nerve damage.

Bondage lite

The bondage practices we're talking about here are just the tip of the whole kinky iceberg. If you're into taking it further there are thousands of resources and Internet sites that can cater for your fantasies. Have fun with your raunchy research!

SEX FACT: *58 per cent of* Cosmo *readers say they'd like to be tied up, with 45 per cent initiating the request.*

BOTTOM
See also: anal sex, spanking

Yup: that fleshy bit you sit on is can be another super-sexy erogenous zone. Here are some cheeky ideas . . .

Massage Techniques

Your buttocks and lower back can feel sensational if aroused in the right way. Teach him these moves:

1) Get him to sit between or astride your legs (depending on how comfortable you feel with your legs open or closed). He should start with long sweeping movements from your lower back over your buttocks and back again.

2) Next, he should move his hands in large circles without breaking hand-to-bottom contact (warmed massage oil between the hands helps). This indirectly stimulates the anal area, which is rich in nerve endings, without actually touching it.

3) Get him to play around with the area where your buttocks meet your back. Two points either side of the base of your spine are usually sensitive, as is the crack at the top of your butt cheeks. Try a combo of kneading, stroking, pummelling and slapping motions.

4) With the balls of his thumbs, get him to gently work his way down the sides of your buttocks (near but not touching the crack in the middle). He could continue with his fingers all the way down so eventually they reach your vaginal lips and clitoris.

5) If you want to be truly teased within an inch of your life, he should massage down your buttocks, over your vagina, just brushing his hands over your clitoris, then pulling back to your buttocks again.

> **Cosmo tip:**
> Some people are highly sensitive (in a positive *or* negative way) around the anal area and can tense up if your hands stray anywhere near their butt hole. Think of bottom massage and anal play as two separate activities until you know what your lover is into.

Other Bottom Treats . . .

Cheeky sex

As an alternative to penetrative sex, some couples like to have sex between the butt cheeks. You lie face down while he runs his penis between your cheeks without any penetration. This feels especially good if your bottom and his penis are highly lubricated, maybe as the finale to your butt massage. You can stimulate your clitoris by reaching underneath you at the same time.

Vibrating heaven

Try using your vibrator over your buttocks or his: experiment with different areas that feel good. You might like it against your anus (just resting there rather than penetrating) or around the sides of your body.

'It's such a turn-on when my girlfriend grabs hold of my buttocks while we're having sex and pulls me in towards her: it's like she wants me to go deeper and deeper.'
Neil, 24, plumber

Nip 'n' suck

As part of oral sex, get him to gently nip your butt cheeks before moving round for the main event. You can try this on him too: it can create a delicious build-up. Sucking and releasing the fleshy parts of your buttocks feels good, too.

Dirty dog

Having sex doggy style (with him penetrating you from behind) is the perfect opportunity for him to gently slap your buttocks while he thrusts

'I love it when my boyfriend penetrates me from behind and thrusts quite powerfully: his balls slapping against my buttocks are such a turn-on!'
Julia, 29, advertising

into you. Alternatively, if he pushes your buttocks upwards as he thrusts into you, this will indirectly stimulate the anal and vaginal area, causing the vaginal lips to pull slightly on the clitoral hood.

BRAIN
See also: fantasy

The brain is the biggest erogenous zone of all. It:
- must be engaged in order to start the physical process of sexual arousal.
- will never run out of batteries, ideas, fantasies, scenarios or turn-on tactics.
- will also never run out of worries, questions and insecurities about sex.
- needs constant oiling: the more you use it in bed (we're thinking fantasies here, not insecurities) the better sex you'll have.

BREASTS
See also: erotic massage, nipples

Fact you know: Men don't have breasts.
Fact you also know: Men are fascinated by what they don't have.
Fact you should get into your head right now: Men will love your breasts no matter what size or shape they are. Whether you're melon-endowed or pancake-flat, handle your breasts with confidence to get the best out of this sexy erogenous zone.

Breast Intentions #1: Sexy Turn-ons for You

Get to know them
Experiment on your own with your breasts while you're masturbating to find out which sensations you like. Try rubbing, caressing or pinching your nipples. Spread your arms wide and then trace a line along your inner arm towards your breasts: breasts are more sensitive when the skin around them is taut. While having sex, repeat these actions for added arousal or guide his hands as to how

you like to be touched. Your breasts swell up to 20 per cent more than their original size while you're aroused. Your breasts will also feel more or less sensitive at different times in your menstrual cycle.

SEX FACT *Some women can climax from breast stimulation alone as the neural pathways that send messages from your clitoris to the brain also form connections with your breasts.*

Hands-on for you

If your man is giving a breast massage, make sure he knows to leave your nipples till last, as they're the most sensitive part. He should start with firm strokes all the way around your chest area (doing this while you're still dressed or at unexpected times like the middle of the washing-up can be sexy). Holding them in both hands, he should use upward strokes diagonally across each breast. He can try deep kneading, flat palms or swirling motions. Don't let his hands lose contact with your skin.

'When I'm about to come, my boyfriend pinches my nipples hard with both hands – it really sends me over the edge.'
Rhianna, 25, tourism officer

Nipple magic

Nipples will be erect when you're turned on and, depending on how sensitive you are, he could try stroking, pulling, flicking, licking, nipping or tugging them. He could even massage them with his erect penis. While he's sucking or licking your nipples, take one of his fingers in your mouth so you can mimic the action you'd like him to be doing to you.

⚠ *SAFETY INFO: Nipples are quite resilient, especially when you're near orgasm but be careful if you're using nipple clamps or clips not to damage the tissue. Don't use clamps or toys for more than ten minutes at a time to be extra safe.*

(For breast-play for him, see **nipples**)

Breast Intentions #2: Sexy Turn-ons for Both of You

'My fiancée presses the softest part of each breast on to my cheeks, which is an amazing tease.'
Henry, 27, insurance salesman

Body beautiful

Use your breasts to massage the whole of his body. Start with him lying on his front and trace your nipples slowly down his back, buttocks and legs. Covering yourself with massage oil will up the intensity for both of you. Turn him over and trace your breasts across the front of his body, teasing his nipples with yours, then moving to his face. Don't let him take your nipples in his mouth until *you* say so. Finally, use your breasts to massage his genitals. Try getting him to hold your breasts together while he slips his penis between them – this leaves your hands free to caress yourself to orgasm as your body rubs against his shaft.

'Most men aren't that fussed about size: it's what you do with them that counts. My ex was quite flat-chested but, when she was on top, she'd lean back, close her eyes and pinch her breasts as if she was lost in ecstasy. It made me feel like the greatest lover in the world.'
Mikey, 25, barman

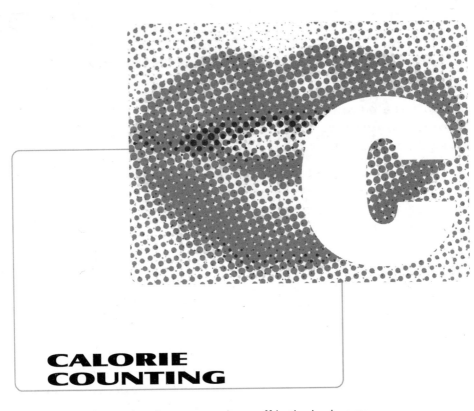

CALORIE COUNTING

Fact fans: here's what you can burn off in the bedroom:

- The average French kiss (that's three and a half minutes with tongues) burns off twelve calories. That's about an apple slice.
- Half an hour of rigorous penetrative sex burns approximately 150 calories.
- Fifteen minutes of oral sex burns around 35 calories.
- Swallowing after giving oral sex won't ruin your diet: it's just five calories per pop . . .

CAT POSITION
See also: positions, orgasm

Otherwise known as the *coital alignment technique*, this is a magical spin on the missionary position that's specifically designed to heighten a woman's chance of orgasm during penetrative sex.

SEX FACT: *Around 80 per cent of women don't climax through penetrative sex alone. Most need some form of extra-clitoral stimulation. After trying the CAT position, 77 per cent of women achieve orgasm during penetrative sex, according to research.*

How does it work?

This technique moves the position of your body and his so that your clitoris gets more direct stimulation during intercourse.

How can I do it?

Start in the basic missionary position (him on top, you underneath). He then moves upwards and forwards slightly and rests his whole body weight on top of you rather than resting on his hands or elbows. Wrap your legs around his body, resting your ankles on his calves. When he's inside you, the base of his penis will now be resting on your clitoris, giving you that all-important extra stimulation. Instead of thrusting, rock backwards and forwards. On the upwards stroke you control the movement, forcing your pubic bone upwards. On the downwards stroke, he controls the movement, forcing you downwards.

'It does take practice and feels quite weird at first but because you're so close together it feels really intimate. The fact that it's easier to orgasm is a fantastic bonus.'

Charlotte, 29, press officer

Any secret-of-success tips?

Keep your bodies in constant contact so your clitoris and the base of his penis are touching all the time. Forget deep thrusts and keep up a steady pace with the rocking/rubbing movement rather than speeding up or slowing down at any point.

Does it take long to master?

Because we're conditioned to enjoy thrusting during intercourse the rocking motion does take a while to get the hang of. His penis receives gentle stimulation so he lasts longer and your clitoris gets all the attention it needs for an explosive climax.

CELIBACY
See under: abstinence

Who are you trying to kid? Bizarrely, abstaining from sex can actually be a huge turn-on.

CHLAMYDIA
See under: sexually transmitted infections

A sexually transmitted bacterial infection, often with no symptoms.

CLITORIS
See also: CAT position, masturbation, oral sex for you, orgasm

What a clitoris is	What a clitoris is not
An organ packed with highly sensitive nerve endings culminating in the clitoral head, the little nubby bit you can see and feel at the top of the vulva.	A mini-penis, so don't treat it as such (men: think softer, slower; girls: when you touch *him*, think harder, faster).
More delicate and sensitive than a man's bits (and somewhat less obvious!).	The be-all and end-all of female sexual pleasure: yes, we like being touched there but there are other bits to play with too.

SEX FACT *The clitoris is the only part of the body with pleasure as its only function. The clitoral head contains 8,000 nerve endings – twice as many as the penis.*

The Anatomical Stuff: X Marks the Spot

The bit you can see is the pea-sized clitoral head at the top of the vaginal area. Made from similar tissue to the head of the penis, it feels harder than the rest of the vaginal tissue and hardens and enlarges when you're sexually aroused. The shaft of the clitoris, which stretches back into your body, can be felt by rolling a fingertip from side to side just above the head. When you're aroused the head can more than double in size as blood rushes to your genitals.

Protected we stand

The head is protected by the top of the vaginal lips, which come together to form a hood over it (a bit like the male foreskin). Tiny oil-producing glands keep it lubricated and shiny, and allow the clitoral hood to glide across the head. Rubbing on the vaginal lips during masturbation or oral sex, or indirectly via penetration (his thrusting will cause pleasant friction), will cause this hood to rub against the clitoris, feeling oh-so special. When you're aroused, everything becomes engorged with blood and, at the point of orgasm, the clitoris retreats under its protective hood (which can be frustrating for your lover, who's been concentrating on it for the last 20 minutes).

Does size matter?

No. The size of the clitoral head can vary from 2 mm to 20 mm and will swell and stand to attention when you're sexually aroused. Size does not affect sensitivity, so bigger isn't necessarily better (although it may be easier to get clitoral stimulation during penetrative sex as it brushes against his pubic bone).

SEX FACT: *A clitoris is not a mini-penis. For the first eight weeks of life, the clitoris and the penis are the same. Once a foetus's sex is established, they develop into different forms. Yes, they're both made of erectile tissue, but the design of the muscles, nerve pathways and blood flow is different.*

Is that it?

No – far from it. In 1998 a urological surgeon, Dr Helen O'Connell, discovered that erectile tissue isn't just concentrated in the clitoral head. In fact, around two-thirds of the clitoris is buried under the surface of the skin. From the clitoral head, two arms of erectile tissue up to 9 cm long stretch down behind the vaginal lips and back towards the pelvic bone (imagine an upside-down Y shape like a wishbone). This explains why many women love to have their vaginal lips stimulated and why the areas *around* the clitoris are particularly sensitive. The muscles that surround and protect these 'wings' are also sensitive and contract at the point of orgasm.

Are all women built the same?

Nope. The concentration of nerve endings in the vaginal area is different in all women. Some find clitoral stimulation the most arousing; others aren't so fussed, as their nerve endings are more concentrated in the vaginal lips, around the urethral opening (the tiny hole above the vagina where you pee) or inside the vagina itself. Clitoral sensitivity also varies depending on where you are in your menstrual cycle, your mood and how closely your brain is engaged. Safe to say, most women find direct clitoral stimulation sexy: around 80 per cent of us need it to achieve orgasm.

What happens at orgasm?

The shaft (the bit behind the clitoral head stretching back into your body) stiffens and the wishbone extensions become harder and fuller. Muscles and ligaments contract rhythmically around the clitoris. At the point of orgasm the muscles contract rapidly and the blood that's been filling the clitoris and the rest of your vagina is expelled back into the bloodstream along with a whole host of feel-good hormones.

'When I was younger the blokes I had sex with were so pleased they actually knew where my clitoris was, they expected a medal for finding it. These days my boyfriend knows that not touching it for as long as possible is the biggest turn-on.'
Lisa, 29, hospital manager

Head straight for it, then?

Definitely not. Tease before you please. Zoning straight in on an unaroused clitoris with a dry finger or a flat tongue can be uncomfortable. Some women even find the clitoris too sensitive to touch directly at all when they're aroused, so playing around the area is a much better bet.

The Fun Bit: Clitoral Tricks to Try Tonight

1) Material girl

Before your knickers come off, try cupping the whole of your vaginal area with a flat hand, reaching downwards from your pubic bone.

Rub the whole area up and down or in circles using the heel of your hand (or his) on top of your pubic bone, pressing down on the clitoris from above.

2) V-Day

Spread your fingers in an upside-down V position and place them directly on top of the clitoral hood with your fingers extending down over the vaginal lips. By moving your hand in this position you'll be indirectly stimulating the clitoris. Experiment with different pressures and motions.

'My girlfriend taught me how to use her vibrator on her. I was amazed at how sensitive other areas around the clitoris were. It felt really intimate to be exploring with her and now I know where she likes being touched the best: left-hand side at the top of her lips!'
George, 31, banker

3) Good vibrations

Go easy on where you place your vibrator: direct clitoral stimulation may be too much, so experiment all over the area, starting with the inner thighs, then moving inwards. When you feel your arousal level rising, take the sex toy away to a less sensitive area again so you feel your passion building, then subsiding. The more you do this, the more intense your final orgasm will be.

4) Clock it to her

To discover where you're most sensitive, imagine the clitoris as a clock face with twelve o'clock being directly above the clitoral head and six o'clock being below it (or even at the base of the vagina). Most women are the most sensitive between ten and two but it's fun to run through twelve (or even twenty-four) hours either with your fingers or his tongue to find out which 'time' you like best.

'My clitoris is so unpredictable, the pressure and strokes I need vary so much – sometimes I want a hard finger thrusting from above, other times I just need to circle around it. It's best to let your partner know what feels good today, rather than relying on the same moves every time.'
Jessica, 34, caterer

5) The wetter the better

Like the vagina, the clitoris loves moisture and hates feeling dry and scratchy. If you feel yourself drying out, open your vaginal lips to let out some more lubricant or alternate clitoral attention with rubbing and stroking the rest of the vaginal area to bring more moisture up to the top. Alternatively, try using a shop-bought lubricant.

6) Two-handed tango

Try reaching one hand down from above to stroke the clitoris up and down while the other hand is under your bottom reaching upwards. The bottom hand can gently massage your perineum (the sensitive patch of skin between the bottom of the vagina and the anus) or gently pull or stroke down the length of the vagina.

SEX FACT: *According to sex therapist Dr Andrew Stanway, right-handed women tend to prefer clitoral stimulation on the left of the clitoris while left-handed women favour the right side. Have fun testing out the theory!*

7) Awesome oral

Mouth-to-clitoris action can be sensational or so-so depending on your partner's technique and your confidence. The key is for both of you to be relaxed and comfortable, as it can take some time for you to reach orgasm (20 minutes on average). Get him to vary direct up-and-down licks on and around the clitoris with long surprise licks down the length of the vaginal area. He could also try coming from the side (so he's leaning over one thigh rather than between your legs) and licking across the top of the clitoris rather than just up and down. See **oral sex for you** for more info.

8) Hands-on approach

In most penetrative positions the clitoris doesn't get much direct action, so, when you're on top, try reaching down and touching yourself in the same rhythm as your thrusting actions. (He'll love to watch!) Or get him to reach around you while he's penetrating you from behind. Alternatively, see the **CAT position** for the best clitoral stimulation during intercourse.

> **He has a clitoris?**
> According to sex therapist Dr Andrew Stanway, men too have a 'clitoris' on the underside of the head of the penis just around the frenulum (little flap of skin at the base of the head). It's a high concentration of nerve endings that respond to deep rubbing motions. Other sex therapists don't agree that this spot is actually the equivalent of what we've got – but who cares? Just knowing he has another undiscovered erogenous zone is enough to please most men.

COMMUNICATION
See also: confidence

Seven ways to communicate better in bed:

1) **Compliment each other:** nothing boosts the sexual ego and increases sexual confidence like a compliment.

2) **Masturbate:** the more you know about how to turn yourself on, the easier it'll be to show your lover.

3) **Use one-word commands:** 'left', 'harder', 'slower', 'softer', and 'yes!' are much easier to understand than complicated instructions. One-worders also sound less critical.

4) **Share your fantasies:** describing the dirty deeds that run through your head opens up a whole new world of opportunities (but remember: you don't necessarily need to act things out, just sharing them is often enough). See the **fantasy** section for how-to-share details.

5) **Take turns to be a demanding diva:** it's hard to concentrate on giving and receiving pleasure at the same time, so take turns to ask for what you want.

6) **Talk outside the bedroom:** if you do have a problem, never discuss it in the heat of the moment; pick a quiet time outside the bedroom where post/pre-orgasmic hormones won't complicate the issue.

7) **Put sex into context:** your sex life does not exist in isolation; romance, affection, respect and love all complement raunch.

The 'I-love-that' game

Try this ego-boosting sexual communication game. Take it in turns to finish the sentence, 'I love it when you . . .' Be as specific as possible, so, instead of saying, 'I love it when you kiss my ear' say 'I love it when you nibble my left earlobe, then run your tongue along that sexy spot just below it'. See if you can exchange 'I love that' at least ten times, getting raunchier as you go along.

CONDOMS

See also: contraception, safer sex

SEX FACT! *When used correctly, condoms offer 98 per cent protection against infection and unwanted pregnancy.*

How to put on a condom

Just to refresh your memory . . .

1. Take care opening the packet (never use your teeth, scissors or the ends of sharp fingernails, as you may tear the condom).
2. Hold the condom in one hand and squeeze the teat at the end so no air gets in.
3. Place the condom on top of his erect penis (before it comes anywhere near the vagina) and gently roll the condom down to the base of the penis.
4. As soon as he's ejaculated, the condom must be held firmly in place while he pulls out so you don't spill any semen.
5. Take the condom off, wrap it and place it in a bin (not down the toilet).
6. Use a new condom every time you have sex.

That Condom Moment: How to Handle it

SEX FACT: *Women aged 19–30 are the group least likely to use a condom the first time they have sex with a new partner.*

When you're in a new relationship or about to have penetrative sex with a new partner for the first time (or even the fifth time), broaching The Condom Moment can be tricky. Here's how to handle it with style:

Be prepared

Don't rely on your partner to supply condoms. Every smart girl should carry condoms and long gone are the myths that girls who carry protection are easy.

'I find I can let go more when I'm having sex with a condom on. There are no niggling worries in the back of my mind to stop me enjoying myself.'
Josh, 21, delivery driver

Be practical

Stash them near your bed so you don't have to rummage through a box at the bottom of your wardrobe to find them.

Be practised

Know what you're doing: read the instructions and feel confident that you'll know what to do once you get the packet open. (The old try-it-on-a-courgette trick might be a schoolgirl cliché but it's also quite handy.)

Be assertive

Most men are simple creatures: if it's a choice between no condom = no nookie, and using one, they'll usually take the condom option. The less embarrassed you are about mentioning it, the less embarrassed he'll feel.

'I love it when my girlfriend puts a condom on me – it's so much part of our sex sessions and sometimes I have to beg her to do it. Making me wait is all part of the fun!'
Jamie, 23, press officer

Be confident

Make putting a condom on part of your foreplay repertoire. If you're taking control, it's possible to make that condom moment arousing rather than awkward (see below for ideas).

Be honest

Admit that you're nervous/embarrassed/find it difficult to mention. Chances are he does too but once you're both protected, you'll be able to relax into what you're doing. Using a condom has to be more fun than worrying about STIs or pregnancy.

Sex it Up: How to Make the Condom Moment Part of Your Seduction Routine

Undress to impress

Perform a sexy striptease where he can look but not touch. As part of your routine, gradually take all *his* clothes off, too. Once you're both naked, it's his turn to be 'dressed' to impress. Take a condom and wave it in front of his eyes: he'll know what's coming. Tease him by pretending to open the packet and then changing your mind about it. Finally, take his penis between your hands and roll the condom down his shaft. Straddle him by sitting on his knee with your arms around his shoulders.

Hide and seek

Hide a condom somewhere about your person and tell him that you can make love only if – and when – he finds it. The only way he's allowed to look for it is with his mouth. Not only does he have to kiss you all over but he also has to undo your buttons/zips/bra with his teeth. By the time he's discovered your secret hiding place (naturally, it'll be in your sexiest item of clothing), you'll both be gagging to use it.

Cosmo tip:
If you're using condoms while having oral sex, try using the polyurethane varieties rather than latex: they transfer heat better so your mouth will feel warmer and sexier.

Mouth magic

Try putting a condom on him with your mouth: form your mouth into an 'o' shape (no teeth, please) and hold the condom gently between your lips with the teat facing into your mouth. Next, hold his erect penis in one hand and lower your mouth (and the condom) over the top so the condom sits there like a hat. Use your lips to gently roll the condom down over his shaft, finishing it off with your hands.

CONFIDENCE

See also: body confidence, communication, mind tricks, sexual signature

How to Boost Your In-bed Confidence:

1) Accept yourself and him

- Accept yourself for who you are and forget everyone else: sex isn't a competition of size, shape, stamina or experience.
- Know that you deserve sexual pleasure and satisfaction and, goddamn it, you're going to get it.
- Know you are a sex goddess regardless of whether you're single, attached, young, old, gay, straight, shy, outgoing, experienced, inexperienced, kinky, kooky or downright dirty.
- Accept and respect the likes, dislikes, persuasions and quirks of others, particularly your partner.

2) Communicate with each other

- Have the courage to communicate what you like and don't like with your lover: see **communication** for how-to details.
- Know it's OK to say no to the things you don't like (and yes! yes! yes! to the things you do).
- Dare to share your innermost desires and fantasies with your lover: see **fantasy**.

> **Cosmo tip:**
> If you have serious self-esteem or confidence issues (sexual or otherwise) it may help to see a counsellor or sex therapist.

3) Enjoy everything!

- Enjoy giving pleasure as much as receiving it.
- Perfect the sex moves you particularly love (see **sexual signature** for more detail).
- Give, accept and remember compliments both in and out of bed.
- Be a little selfish in bed: you deserve orgasms just as much as he does.

4) Experiment

- Try something new in bed, just for the hell of it.

- Laugh if things go wrong (they're bound to at some point).
- Have the courage to take a few risks in bed and outside it.

5) Never stop learning
- Masturbate to learn what turns you on the most.
- Be as informed as you can: this book is packed with pleasure-activating info. Read it and enjoy – then go on the Internet or buy some more books/videos/toys/fun.

6) Practise
- Practise safe sex so you can enjoy the moment.
- Practise new sex moves: you wouldn't expect to jump straight into the driving seat of a car and know exactly what to do. Same goes for sex.

CONTRACEPTION
See also: condoms, sexually transmitted infections, safer sex

Contra-ception literally means 'against conception'; in other words, the methods outlined below, when used correctly, are extremely effective at preventing unwanted pregnancy. If a method offers 98 per cent protection, this means that if 100 women have regular sex for a year using this method correctly, two will become pregnant. Crucially, most contraceptives don't offer much protection from sexually transmitted infections (STIs).

SEX FACT. *The first commercial condom available in the UK in the 1930s was reusable: you just had to wash it out after use.*

Your contraceptive choice is totally up to you – experiment with a few contraceptives to find out what suits your lifestyle, relationship status and personality. There are more than thirty different contra-ception pills, hundreds of different condoms and another thirteen alternative methods of contraception available in the UK. If you're looking for reliable protection against STIs, condoms are *always* your best bet. See **Useful Addresses and Contacts** under 'Resources' at the back of the book for organisations that can provide more info and advice. Here are your options:

Contraceptives #1: The Rubber Stuff

Condoms
Usually made from thin latex (rubber), a condom is a tightly fitting sheath that fits over an erect penis, protecting you from unwanted pregnancy and sexually transmitted infections (STIs). When buying condoms look for the BSI Kitemark, which means they've been thoroughly tested, and check the expiry date. A tiny proportion of people are allergic to spermicides used on condoms or to the latex itself, and so can use polyurethane (plastic) condoms produced by most major manufacturers. They are 98 per cent effective.

Advantages: If used correctly, condoms provide excellent protection against unwanted pregnancy and STIs including HIV.

'I tried three different brands of Pill. The first one gave me terrible headaches, the next made me feel fat and spotty and the third killed my sex drive, which was the worst. What's the point of being on the Pill if you don't want sex? I'm sticking to condoms from now on.'
Olive, 28, call centre manager

Disadvantages: Can interrupt the 'flow' of sex. Many new partners find addressing 'the condom moment' difficult. See **Condoms** for more info.

Available: Free from family-planning clinics and sold widely.

Femidom
The Femidom, or female condom, is a thin polyurethane (plastic) bag inserted into the vagina. His penis then goes into this bag inside the vagina, protecting you both from STIs and unwanted pregnancy. You need to be careful that the Femidom is firmly in place and that the penis slides into it rather than down the side. It is 95 per cent effective.

Advantages: Protects against STIs and unwanted pregnancy. Can be used with oil-based lubricants or by people allergic to latex.

Disadvantages: Can be tricky to insert correctly. Disrupts the flow of sex and can be noisy. Also expensive when bought over the counter.

Available: Free from family-planning clinics and widely sold.

Contraceptives #2: The Pill and the Patch

SEX FACT: *It's estimated that the Pill is taken by 70 million women worldwide.*

The Combined Pill

The Combined Pill contains two hormones naturally produced by the body during the menstrual cycle: oestrogen and progestogen (the artificial version of the female hormone progesterone). They work together to stop ovulation and prevent pregnancy. Depending on which brand you use, you either take the Pill for 21 days, then have a seven-day break, or take the Pill continuously (with the last seven in the packet containing no hormones). There are different brands of the Combined Pill available which contain slightly different levels of hormones. It is 99 per cent effective.

'I've been on the Pill for the last ten years on and off. I've never had any side effects that I can remember. I'm really happy with it. It suits my lifestyle and my relationship.'
Cerys, 31, Nurse

Today's contraceptive pills have around a tenth of the hormones that the first pills that came out in the 1960s had, which means radically reduced side effects. If you're prescribed one brand and it doesn't suit you, another might. Some pills, known as 'phasic' pills, are of different colours, indicating different levels of hormones. These can be useful if you've had side effects with the normal 21-day version. The Combined Pill is not recommended for smokers over 35 or those with some medical conditions (your doctor will advise).

SEX FACT: *Contrary to popular belief, it is safe to take the Pill for long periods of time – even up to the menopause.*

Advantages: Beneficial side effects include lighter or nonexistent periods, reduced symptoms of PMS plus protection against ovarian cancer and some pelvic infections.

Disadvantages: Offers no protection against STIs. Can have temporary side effects and, in very rare cases, can cause blood clots (thrombosis). You also have to remember to take the Pill every day, so it's not for forgetful types.

Available: Prescribed free from your GP or local family-planning clinic.

The Progestogen-only Pill

The Progestogen-only Pill (POP), formerly known as the Mini-Pill, contains just one female hormone: progestogen. It works by thickening the cervical mucus to prevent sperm getting through. Because you may ovulate while on the POP (some women do, some don't), it's crucial that you take it at the same time every day in order for there to be enough hormone in your system to keep the mucus thickened. You may experience lighter, irregular periods or they may stop altogether, which is perfectly normal, but some women find it alarming. It is 99 per cent effective.

Advantages: Suitable for smokers over 35 or women who have problems taking oestrogen.

Disadvantages: Irregular periods may be worrying. Offers no protection against STIs. May be less effective for women over 11 stone (70 kg), so check with your doctor.

Available: Prescribed free from your GP or local family-planning clinic.

SAFETY INFO: The Pill is 99 per cent effective if used correctly but some medications or medical conditions (such as vomiting or diarrhoea) radically reduce this figure. Read the advice leaflet for the brand you're using for exact details or contact a contraception expert for advice (see back of this book for details).

Cosmo tip:

Don't want your period for your wedding day/holiday/ important exam? If you're on the regular 21- or 28-day Pill it's perfectly safe to take three sets of pills in succession (it's technically known as tri-cycling, i.e. having three cycles of pills without a break). There are no added side effects or risks and, if you do this, you'll have a period every 63 days rather than every 21. (If you're on tri-phasic pills, the ones that have three different types of pill in one packet, check with your GP first.)

Contraceptive patch

A patch that works like a nicotine patch, administering oestrogen and progestogen into your body through your skin. It lasts for seven days, so you wear a new patch every week for three weeks, then have a week off, just like taking the Pill. It is 99 per cent effective.

Advantages: Works like the Pill but you have to remember to change it only once a week.

Disadvantages: Will have similar side effects to the Combined Pill and you have to have a patch on your body. No protection against STIs.

Available: From your GP or family-planning clinic.

Contraception #3: Pop it in . . .

The diaphragm and cap
A diaphragm is a small soft rubber dome with a firm flexible ring that is inserted into the vagina. It fits over the cervix, preventing sperm reaching an egg. It is used with spermicide, a chemical gel or cream that kills sperm. A cervical cap is similar but smaller and some newer varieties are made of silicone rather than rubber. Diaphragms and caps come in different sizes and you'll need to be fitted with one by a doctor or nurse to make sure it's the right size. They can be inserted any time before sex and must be left in for at least six hours after you have sex to prevent sperm entering the uterus. They are 92–96 per cent effective.
Advantages: Has few side effects and can be used any time before sex (so not as intrusive as using condoms). Does not affect your periods or natural hormone levels.

Disadvantages: Offers no protection against HIV/AIDS but does protect you against some STIs such as chlamydia and gonorrhoea. Cystitis can be a problem for some women if the diaphragm is the wrong size.

Available: Free from your GP or local family-planning clinic.

Contraception #4: The Longer-Term Options

The intra-uterine device (IUD) and intra-uterine system (IUS)
The intra-uterine device (IUD) – formally known as the coil – is a small plastic or copper device that's inserted into the womb and stops

sperm meeting an egg or stops a fertilised egg settling in the womb. The IUS is similar but also releases progestogen, which thickens cervical mucus. Both devices have thin threads that come through the opening in your cervix so you can check it's still in place. Once fitted by a trained doctor or nurse, the IUD can stay in place for three to ten years (the IUS for up to five years) depending on the type. They are 98–99 per cent effective.

Advantages: Once inserted, is there for the long term. Usually can't be felt by either partner.

Disadvantages: Offers no protection against STIs. IUD can cause heavier or more painful periods. Some women's bodies react to the IUD or IUS and reject it.

Available: Free from your GP or family-planning clinic.

Contraception injections

A single slow-release dose of progestogen is injected into your system (usually into the muscles in your buttock), and lasts for twelve weeks (Depo-Provera) or eight weeks (Noristerat). They are 99 per cent effective.

Advantages: No pills to remember every day. You may also get lighter or no periods and fewer PMS symptoms.

Disadvantages: Progestogen side effects, including possible weight gain or loss, acne, headaches etc. Once you've had the shot, any side effects you have are likely to last 10–14 weeks. Also, normal fertility may take a year or more to return after you've had the injection (although can return more quickly, so don't delay in getting a repeat injection, or use barrier contraception). No protection against STIs.

Available: From your GP or family-planning clinic.

Contraceptive implants

A small (4 cm) plastic tube is inserted just under the skin in the upper arm and releases progestogen over a period of three years. Implants are inserted under local anaesthetic. You can usually feel but not see them. They are 99 per cent effective.

Advantages: Can be removed at any time. If removed, normal fertility returns immediately, as it hasn't actually stopped ovulation (as the injections do).

Disadvantages: The usual progestogen side effects apply. No protection against STIs.

Available: Fitted free by a trained doctor or family-planning expert.

Contraception #5: Going *au Naturel*

Q: What do you call a woman relying on the withdrawal method of contraception?

A: Pregnant!

The Withdrawal method

He faithfully offers to withdraw his penis before ejaculation occurs. This is an extremely unreliable method of contraception for a number of reasons: (1) in the heat of the moment, withdrawal can be difficult; (2) ejaculate leaks out of the penis before he climaxes (pre-come), which can, in rare circumstances, cause pregnancy; (3) neither of you has any protection against STIs. The FPA (Family Planning Association) doesn't recognise withdrawal as a method of contraception because it's so unreliable.

Advantages: Involves no preparation or hormone-taking on your part (but a lot of control on his).

Disadvantages: It's totally unreliable and offers zilch protection against STIs.

Available: Any time, any place.

SAFETY INFO: Be warned – contraceptives are only as effective as the people who use them. If you forget to take a pill or tear your condom, the effectiveness of your chosen method is greatly reduced.

Natural family planning/the rhythm method

If you don't mind getting pregnant or actively *do* want to start a family, you can try natural family planning. This involves working out when you're likely to be ovulating so you can either avoid having sex (or use a barrier method of contraception) at this time (or go for it if you *do* want to get pregnant). Ovulation occurs in the middle of your menstrual cycle (usually around fourteen days after the first day of your period). You need to observe and monitor certain changes in your body that indicate ovulation has occurred, including your body temperature (it rises slightly when you ovulate), your cervical mucus (which becomes clear and stretchy when you ovulate) and how long your normal menstrual cycle lasts. You can remain fertile for eight to nine days of your menstrual cycle, so on these days you'll need to use other methods of contraception (or abstain) if you don't want to get pregnant.

Advantages: Up to 98 per cent effective if used according to teaching and instructions. It doesn't involve anything other than commitment and doing what you both do . . .

Disadvantages: Will require training from a qualified FPA teacher, as other factors affect your menstrual cycle and body temperature such as flu, stress and medication. It takes three to six months to learn effectively and both partners need to be very committed to the method and the relationship. No protection against STIs.

Available: Theoretically any time, any place, but in reality it's best to get some advice if you intend to use this method. Plenty of books are available, or talk to a family-planning expert.

Contraception #6: The Really Long-Term Options

Female sterilisation

For a truly long-term – OK – permanent – solution, you could opt for sterilisation, where the fallopian tubes are cut or blocked so an egg can't travel down them to meet sperm. It's a simple operation done under general anaesthetic and permanently stops your fertility.

Advantages: Once you know the operation is a success, it's permanent, so you don't have to think about contraception at all.

Disadvantages: You may need a few days in hospital and rest is needed afterwards to recover. No protection against STIs. Not recommended if you're in any doubt that you might want children in the future, as it's extremely difficult to reverse the process.

Available: Free on the NHS or from a private GP or family-planning clinic.

Male sterilisation (vasectomy)

Male sterilisation, a.k.a. a vasectomy, involves having the tubes that carry sperm from the testes into the penis cut, so sperm aren't present in the man's semen when he ejaculates. It's another permanent option and has few side effects. It's a minor operation that takes 10–15 minutes and can be done at a doctor's surgery or clinic.

Advantages: Simple procedure and, once you know it's worked, you don't have to think about contraception.

Disadvantages: It's another permanent method, so he has to think carefully about whether he definitely won't want children at any time in the future. No protection against STIs.

Available: Free from your GP or family-planning clinic or via a private doctor.

What the Future Holds

New methods of contraception are being researched all the time but often take a while to be approved in the UK. Coming to a family-planning clinic near you sometime soon are:

1) The contraceptive ring

Nuvaring is a small flexible ring that's inserted into the vagina and sits near the cervix. It releases the contraceptive hormones you need, right in the area you need them, so they don't have to travel through your bloodstream and digestive system. You use the ring once a month so you don't have to worry about taking a pill every day or changing a patch every week. Currently available in the US, it's due to be available in the UK at some point towards the end of 2004 or the beginning of 2005.

2) New pill developments

Seasonelle: A hormonal combined contraceptive pill that you take for three months continuously (so you have only four periods a year rather than twelve). It has been approved by the Food and Drug Administration and is available in the US.

Mifepristone: A single pill you take just once a month is currently on trial in the US. It works using slow release-technology like the patches and implants but within your system rather than outside it. It's still in the early stages of development but may be a popular alternative to the once-a-day pills in the future.

3) Combined injections

Lunelle, currently available in the US, is a once-a-month injection of the combined hormones oestrogen and progestogen. Trials are currently in place for a self-injecting system, like the one diabetics have for insulin, that would mean you have to remember to inject your hormones only once a month. No date yet from the manufacturers for general release in the UK.

4) The male pill /male contraceptive implants

Trials are ongoing with a male progestogen-only contraceptive pill and contraceptive implants and patches, and have been for some time. The major side effect in men is that, because progestogen counteracts the effect of his male hormone testosterone, it considerably shrinks his sex drive. The trials are continuing to look at ways to counteract this side effect and combined progestogen pills with testostergen (artifical testosterone) booster shots or patches are being researched in London and Manchester. However, it may be years before the pills and implants become available.

Emergency Contraception

See the **emergency contraception** section for what to do if you've had unprotected sex (sex without a condom) or you think your contraceptive may have failed (i.e. the condom split).

With thanks to the Family Planning Association for help with the research of this section.

CRABS

See under: sexually transmitted infections

Another name for pubic lice (because of their crablike appearance).

CUNNILINGUS

See: oral sex for you

A fancy Latin name for oral sex practised on a woman.

CYSTITIS

See also: genito-urinary infections

Inflammation of the bladder, usually caused by bacterial infection. Sometimes it can be caused by over-enthusiastic sex.

DEEP THROAT
See also: oral sex for him

What is it? An oral sex technique, made famous by the 1970s porn star Linda Lovelace, in which you take the whole of his penis into the back of your throat like a sword swallower swallowing his weapon. Men often want deep throat because they've seen it in porn films and think it's the best blow-job technique ever. It isn't, but they're not to know that until you show them differently. There are two vital things to know about deep-throating: (1) it's pretty over-rated, as the first third of the penis is the most sensitive and, with it shoved down the back of your throat, you can't actually pay it much attention; (2) you don't need a special throat (or a special 'sword') to do it, just a little patience and practice.

What makes it tricky? When you put anything near the back of your throat it triggers an automatic 'gag' reflex as you try to swallow whatever it is. A penis is no exception.

How do I to it? The secret is to learn to relax the back of your throat so your gag reflex isn't triggered. You can try practising on a dildo or vibrator to get used to the feeling before moving on to your man.

Start by gently pushing his penis towards the back of your throat. You may gag at first but, with a bit of practice, you'll learn to relax. Breathe through your nose and swallow if saliva builds up. Gently move your mouth backwards and forwards along his shaft. Once you're really confident with the technique, he can thrust into you while you keep still. (This takes a lot of trust and practice, so wait till you're ready.)

What if I can't get the hang of it? Don't panic: licking and sucking his penis rather than taking the whole lot in your mouth is often more pleasurable for you and him.

DEHYDRATION
See also: alcohol, arousal, lubrication

You may suffer from dehydration down below if . . .
- you've had too much alcohol or taken too many drugs.
- you're on certain medications such as antihistamines, some cold cures or antidepressants.
- you're not turned on enough.
- you're using sex toys or vibrators, which can dry you out.
- you've been in the same position for too long.

Sex without lubrication can be a best awkward, at worst painful. The more turned on you are, the more natural lubricant you're likely to produce, but sometimes what Mother Nature provides just isn't enough. Sexy artificial lubes (from sex shops or from the Internet) can be extremely arousing and enhance your enjoyment.

SEX FACT! *Vaginal secretions are actually produced from the internal vaginal walls so sometimes, if you're receiving oral sex for example, putting a finger inside you to draw out some more natural lubricant is all you need to rehydrate.*

DELAY TACTICS
See also: premature ejaculation, multiple orgasms

SEX FACT: *Many men have learned to ejaculate fast because, when they started masturbating as adolescents, they had to finish quickly before anyone caught them at it. This can be a hard habit to break.*

Here are some red-traffic-light techniques to slow your man down during sex:

The pull-down
A man's balls pull up towards his body when he climaxes. If you sense he's about to come, gently pull them away from his body.

The squeeze
Another telltale sign it's nearly all over is that the head of his penis becomes fully engorged and turns a deep shade of purplish red. To delay ejaculation, squeeze it firmly for about four seconds,

> **Cosmo tip:**
> He can try these techniques on his own while masturbating to learn more about his body and levels of arousal.

which temporarily causes his erection to subside. Continue with a different form of stimulation for a while so his arousal can build up slowly again. The squeeze needs to be firm enough to work, but not painful: this is not an S&M procedure!

Count him down
Imagine arousal for both of you works on a scale of one to ten, with ten being orgasm. Experiment with these different levels of arousal by kissing, touching or licking your partner all over and getting him to identify which level of arousal your action produces. A kiss on the inner thigh might be six, a lick seven, a kiss on his penis seven, a lick or suck eight or nine etc. Next, try the same technique during penetrative sex, experimenting with different positions, speeds or levels of thrusting. Once you're both used to the scale, you can use it to slow each other down. For example, if you're doing something to him that registers eight but you don't want him to climax you can take it down to, say, six and build it back up again. He can also

experiment with this technique when masturbating to learn to control ejaculation using different speeds and techniques.

Stop right now . . .

. . . and feel the moment. In the middle of passionate penetration simply stop all movement and stay totally still and silent. Listen to each other's breathing and your pounding heartbeats; drink in all the senses of the moment. Look at each other and re-engage mentally. This will bring both your levels of arousal down a little so you can have fun bringing them back up again. It's also sexy and intimate.

> **Cosmo tip:**
> If he's worried about coming too quickly on your first night together he could try masturbating first. That way his second ejaculation will take longer than the first. (And you need never know – sneaky but worth it for both of you!)

Breathe through it

As his breathing and pulse rate peak at the moment of orgasm, getting him to concentrate on his breathing can delay his climax. Get him to focus on his breathing and to slow it right down. Breathe deeply and fully together to deliver more calming oxygen to your bodies. With practice, you should both be able to use this technique over and over again.

Mix it up

Get him to alter the types of thrust he uses during penetration. Most men need a steady rhythm at the moment of climax, so simply by slowing down, altering the angle or going from fast shallow thrusts to deep slow ones can slow him down.

Engage his PC muscles

Normally during ejaculation a man's PC (pubococcygeal) muscles (the ones he uses to stop or start the flow of pee) contract involuntarily, but, by learning to control these muscles, he should be able to control when he ejaculates and use them to pause or stop himself. Practice makes perfect with this technique – see **Kegel exercises for him** for more info on exercises to strengthen these muscles.

DILDOS
See also: sex toys

Since ancient times penis-shaped sex toys have been made from a huge variety of materials for use by both men and women. The Egyptians used wood, the Romans carved giant candles in the shape of phalluses and the ancient Greeks used leather, which they would lubricate with olive oil (how Mediterranean!). And, as we all know, Monica Lewinsky used Bill's cigar. With such an illustrious history, how could you fail to be interested in their enduring pleasure?

DREAMS
See also: fantasy

Analysing Your Sexy Dreams
Although there are common themes in sex-dreams (see below) it's most useful to analyse them in the context of what's going on in the rest of your life. Think about how you're feeling, your hopes, dreams and expectations. What's going on in your relationships, at work and at home? What are you worried about? What is your dream telling you about your feelings or emotional state? Sometimes extremely sexual dreams might not have a sexual meaning at all and could actually be related to other aspects of your life. Also bear in mind that dreams are often our brain's way of sorting out the detritus from the day – characters, experiences or stories from newspapers, TV programmes or significant events that happened during your day often filter through your dreams. Try keeping a dream diary by your bed so you can write down your sexy dreams as soon as you wake up. You never know what your subconscious will pop up with next . . .

Common Sexy Dream Themes: What They Mean

Dream sequence #1: sex with a celeb
Possible interpretations:

- You're being adored and worshipped by someone the world thinks is gorgeous. Are you craving more attention from your current partner?
- If you're single, you could be craving a sexy no-strings fling. Organise a girls' night out and go for it.
- Your dream lover could also reflect your own hidden talents or desires. What qualities does he or she have that you could bring out in yourself?

Dream sequence #2: sex with your ex
Possible interpretations:

- Fear of commitment with your current partner or unresolved issues with your ex that you may need to sort out before you can move on.
- Are you going over old ground or repeating a familiar pattern with your current partner or maybe even somewhere else in your life, like at work?
- Are you anxious about something unconnected with the past like a big work project? If your relationship ended badly this could be an anxiety dream like having to take your school exams or driving test over and over again.

Dream sequence #3: sex with someone you know
Possible interpretations:

- Even if you don't want to be unfaithful, a sex dream may help you play out fantasies that you'd never act out in real life.
- You could be comparing this man (or woman) to your partner: what qualities do you like or admire?
- If you're single, having dream sex with a platonic friend may help you suss out whether it's right to take things further.
- It may be giving you signals about unfulfilled fantasies you'd like to act out with your current partner: think about what you actually got up to and whether this could improve your current sex life.

SAFETY INFO: Recurring sexual or violent dreams can be extremely disturbing. Visiting a counsellor, therapist or psychologist may help.

Dream sequence #4: sex with your boss
Possible interpretations:

- This is usually more about your desire to 'get on' at work or how you feel emotionally about your position than actually wanting sex with your manager.
- It can often reflect how you feel you're treated (or want to be treated) at work, particularly if the dream contains lots of issues about power and control.
- It can give you clues about your hidden talents or what you think is expected of you.
- It could just suggest you're passionate about what you do, or, alternatively, you're spending too much time at work and it's taking over everything in your life, including your subconscious.

Dream sequence #5: Sex with another woman
Possible interpretations:

- It doesn't necessarily mean you're gay or bisexual. You may feel particularly close and loving towards a female friend (or even member of your family).
- Your dream lover may be a reflection of the sexual identity you'd like to have or the image you'd like to portray. What is it about her you find sexy? How could you bring that out in yourself?
- You may want your current lover to be more 'feminine' in his approach to sex: try gentler foreplay or discuss how you'd like your sex life to change.
- If you have this dream regularly, it may be a safe way for you to explore lesbian or bisexual desires. It might be worth talking to a counsellor about how you feel and how to take the next step.

Cosmo tip:
Saying, 'I had this amazingly sexy dream last night' is a great way to introduce a lover to one of your favourite sexual fantasies (and he never needs to know whether it's a real in-your-sleep dream or not).

Dream sequence #6: Sex with a stranger
Possible interpretations:

- Again, this man or woman may indicate what qualities are lacking in your current relationship or what you're looking for in a partner.
- You may not be getting enough sex in real life (or getting too much, so sex is on your mind all the time).
- You may feel freer in your dream to let go of inhibitions you have and experience things you wouldn't normally dare do. Analyse what they are and think about any elements that could enhance your real relationship.

Dream sequence #7: Explicit fantasies you've never tried in real life

- Often these are 'facing-your-fears' dreams and could relate to things you're scared of or risks you need to take in any part of your life, not just sexually.
- These could be your secret fantasies: think about what you enjoyed/didn't enjoy about the dream and work out what you'd like to try (or discuss with your partner) in real life.
- Think about the 'themes' of these acts: if you dream about having sex in front of an audience, you could be craving more attention from your current partner. If you're being tied up, you could be feeling restricted in your relationship or maybe even at work.
- These could simply be an outlet for your creative imagination: the weirder and more wonderful the better. Enjoy them!

DRESSING UP
See also: fantasy, role-play

Five reasons why dressing up for sex is great for your love life:

- It instantly changes your identity in the bedroom.
- It allows you to act out your fantasies (or his), adding erotic visual details that turn you both on.
- It gives you licence to act in a way the 'real you' wouldn't dare to.

- The feel of the fabrics adds instant sensuality to you lovemaking.
- It makes the process of getting ready for sex, sexy.

Three reasons why dressing up for sex is bad for your love life:

- It can make you feel stupid or uncomfortable.
- It can make you feel detached from the real you.
- If you're doing it purely for the enjoyment of your partner and don't get anything out of it yourself, it can inhibit your enjoyment.

Dressing up works best when you're both really into it. The more you get into your character, stick to it and act the part, the more arousing the whole experience will be. Go for it: your starring role awaits . . .

Your Sexy Dressing-Up Box
Have these naughty items at the ready:
1. Sexy underwear – have a selection of different types suitable for different bedroom roles: pure white items for vestal virgins, raunchy red for call-girl play, basques for bordello raunch, not forgetting those old classics, stockings and suspenders.
2. Hats – an incredibly simple way to take on a new persona in bed. Ride him like a cowgirl in your Stetson, turn into Chantelle the sexy cigar-smoking chanteuse with the addition of a simple beret or play the princess and have posh sex in your tiara.
3. Wigs – nothing transforms your persona more quickly than going from a blonde to a brunette to a redhead. Wigs offer you something to hide behind and create a stunningly novel visual image for him.
4. Masks – again, you have something to hide behind that adds an element of mystery and surprise to your lovemaking.
5. Shoes and boots – wearing your favourite shoes in the bedroom gives you *Sex & the City*-style confidence and, if you're wearing heels, makes you look taller and sexier.
6. Tactile fabrics – anything that feels sensual against your skin or his is going to feel great in bed.

7. Uniforms – think saucy French maid (don't forget your feather duster), Britney-style sexy schoolgirl, naughty nurse, police-woman, traffic warden, security guard. Check out specialist uniform shops for the real deal or sex-toy websites for the sex-rated versions.

8. Accessories – simple things like a feather boa, a string of pearls or a bondage-style choker can all enhance your lust life. Bonus: they can be used as naughty sex toys against his body too!

Cosmo tip:
You don't have to go for a full top-to-toe outfit to enjoy the benefits of dressing up. Just wearing something you don't usually wear to bed, like full makeup, a sexy bra or even new sensual body lotion, can allow you to behave in a sexy new way.

DRUGS
See also: alcohol

For thousands of years, drug taking and sexual activity have gone hand in hand. Some people say taking drugs can enhance sexual experience. Others say it destroys it. The jury's still out on this one, so it's best to be cautious. Prolonged or habitual drug use almost always kills your sex drive and can have potentially fatal effects on you and your relationships. Here's a rundown of common illegal drugs and their effects in a sexual context.

Cannabis/Marijuana

Pros: Can increase sensitivity to touch, sight and smell. Can make you feel less inhibited and more touchy-feely. Your sense of time may be altered so sex seems more intense or to last longer than usual.
Cons: Can make you feel sleepy rather than sexy. Habitual users may lose their sex drive due to lower testosterone levels, and ability to orgasm in both sexes is affected. Affects fertility in women. Smoking also restricts blood flow to the genitals, so arousal is more difficult/takes longer.

Ecstasy

Pros: Feelings of empathy, love or warmth for your partner are common. Physical sensations are sometimes increased, making sex feel more intense. Sense of touch is often heightened.

Cons: It's known as the hug drug, so hugging (or smiling at random strangers) may be all you're good for. Ability to orgasm is affected and climaxing may be difficult. Long-term effects may lower sex drive as levels of feel-good hormones are depleted.

Cocaine

Pros: Can make you feel more confident and can temporarily increase your sex drive and levels of arousal. Increases levels of dopamine in the body, which raises libido levels. (Interestingly, dopamine levels also rise when you first fall in love/lust.)

Cons: Can make you feel paranoid and want to avoid sex. Can cause numbing of the sex organs and inability to get an erection or to orgasm. Long-term use can affect the body's ability to produce dopamine, dulling your natural sexual responses over time.

SAFETY INFO: Mixing drugs and sex is a dangerous combination, particularly (as is the case with most illegal drugs) when you don't know exactly what you're taking. The bottom line: there are many better ways to enhance your relationship.

LSD/Acid and Magic Mushrooms

Pros: Can cause altered state of consciousness or altered sensory perceptions, which can enhance sexual experiences.

Cons: Can cause altered state of consciousness or altered sensory perceptions that are bad, scary or disturbing. Hallucinating during sex can be unpleasant or traumatic and can adversely effect your relationship (say if you perceive your partner in a disturbing way). Even worse, you have no control over what happens to you.

Amphetamines (Speed)

Pros: Is a stimulant, so can sometimes temporarily increase sex drive.

Cons: Sex organs can decrease in sensitivity, making sex last too long. This can cause dryness, numbness and pain. Users can be too jittery or hyped up to want sex in the first place.

SAFETY INFO: If you're considering using illegal drugs for sexual purposes check out the wealth of information on the Internet, but remember that some sources of info are more reliable than others. Mixing illegal drugs or mixing drugs with alcohol is never a good idea.

Poppers (Amyl Nitrate)

Pros: Can increase sensitivity to light and music and increase desire for sex. Can relax muscle fibres, so are sometimes used to heighten the enjoyment of anal sex.

Cons: Overuse can lead to inability to gain or maintain an erection and vaginal dryness.

Opiates (Heroin, Morphine)

Pros: For sex, none.

Cons: Dramatically decrease sex drive, interest in sex, ability to become aroused, maintain an erection or orgasm plus other long-term health problems.

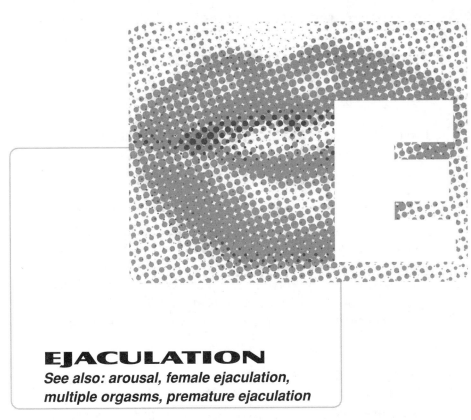

EJACULATION
*See also: arousal, female ejaculation,
multiple orgasms, premature ejaculation*

Ejaculation is the physical sensation of semen being propelled from the body at the point of male orgasm. Please note: ejaculation and orgasm for men are not exactly the same thing. For most men, they happen pretty much simultaneously with the muscular contractions and feelings of intense sexual pleasure of orgasm being followed swiftly by a warm rush of fluid from the penis. To experience multiple orgasms, some men can control ejaculation (i.e. hold back from the point of no return) yet feel waves of orgasmic pleasure. Others (those highly trained Taoist or Tantric types) can even experience full orgasm while withholding their ejaculate completely. **Female ejaculation**, the expulsion of a clear semen-like fluid at orgasm, is extremely rare but does exist (and, no, it isn't pee).

EMBARRASSING NOISES
See also: vagina

If you're sexually active and have ventured beyond the missionary position, you've probably experienced the undignified sensation of your vagina making embarrassing fart-like noises after intercourse or foreplay.

This noise is not your vagina rudely breaking wind purely to shame you (although these noises are commonly known as 'fanny farts'). It's the air that's been pumped into it by the energetic activities of your lover/dildo/vibrator/fingers escaping. A cunning way to avoid this noise is to subtly insert a finger into your vagina, expand the wall slightly, then bring your finger out very slowly. This lets the air out gradually without the accompaniment of any sound whatsoever.

EMERGENCY CONTRACEPTION
See also: contraception, sexually transmitted infections

Had sex without a condom and don't want to get pregnant? Here are your options:

Option 1: Within three days . . .
The Emergency Contraceptive Pill can be taken up to 72 hours after you've had unprotected sex. It's available free from your GP or family-planning clinic or over the counter at pharmacies for around £25. The sooner you take it after having unprotected sex, the more effective it is.

Option 2: Within five days . . .
Up to five days after having unprotected sex (and possibly even longer), you can have an IUD (intra-uterine device) fitted by a doctor. This works by thinning the womb lining so a fertilised egg can't be implanted. Obviously this is much more intrusive than the Emergency Contraceptive Pill but can be useful if you've missed that 72-hour window.

> **SAFETY INFO:** *Emergency contraception does not protect you against sexually transmitted infections (STIs). If you've had sex without a condom you're at risk of contracting an STI, so get tested.*

ERECTILE PROBLEMS

See also: erection, performance anxiety, premature ejaculation, Viagra

When Things Go Wrong . . .

Failing to get or maintain an erection can happen for all sorts of reasons: stress, too much alcohol, heavy smoking, lack of desire, various medications (including antidepressants), low testosterone levels, feeling under the weather or just being exhausted can all cause his penis not to perform as it should. Serious conditions such as diabetes, heart disease and high blood pressure also affect his hardness. Erectile dysfunction (i.e. malfunction of his favourite toy) varies in degrees and can include:

- getting hard when he's on his own but not with a partner.
- waking up with an erection but not being able to sustain it during any sexual activity (either during masturbation or with a partner).
- getting hard just before sex but not being able to stay hard through penetration.
- getting hard then going floppy again very quickly.
- never getting hard.

This becomes a problem only if this is a recurrent or ongoing event. Serious erectile dysfunction is more common in older men.

What can cause erectile dysfunction?

The causes are sometimes psychological, sometimes physical. A common physical cause is when the cells that usually keep the blood in the penis fail to do the task effectively, so the blood that's been pumped in leaks out again, causing him to lose his erection quickly. Psychological causes often include performance anxiety and times of extreme stress or pressure. Various illnesses and medications can also cause erectile dysfunction.

SEX FACT: *Smoking can seriously affect his ability to get and stay hard, as nicotine constricts the arteries, particularly around the penis.*

What He Can Do About It

First he needs to discover whether the cause is physical or psychological. All men have a number of unconscious erections while they sleep. A doctor or sex therapist can prescribe a special penis ring that can measure nocturnal erections. If he's getting erections in his sleep or only at some times (like on his own rather than with a partner) it usually means the problem is psychological rather than physical.

If the problem is psychological, sex therapy can be extremely effective. This usually consists of lots of massage, taking the focus away from penetrative sex (so calming performance anxiety) and using nongenital touching to become aroused rather than putting all the focus on the penis. Physical causes can be treated by a doctor and involve any of various measures, such as a penis ring round the base of the penis (preventing the blood flowing out again), penis pumps (which help him get hard), drug therapy such as testosterone or Viagra, penis injections and sometimes surgery. A doctor will need to do a number of tests in order to prescribe the right treatment, often combined with some form of counselling.

> **Cosmo tip:**
> Keeping physically fit helps keep the blood pumping round your body and will help keep the penis happy, hard and healthy, too.

What *You* Can Do About It

- Don't take it personally: it really isn't you.
- Be sympathetic; listen if he wants to talk about it but don't push him if he doesn't.
- Avoid penetrative sex but don't avoid sex altogether: go for oral action and as much nongenital touching as you can stand.
- Compliment him on his other sexual techniques: boosting his confidence can often be the sexual boost he needs
- If the problem is long-term, advise him to go to see a doctor or sex therapist: these problems can usually be sorted over time with the help of a supportive partner.

SEX FACT: *Depression is a major cause of erectile dysfunction in men and can often be a vicious circle: the more depressed he feels, the more downtime his penis has, the more it affects his self-esteem and so on.*

ERECTION

See also: arousal, erectile problems, penis

SEX FACT: *The average time a man can maintain an erection is around 40 minutes. The younger he is, the longer he'll stay up.*

The Biological Bit

When a man is sexually aroused, stimulating messages are sent from the brain to a set of muscle cells around the base of the penis. These then relax, allowing blood to be pumped into the penis. The penis becomes engorged with blood, darkens in colour and stands to attention, causing an erection. The pressure of these engorged cells closes the veins around the base of the penis so the blood doesn't flow out again.

The Fun Stuff

The direction of his erection may not be the same as the man standing next to him. Some erections can point straight outwards at 90 degrees, others can look kind of kinked. Some can even point down. These are all perfectly normal. You can increase your sexual pleasure and his by choosing your sexual position to match the angle of his dangle. Here's how:

If it's at 30 degrees (i.e. upwards towards his stomach): have sex with you on top leaning forwards towards him.

If it points straight up: sex standing up or in the standard missionary position will be good for you both.

If it points straight out (at 90 degrees to his body): crouching on top of him (rather than sitting) in an upright position will feel good for both of you; the missionary position with your knees up to your chest is also good.

If it points downwards: try the reverse cowgirl where you're on top but facing his feet rather than his chest; lean forwards slightly towards his knees.

If it points to one side: experiment with you on top leaning over whichever shoulder his penis points towards; you'll need to adjust yourself a bit to work out what's best for both of you.

SEX FACT: *An erect penis can hold eight times as much blood as a non-erect penis.*

EROGENOUS ZONES
See also: astro hotspots, nerve endings, zone orgasm.

Dictionary definition: an area of the body sensitive to sexual stimulation.

Cosmo **definition:** any part of the body that tingles, zings, throbs, pulses, warms, tickles or thrums when stimulated by another part of your body, his body, a foreign body or even just by thinking about it sexually; otherwise known as moan zones, hotspots or sites of specific sexual interest.

Bleedin' obvious erogenous zones (don't pretend you don't know these already):
- the genitals (in both sexes, obviously)
- the breasts/nipples (yup, that's in both sexes too)
- the lips: that's what makes kissing so electric
- the bottom

Not-quite-obvious erogenous zones:
- the perineum (the patch of skin between the anus and the penis/vagina)

- the hairline (all the way around the face and neck)
- below the ears
- the inner arms/elbows
- behind the knees

'Ooh – those indents at the base of my spine in between those two little knobbles – just a light stroke there and I'm anyone's!'
Lisa, 34, care worker.

Obscure erogenous zones you might not know about:
- the soles of the feet (especially the instep for women)
- the spot below the ankle bone (especially in men)
- the skin between the fingers and toes
- the brain: yup, your sexual imagination is the powerhouse behind all your sexual responses – see the **fantasy** section for details on how to get it into training

Everyone has unique-to-them erogenous zones just waiting to be discovered. Try the techniques below to find out yours and his . . .

Discover Those Moan Zones

Technique 1: On your own
Start by relaxing in a warm bath. Afterwards, arouse yourself by stroking and caressing your body with a little massage oil or body lotion. Start at your feet, working the oil in between your toes and around your ankles. Make a note of all the sensations you feel as you touch each part of your body. Work your way up your legs, around your thighs and belly (avoid your genitals). Caress the backs of your knees and your thighs, move up to your buttocks and the small of your back, then move on to your upper body, stroking your arms until they tingle and massaging the back of your neck with your fingertips. Stroke your abdomen, down to your pubic hair, around your breasts and across your hips (again, avoiding obvious zones like your nipples). When your body is fully awakened, try thinking through your sexiest fantasy. Continue caressing different parts of your body, experimenting with different touches from light strokes to deep massages. Finally, finish the exercise by moving one hand on to your genitals but keeping the other on a new erogenous zone you've

> **Cosmo tip:**
> Try running your hands all over his body mere millimetres away from the skin so you're just brushing the hairs rather than actually touching him. It's incredibly erotic.

discovered. Continue stimulation in both places until you climax. (Note: he can do this exercise on his own, too.)

Technique 2: With a partner

This time you're going to be mapping each other's secret hotspots. Start with both of you relaxed and naked. You go first by touching him in any area of his body away from his obvious zones, either starting with his feet (working upwards) or with his head and neck (working downwards). This time, you need to stroke areas no bigger than 5 cm (2 inches) at a time.

Every time you touch a new area, he has to rate how your touch feels from minus three for totally annoying, to zero for not so sensitive, to plus three for extremely erotic. If he gives a low rating, experiment with different touches and strokes to see if it ups the arousal level on that part of the body. If it doesn't, move on to the next area. Once you've been all over his body finding new hotspots, he does the same with you. When you're having sex you can use this

> **Cosmo tip:**
> Rubbing any part of his body in the direction of the penis sends blood pumping to his most obvious erogenous zone. Try firmly massaging his inner thighs with upward strokes or using flat palms with a downward motion on his abdomen.

new-found knowledge to tease these sexy new spots with your tongue, fingers or any other object, such as a feather or a silk scarf.

'My secret sexspot is that little indent where the ear joins the neck. A hard tongue pressing and rolling around there makes me forget where I am.'
Paul, 23, furniture restorer

EROTIC MASSAGE

See also: masturbation for him, mutual masturbation

Your Back-to-Basics Masterclass

What you need

A warm room, a naked partner, a towel to lie on, a flat comfy surface, such as your bed, and some massage oil. Either choose a neutral base oil, such as sweet almond, plus a few drops of your favourite essential oil, or try some erotic oil from a sex shop or toy website.

'The thing I love about massage is that it can suit any mood. Sometimes I just want to be totally relaxed; other times it's an incredibly intimate part of foreplay that gets really raunchy.'

Belinda, 32, product manager

What to do

1) Get your partner to lie on the bed on his front and sit astride him on top of his buttocks (avoid sitting on his lower back).

2) Rub a generous amount of oil between your fingers to warm it up so your hands will glide across his body. Next, start to explore your lover's body with long, sensuous strokes: take it as slowly as you can. Always keep one hand in contact with your partner's body at all times during a massage even if you're reaching for more oil or changing a CD. It emphasises your carnal connection.

3) Start with the neck and shoulders, which are packed with nerve endings. Use your hands to stroke and knead his skin, experimenting with different pressures and speeds.

4) Move on to his back using strong sweeping movements. Try placing both palms on his shoulders, then move them firmly in opposite circles. Work outwards and away from the spine, moving down the back and over the buttocks; then work back to the shoulders again.

5) Once you've reached the buttocks, spend time kneading and caressing them with slow sensual strokes. Make fists with your hands and swirl them over his skin. Reach between his legs with flat palms and move them down his thighs. You're aiming here to get tantalisingly close to his penis but not quite close enough.

6) Move down his legs, focusing on long strokes up and down his thighs and calves. Once you've stroked right down to his calves, start to move up again with long sweeping movements till you're back between his legs and around his buttocks.

7) Next, turn him over and repeat the whole process from top to bottom, avoiding his penis. Top up the massage oil so your hands are constantly slippery.

8) Once you've caressed him senseless, move on to his penis. Keep your strokes long and flowing in tune with the rest of your massage. See **masturbation for him** for some specific new moves. Alternatively (if you can both bear it) leave the massage without touching genitals and swap roles so you get to be massaged.

> **Cosmo tip:**
> Don't talk when you get hands-on. This heightens the effect of any massage, as it means all his attention is focused on your touch rather than being distracted by your voice.

Sex it up by . . .

• using the pads of your fingertips all over his body as if they were spider's legs wandering around: it's a highly arousing yet light touch;

• performing the whole massage with both of you naked; avoiding the obvious erogenous zones gets oh-so-much harder;

• massaging his body with your body – once you're both smothered in oil, use each other's body (rather than your hands) as the massage tools.

SAFETY INFO: If you're moving from erotic massage to penetrative sex, remember that any oil-based lubricants (including most massage oils) aren't compatible with rubber or plastic (polyurethane) condoms, as they rot the latex. Either use a water-based lubricant or keep the massage oil away from your genitals.

Ex-boyfriend sex
See under: X-boyfriend sex

EXHIBITIONISM
See also: outdoor sex, stripping, voyeurism

Although exhibitionism usually means you love to be watched in a sexual context, the heart of the experience isn't usually the putting-on-a-show part. It tends to be the feeling of being adored or worshipped by others while you're lost in sexual ecstasy.

Here's how to get a little exhibitionism into your life:

Use Your Mind
Often it's the *idea* of exhibitionism that's actually the arousing part. Think carefully whether you want to turn your show-off tendencies into reality. Fantasy is often a lot more fun. Think about it. How else can you be on stage in front of, say, all your ex-boyfriends with jealousy seething in their eyes, making love spectacularly to your current partner? How else can you safely be on set at your very own porn film, where you – the star (and director/producer, naturally) – have the biggest trailer, the hugest entourage and the sexiest co-stars? Your fantasies are limitless, so you can indulge in any kind of showing-off activity you like (without the risk of disappointment or arrest). See the **fantasy** section for more info.

> **Cosmo tip:**
> Remember that flashers are extreme exhibitionists who cause offence or distress. If you fancy showing off, consider the effect of your actions on innocent bystanders. If you expose yourself in public you can be arrested, so be careful and considerate.

Have Sex Outdoors
The thrill and possibility of people watching you get down and dirty in the great outdoors is often more arousing than actually having others' eyes upon you. As the law stands at the moment, sex outdoors is legal in the UK so long as no one can see you (it's deemed an offence if they can). See the **outdoor sex** section for more info.

Put on a Strip Show
The anticipation of showing off can be an incredible turn-on, so, if you fancy stripping, make sure you plan your sex show down to the last dirty detail. By the time you tie your naked man to a chair ready

for your show, your adrenaline and arousal levels will be sky high. Make the music loud and your moves outrageous. See the **stripping** section for step-by-step how-to info.

Exhibitionism for the shy
Try These Not-So-Blatant Suggestions For Shy Show-offs
• Make love with the light on if you usually do it in the dark.
• Have sex in front of a mirror so you can watch yourself and watch him watching you.
• Have sex with the window open so you're almost-but-not-quite doing it in public.
• Have sex on a balcony on holiday. If he's behind you and you're both leaning over the balcony, you should be able to get away with it.

'We came home quite drunk one day and had sex in the living room with all the lights blazing. Although the blinds were down, the thought of people in the street being able to see what we were up to gave me a huge buzz.'
Ellie, 35, printer

EXPECTATION

Get your sexpectations right: sex therapists talk about the 2–2–6 rule. Out of every 10 times you have sex, twice will be mind-blowing, twice you'll wish you hadn't bothered and six times it'll be 'nice'. With two of you involved, there'll be the times when your 'wish you hadn't bothered', is his 'mind-blowing'.

FAKING
See also: orgasm

Ninety per cent of young women admit to faking. Reasons include 'to flatter him', 'because I was tired', 'because he'd had too much to drink' and 'to see if he'd notice the difference'.

Thirty per cent of young men admit to faking. Common reasons include 'not to hurt her feelings', 'because I was tired', 'because I'd taken too many drugs/had too much to drink'.

'Sometimes you just know you're not going to come, whatever he does. So long as you both know that, then there's no need to fake anything.'
Sarah Jane, 22, student

'I only ever fake it for women I like or the ones who aren't so confident in bed. It really boosts their ego – I like to think of it as a service I'm providing them with.'
Mark, 31, estate agent

Reasons For Faking

- You're knackered and just want to get it over and done with – just this once . . .
- It'll boost his ego (fine, if he's a fragile little soul but it won't make him better in bed in the long run).
- You fancy yourself as the next Meg Ryan and enjoy 'performing' in public places.
- He really is crap in bed, nothing he does is ever going to work.

Reasons Against Faking

- He'll think he's fantastic in bed when he isn't.
- Whatever he's doing that isn't rocking your world, he'll do again because he thinks it works.
- A faked one-night stand could lead to a ten-year marriage, in which case back-tracking may be a little tricky.
- You won't be getting the pleasure you deserve.

FANTASY
See also: dressing up, role-play

Fantasies are fun, free and flexible and, if kept to your imagination, totally safe sex. Also, the more you fantasise the better your sex life will be. Fantasies are a safe way to let your mind wander into forbidden territories you might not go to in real life. Just because you imagine something, it doesn't mean you necessarily want to act it out (although that could be an option). There are absolutely no rules in fantasy land. Nothing is right or wrong, good or bad (and remember that bad can feel very, very good!), forbidden or impossible. You are ultimately in control and have the power to make whatever you want happen. It is incredibly empowering to know that *you* are responsible for your own sexual pleasure and don't have to wait for someone else to turn you on.

SEX FACT: *The hormone testosterone is thought to be responsible for the development of the sexual imagination, which may explain why men fantasise twice as often as women do (and explains why adolescent boys' sexual imagination goes through the roof when they hit puberty).*

Male v. Female Fantasies

Although themes are common, the way fantasies are played out in the male and female sexual brain are subtly different. Here's how:

Male fantasies:	Female fantasies:
concentrate on explicit action.	concentrate on details and build-up.
tend to isolate the physical sex act.	tend to have a detailed storyline before the sex.
tend to be visually oriented: he can see an exact picture of what's going on.	tend to be more sensual: you can hear, feel, smell *and* see what's going on.
are action-oriented, concentrating on what he's doing/how he's acting.	are emotion-oriented, concentrating on how you're feeling in a situation.
are often impersonal, involving strangers or several partners there only for sex.	often involve relationships and emotional attachments forming with specific people.
tend to be more common when he's not getting any sex.	tend to be more common when you're having a lot of sex.

Most Popular Fantasy Themes for Both Sexes
1. Sex with your current partner
Men are more likely to visualise their partners in scenarios they are yet to experience together whereas women are more likely to replay past sex scenes you've already enjoyed together.
2. Sex with someone you know who isn't your current partner

3. Sex with a celebrity
4. Sex with another woman
5. Forced sex
Even though your imagination might conjure up a masked man, you are in control of this fantasy and the actual sex tends to be arousing rather than painful or violent.
6. Taboo acts
A catch-all category for all those really forbidden things we may daydream about (and wouldn't dare to share with anyone else). Sex with animals, relatives, religious figures, satanic sex rites all come into this category.

SEX FACT: *Two in three men have fantasised about their female colleagues and friends naked.*

Fantasy Fun Stage One: Developing Your Sexual Imagination
Try these exercises to develop your inner sexual world and unleash the fantastic potential locked up in the naughty part of your brain.

Visualise your desires
The best time to develop your fantasies is while you're masturbating. First, conjure up a fantasy scenario or character that usually turns you on. Once you have the basic image in your head, fill in extra details so you're visualising everything in the scene and connecting yourself to all your senses. The point is to make this 'picture' as vivid as you can, using as much detail as you can muster. As you touch yourself, really let your mind go and involve yourself in the images you're creating.

> **Cosmo tip:**
> Use your fantasies as before-play. Start thinking about sexy scenarios in the bath, the taxi home after a night out or while you're snuggled on the sofa together. It'll heat up your body and mind and make you ready for action.

Develop the story
Once you've created a detailed image, take your fantasy partner into different situations in your head, playing with other ideas that you think might

turn you on, such as people watching or a change in location. Again, engage all your senses.

Use your fantasy when you like

Once your fantasy is fully developed, you can use it whenever you need it either during sex with your partner or when you're on your own. If your fantasy involves your current partner, fantastic: use all the details of that fantasy next time you're with him. Unless you choose to share your fantasies, the secrets of your imagination are totally safe.

Use it where you like

Practise developing your fantasies any time, any place, rather than just saving them for the bedroom. Try using your commute home for a little sexual self-help. Spot the sexiest man in the train carriage and imagine exactly what you'd like to be doing with him right now. Think of it as a sexual workout for your brain – the more you exercise it, the fitter (and more flexible!) it'll become. Think of a different sex scenario every day to build up a great repertoire.

> **Cosmo tip:**
> For a secret head trip that'll make you think and act differently in bed, try imagining you're the man and he's the woman: it'll make you behave in a sexy new way (and he'll never know why . . .)

Fantasy Fun Stage Two: Sharing with Your Lover

Sharing your fantasies with your lover can be incredibly erotic – just the sound of your voice describing dirty desires is a turn-on for both of you – and amazingly intimate, making you feel closer to your man's body and soul. Sharing your secret sex thoughts, even if you have no desire to actually act them out, can also send out subtle I-want-that messages to your man that may change your bedroom behaviours for the better. It also allows you to discuss sexual scenarios that you'd never dare try in real life. Alternatively, discussing them with your

'I love it when my girlfriend tells me her fantasies. She whispers them in my ear as she kisses my neck, and it turns us both on. We don't even need to act them out – just hearing them is enough.'
Toby, 25, account manager

partner can be a kind of rehearsal for something you'd like to try: you're testing the water to see if similar activities would appeal to him.

Sharing: The Rules

Before you dare to share, follow these rules:

1. Be open and honest but also non-judgemental – it takes a lot to share fantasies, so don't laugh, cringe or tease each other about your raunchy revelations.

2. Be careful whom you choose to share with: exchanging fantasies is incredibly intimate and takes a huge amount of trust.

3. Whatever happens in your relationship, never use your knowledge of each other's fantasies as a weapon or act of revenge.

4. Don't reveal anything that may hurt your lover or make him feel insecure.

5. Just because you dare to share it, it doesn't mean you or he want to act out your fantasies: make it clear you're just talking at this stage.

Be equal

If you start an exchange of erotic ideas, start with milder fantasies, taking it in turns to get raunchier and ruder. Make it clear you're talking about things in the abstract rather than things you'd really like to act out.

Try erotic story-telling

Try writing down a list of your top five fantasies and put them into a hat. Both of you then pick one out and read what it says on the paper. Whether it's your fantasy or his, you have to start a story involving this sexy scenario. If it's not your fantasy, start telling the story (with you both as central characters if you can) and ask 'what happens next?' to find out how *he* wants to it develop.

Play sex consequences

On a piece of paper start by writing a character's name, fold the paper over, swap it with your lover's and write down a location.

Remember, this should be based on your fantasies so shouldn't be totally random. Next write a sex act or position, swap again and write a prop or accessory. Once you've finished, take turns to create a fantasy story using the words on each piece of paper. You'll end up with stories that combine elements of both your fantasies.

Go online

If you're too scared to talk directly to your lover, try finding a chat room where you can describe your innermost desires while remaining totally anonymous. You'll get all the pleasure of revealing your sexy secrets with none of the embarrassment of watching someone squirm as you tell all.

'I told my fiancée I had a fantasy about being seduced by a policewoman. I was shocked when she came into our bedroom with a police uniform on. She handcuffed me and kissed me all over. It was incredibly erotic and we had fantastic sex.'

Darren, 28, university lecturer

Fantasy Fun Stage Three: Acting Out Your Fantasies

Think carefully about whether you want to move on to this stage. For many couples, simply discussing fantasies is more than enough. Other couples find that, actually, dressing up as Robin Hood and Maid Marion isn't as raunchy as it seemed in their imagination. Be flexible and open to sexperimentation, but never feel forced into something you really don't want to do. If you *do* discover a burning fantasy that you'd both like to try, go for it. Here's how to go about it.

Enjoy the build-up

Once you've settled on your scenario, enjoy the process of getting everything you need in place. Part of the fun of acting out your sexual daydreams is the raunch-inducing build-up. Enjoy shopping around for exactly the right location, venue or accessories.

SEX FACT *Fifty per cent of Cosmo readers have acted out a fantasy, according to Cosmo's latest sex survey.*

Script your scene

If you're going for something for the first time – maybe you fancy pretending to be sexy strangers who have only just met – try thinking up a basic step-by-step script for your encounter. You don't have to write down the exact words you're going to say: just roughly plan out what's going to happen.

Acting out

Choose an unfamiliar location. It's easier to act out a sexy scene or take on a new sexual identity if you're away from the comfort of your own bedroom. Try fantasy play when you're at a hotel or at someone else's house.

'I once casually told my boyfriend I quite like the idea of being tied up while having sex. Next time we went to bed, he held my hands together above my head and ordered me to face the wall: it was such a turn-on to think he'd remembered our drunken conversation and was acting on it in a subtle way. That was enough for me – fantastic!'

Linda, 32, interior designer

Play-act rather than act out

You don't have to be totally literal when you're acting out your fantasies: often just taking a theme is enough. For example, if you fantasise about giving a sex show, try having sex in front of a mirror so you can watch the 'show' yourself. Want to have sex with two men? Try using two vibrators, or a vibrator alongside your lover. Top-to-toe costume and a room full of props is often not necessary.

Go as far as you want

If you get totally involved in fantasy play agree a safe word that means you stop what you're doing straight away. Go for a neutral word like 'red' for stop rather than words like 'no' or 'stop' that might often mean the opposite in the heat of the moment.

Cosmo tip:
Fantasies, like every other sex act, get boring if you use the same one all the time. Try thinking up new scenarios that turn you on, and bring out your old favourites only when you really need them.

FEET

See also: erogenous zones, oral sex for him

As your feet contain a staggering 7,000 nerve endings (that's only 1,000 fewer than the clitoris), it's worth getting to know your tootsies (and his) in a sexual context. The skin on certain areas of the feet and ankles is also extremely thin, so the nerve endings are very close to the surface (hence that ticklish feeling).

SEX FACT *In both men and women, feet tend to curl involuntarily at the point of orgasm – watch his next time!*

Perfect Preparation

No one wants to touch (or taste) anything but the cleanest feet, so start by bathing your partner's in a bowl of warm soapy water. Ideally, leave your lover for ten minutes or so to relax before you get started, then dry his feet carefully.

Moan-some Massage

1) Once his feet are clean (you can skip the preparation if he's shower-fresh), sit somewhere where you're both comfortable with one of his feet in your lap.

2) Warm up some massage oil between your hands and, with firm strokes, rub the oil all over his feet and up past his ankle bone.

3) Using the pads of both your thumbs below the pads of each of his toes (on the underside of the foot), move them gradually across his foot (in a movement a bit like a caterpillar inching forwards) massaging in circular directions. The more relaxed he is, the less ticklish he'll be. He should try synchronising his breathing with the rhythm of your strokes.

4) Take one toe at a time and pull it gently outwards to release tension all over his body.

5) Finish by massaging the whole of his feet with both hands. Clasp his foot with one hand behind the ankle, then pull your hand across the whole length of the foot. When you reach his toes, start with the other hand at the ankle and so on, so his foot is in contact with one of your hands at all times.

Kinky Stuff for Feet-Friendly Folk

Breast intentions

During the middle of a foot massage, take his feet one at a time and massage them with or between your breasts either by lifting his foot up or bending down over it. It'll be a novel sensation for him and having his toes tickle your nipples can also be arousing for you.

Feel the fire

Take his erect penis between *your* feet and roll it around as if you were trying to make fire with it. This is especially effective if you've just received a foot massage and your feet are still covered in oil. (Remember that oil-based products can react with latex condoms causing them to break, so be careful if you have sex afterwards.)

'Toe jobs really don't do it for me: I just become self-conscious about the state of my feet and find it hard to relax.'
Mick, 28, roofer

Toe the line

Once his feet are clean, try giving him a toe job. Start by licking and kissing his feet, then take one toe at a time, starting with the smallest, and slip it into your mouth, running your tongue across it as you do so. Hold it in your mouth and suck hard (toes are more robust than his penis, so can take more pressure). Next, pull it out very slowly and go on to the next one. This is a great warm-up to oral sex, particularly if you can maintain eye contact with him at the same time.

'Having my toes sucked drives me wild, especially if he uses a hand on my clitoris at the same time. The two sensations are amazing, but I have to be careful not to move my foot too much when I climax – I'd hate to kick his teeth out!'
Rachel, 34, courier

Toe-in-the-hole

During foreplay, he can massage your genitals with his feet by running a toe or two up and down your vaginal area very slowly (make sure you're well lubricated). If he's extra-dextrous with his digits, he could try massaging your clitoris with his big toe or even inserting it into your vagina.

FELLATIO
See under: Oral sex for him

Posh word for blow jobs/oral sex practised on a man.

FEMALE EJACULATION
See also: G-spot – female

Ever felt as if you've wet the bed when you climax? If so, you may be one of the rare women who experience female ejaculation.

Come again?
Exactly. Some women ejaculate a small amount of fluid when they climax, particularly after G-spot stimulation.

What, a female wet patch?
In a way. Although it may feel a little like losing control of your bladder, female ejaculate contains little or no urine. In fact, its chemical composition is more like the fluid that comes from the male's prostate gland.

Is it bad for you?
No. Female ejaculation can be extremely pleasurable (if a little alarming at first) and for some women it indicates the highest level of sexual arousal available.

So how can I ejaculate?
You may do already but not realise it. As all vaginal secretions increase at the point of orgasm, it's sometimes hard to tell the difference. Try stimulating the G-spot (the little patch of skin on the front wall of the vagina about 5 cm/2 inches up) until you feel you're about to come, and then push down on your pelvic floor muscles and let go of any tension around your bladder.

SEX FACT: *Female ejaculation is relatively rare. Scientific studies indicate that between 6 per cent and 14 per cent of women experience ejaculation of fluid at orgasm.*

Any precautions?

Other than putting a towel down, make sure your bladder is empty so you'll feel relaxed and confident that you won't pee.

What do men think of it?

They find it pretty surprising at first but once they get used to it they find it arousing and gratifying, as if they've pleased their partner in a special way.

Can everyone learn to ejaculate?

Probably not, as ejaculation is so rare. If you can, enjoy the sensation. If you can't, don't worry about it. At least you won't have to wash so many towels!

Blimey, will I need to wash down the ceiling?

No. Although porn films seem to show female ejaculation as an enormous gush, it's not normally this dramatic: it's only around 5 ml (one teaspoon) of fluid.

FETISHES
See also: bondage, dressing up, fantasy

Psychologists define a sexual fetish as an object or activity that is necessary for sexual arousal or gratification. In extreme cases, fetishes work like addictive drugs: you start off gradually by, say, liking to keep your shoes on while having sex, but eventually need more and more of your fetish to become satisfied or even remotely aroused; you can't get turned on at all without touching, feeling or licking the shoes.

In milder cases, a certain object, material or activity has the ability to turn you on and heighten your sexual enjoyment. In the right environment, this can be used to improve your sex life and create more intimacy between you and your lover.

SEX FACT: *Men are more likely to develop fetishes than women, maybe due to early sexual responses being triggered by certain objects, like sitting on a rubber bath mat or stroking themselves with the satin edge of a blanket. As female sexual responses tend to be discovered later in life, we're more likely to associate them with relationships than objects.*

Common fetishes include tactile materials such as leather, rubber, silk or fake fur, or specific items of clothing that give you a certain identity, such as killer knee-high boots, a sexy hat or seductive stockings and suspenders. In other cases, it's a certain activity rather than an object that has extreme appeal: some people find they become aroused by having sex in front of an open window with the lights on, or by doing the dirty in a parked car when there are others watching. Whatever your particular sexual interest, the trick is to explore your fetish completely – get to know it by touch, feel and smell – then, crucially, to teach your lover to appreciate what you love.

Sex Fact: Top 5 Most Common Fetishes
1. Shoes and feet
2. Leather, rubber and latex
3. Domination and bondage
4. Piercing
5. Uniforms

'I once went home with a guy who took me into a totally blacked out bedroom with chains hanging from the walls. He sat me down on the bed and asked if I wanted to play with his "little friend". I have no idea who or what his little friend was as I got out of there as fast as I could.'

Naomi, 24, accounts assistant

How To Have Fetish Fun: A Beginner's Guide

Incorporate a shared fetish into your sex life gradually, then use it to turn on your partner in any situation. Here's how:

1) Dress up in a material or item that you or your lover finds erotic (stilettos, rubber, satin underwear – whatever). Experiment with different items or materials until you discover what you both really like.

2) Get your lover to lay on the bed, blindfolded. Sit astride him and ask him to run his hands all over your body, caressing you and enjoying the fetish until you're both highly charged. Take turns to be the one blindfolded – losing the power of sight will heighten all your other senses. Lick, kiss, stroke and smell your object of desire and your partner's body.

3) Remove the blindfold, then use the fetish in foreplay, using as much imagination as you possibly can. If it's stiletto heels, gently run them down his back. If it's fake fur, seductively strip, leaving just your fake fur scarf/jacket on. Make him kiss, fondle and stroke your fetish. Finally, make love wearing your sexy item.

'I have these really high black patent-leather shoes – they make me over six feet tall when I'm wearing them and I couldn't possibly walk in them, so we both know they're only for the bedroom. The weird thing is, I take on a totally different character when I'm wearing them and become totally dominating and in control. The rest of the time I'm a shy little pussycat in bed!'
Jayne, 31, PA

Cosmo tip:
Don't let your fetish take over: use it as an occasional treat rather than an every-time obsession otherwise your lover will think that your inanimate object of desire is more important than he is.

4) When the fetish has significance for both of you, take it further afield. If it's an ordinary object – his tie, for example – you only need to pull on it in public to start him fantasising. And just seeing a glimpse of those knee-high boots will remind you both of the last time you were wearing them.

Tempting Turn-ons
Here's how to bring some common everyday items into your sex life:
Kinky boots: Straddle him while he's standing up and cross your legs behind his back – he'll love the contrast of skin and leather. Alternatively, stand in your boots while he gives you oral sex. Let him stroke his hands up your thighs and over your boots. You'll feel powerful, sexy and in control.

Satin: Get him to fondle your buttocks, inner thighs and vagina through your French knickers, then keep them on while you have oral sex. He can lick you through the fabric at first, then pull your knickers aside so his tongue has direct access to your clitoris while he strokes the rest of you through the fabric.

Police uniform: Arrest him for crimes against the female sex and accuse him of using his truncheon for immoral purposes. Offer to give it a thorough inspection while he's handcuffed to the bed.

Stockings and suspenders: A traditional turn-on – just wiggling a fish-netted leg around the bedroom door will get him hot.

FLIRTING

Flirting is a sexy, seductive art form that can be used to either attract a mate or, when you're in a relationship, to signal your intent for the evening (or the next five minutes). At its core, flirting is about (1) making the most of your natural assets (both the physical and the emotional ones) and (2) making people feel good about themselves. This section is designed to give you a few basic hit-him-with-it signals and to inform you of the messages he might be giving out to you.

Know the signals

Although these tips are divided into you and him, most of them are applicable to both sexes, so feel free to use any of them you want.

Cosmo tip: In general men are notoriously bad at picking up I-want-you signals because they're used to dealing in facts rather than reading emotions, as women are.

SEX FACT: *Over 80 per cent of communication is nonverbal, so body language is the greatest flirting tool there is. Most of it is unconscious: we 'leak' physical clues about our feelings and state of mind.*

Section One: From Afar . . .

Here's what to do if you spot someone across a crowded bar and want to get your message across loud and clear.

You	Him
1) Eye contact – hold his gaze for a little longer than usual: two seconds should be enough (any more than three and he'll think you're a psycho).	1) Body position – check out where he's facing We subconsciously turn our bodies towards someone we find attractive, so, even if he's talking to someone else, if his body's facing you, he's probably interested.
2) Eyelash flick – if you catch him looking at you, look up, look down, then look up again through your eyelashes.	2) Simple smile – if your eye contact's rewarded by a smile, it's an obvious 'let's talk' signal.
3) Engage your imagination – imagine the two of you having sex. It makes your cheeks flush in a sexy way.	3) Mouth magic – if he looks at your mouth while you're talking he finds you attractive.
4) The wiggle walk – to attract attention when walking across a room, place one foot in front of the other as if you're walking along an imaginary tightrope. This automatically makes your bottom wiggle.	4) Body brush – consciously brushing past you on the way to the bar means he wants to get closer to your body.

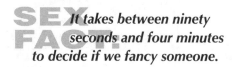

SEX FACT: *It takes between ninety seconds and four minutes to decide if we fancy someone.*

Cosmo tip:

If flirting doesn't come naturally to you, practise flirty body language in front of a mirror. Your body develops 'muscle memory' so it remembers the poses you've practised.

Section 2: In Conversation

You've made a connection and started chatting. Here's how to push things a little further.

You	Him
1) Preen supreme – preening gestures such as running your hands through your hair or twiddling it round your fingers are extremely sexual.	1) Peacock gestures – he'll preen himself, too. If he touches *his* hair it means he subconsciously wants you to touch him there too.
2) Draw his eye to your assets – fiddling with a necklace that draws his eye to your cleavage or touching a sexy shoulder strap points his eyes in the direction of your best bits. It also gives out the message that you're enjoying your body and would like him to enjoy it too.	2) The block – men often use their bodies to block out all the competition. If you're in a group and his body is between you and the rest of your/his friends, he's interested in getting you alone.
3) Touch me – gently brushing your mouth with a finger indicates you want to be kissed. Absentmindedly stroking your throat or the side of your neck shows you want to be touched there too.	3) Touch me, too – if he touches his face while he's talking to you, it means he wants you to touch it soon.
4) Laugh long and hard – using your whole body (rather than just your mouth). This indicates you want to get body to body. It also draws his attention to your open mouth, which makes him think of what you'd do with it in the bedroom . . .	4) Mirroring – to establish instant rapport mirror his body language. If he leans in to pick up his drink at the same time as you, or opens out his body the same way you do, you're probably getting on great.
5) Whisper it – if you speak softly, he'll have to get closer to you to hear what you're saying (lowering your voice a little also makes it sound more seductive).	5) Body alignment – if, when you touch him, he aligns his body so it's facing towards yours, he wants to be touched again.
6) Invade his space – if you're having a drink, try putting something of yours – your hand, your phone, your wineglass – on his side of the table. Subconsciously, you're showing him you want to be in his space. If he leaves it there, he's interested. If he pushes it back, he's not.	6) Open invitation – leaning back with his legs apart means he's inviting you into his space and subconsciously displaying his sex organs.

SAFETY INFO: Although these flirting signs are used by both sexes, it is possible to misinterpret them. Always ask for verbal confirmation if you want to go further than a bit of cheeky banter. And remember that no always means no and should be respected.

Section Three: Back at Yours/His

Up close and personal flirting should be tantalising, tempting and give both of you a teasy taste of things to come . . .

You	Him
1) Lip licking – licking or wetting your lips is an extremely suggestive gesture because it's mimicking what happens to your other lips when you become aroused.	1) Body contact – while you're on the sofa, he'll probably try to get as much physical body-to-body contact as he can. Snuggling up and putting your legs over his knees can help this along.
2) Linger longer – linger over a kiss, hold his head in your hands and hold eye contact for longer than usual to build up the passion.	2) Face stroking – while you're lingering over lip and eye contact, he can stroke your face sing just his fingertips: it's a sensual gesture than can feel electric.
3) Talk dirty – before you remove any clothes, whisper exactly what you'd like to do to him (or for him to do to you) – it's an excellent passion precursor.	3) Longing look – if you're still dressed, his eye will subconsciously be drawn to the parts of your body he wants to touch the most – usually your shoulders, breasts, legs, bottom, and of course, genitals.
4) Footsie index – if he walks across the room to fiddle with the stereo (men always do that), dangle your leg suggestively off the sofa and let your shoe dangle from your heel (works best if you're wearing mules or flip-flops). It's a flirty indication that you'd like to remove more than just your shoes.	4) Multi-tasking – maintaining eye contact and talking to you the whole time while slowly and seductively unbuttoning your clothes can feel extremely sexy (as if it were happening by magic).

FOOD

See also: aphrodisiacs, ice

The Food of Lust: Naughty Nibbles and What to Do With Them . . .

Champagne

Decadent and celebratory, bubbly puts you in the mood for lust. Pour it on to each other's body and drink it down. Try oral sex while keeping the bubbles in your mouth for the ultimate fizzical sensation. Oral also works well with the minty zing of crème de menthe or the creamy texture of Bailey's – those little bottles are perfect for it!

Chocolate spread (or body paint)

Get naked and make your own masterpieces (or write sexy instructions) on each other's body, then get licking. Add a touch of colour with strawberry jam, apricot preserve, blueberry sauce, honey or yoghurt.

Smoked salmon and caviar

Japanese geisha girls entertain their guests by serving sushi on a human platter. Try it at home with some creatively placed strips of smoked salmon and caviar over your torso.

SAFETY INFO: It's always better to use food on **the body than in the body, as anything too alkaline or sugary may upset the natural balance in the vagina, causing an infection.**

Grapes

Play 'find the hidden fruit'. Use your imagination and you'll be surprised at how much fun it can be. There may be a few visible fruits for him to find – but what about the ones he *can't* see?

Raspberries

Skip the ripple and just use the luscious fruits as false nipples. Get him to squidge them into you with his tongue for a sexy smoothie with a difference.

Polos

The minty thrill you feel in your mouth when sucking on a Polo can feel just as exciting on your body parts (or his). Steer clear of the Extra Strong Mints or you'll bring tears to his eyes!

'In my experience, honey and golden syrup are too sticky and chocolate spread looks disgusting. Those smooth fruity yoghurts (the ones without the chunks) give the best texture and taste: you can put them anywhere!'
Issy, 32, solicitor

Mango

Ripe juicy mango has been used in masturbation for centuries. Just cut the skin away from the stone and rub whichever part of your body you'd like to sweeten up. Get him to lick up the juices afterwards. De-luscious!

Cucumbers

So long as it's clean and not too colossal, you (or he) can put it pretty much anywhere.

Food Games

Try these naughty food games next time you're planning a seductive dinner for two.

The naked chef

Try cooking and eating a meal totally naked: you'll look cute in an apron (better still: he will – check out those buns!) and sitting down to a table totally bare can be extremely liberating. Keep food simple (not slurpy!): M&S finger food plus exotic fruit and ice cream are perfect.

Seductive scoffing

This one's more entertaining than strictly sensual, but a bit of a giggle in the bedroom (or at the kitchen table) never did anyone's libido any harm. Take turns to eat as sexily and sensuously as possible, regardless of what you're eating. Act up as much as you can (handy tips are maintaining lots of eye contact, slowing yourself right down and using as much tongue action as possible, or speeding yourself right up as if you have an insatiable appetite, not just for the food). This game works particularly well if you're in a restaurant, where you can order specifically sensuous foods from the menu but at the same time have to maintain some kind of decorum because you're in a public place.

Feeding frenzy

Take turns to feed each other different types of food. This works especially well if the person being fed has their wrists tied gently behind their back or is wearing a blindfold so they have to relinquish all control. Using your fingers rather than a fork will make the whole thing much more sensual.

'I love it when my boyfriend feeds me particularly gooey stuff like ice cream or honey that I have to lick off his fingers. It's the combination of behaving like a naughty child and licking his fingers in a provocative way that turns me on.' Anita, 27, market trader

FOREPLAY

See also: too many sections to mention!

Dictionary definition: sexual stimulation before intercourse. Otherwise known as what happens before 'real sex' begins.

***Cosmo* definition:** what happens, in fantastic sexual encounters before, during and after penetration. Should be renamed: more-play, as women generally want more of it.

SAFETY INFO: Some foreplay techniques (such as oral sex) are of a higher risk than others. If you're in doubt, use a condom.

Top 10 Fantastic Foreplay Rules

1) **Woman always want more:** Teach your man to slow down. The point of foreplay is to enjoy it for itself rather than as a means to an end.

2) **Penetration isn't king:** Since the discovery that over 80 per cent of women need clitoral stimulation to orgasm but don't tend to receive it during penetrative sex, foreplay has taken its rightful place as the important part of lust for women (and men). Penetration is fun, but it's not everything.

3) **Sex is an adventure, not a straight line:** Think of sex as a richly illustrated treasure map with loads of different routes,

adventures and trails. Yes, there's treasure at the end but the fun part is the journey, not just the final destination.

4) **Mix it up:** Surprise your lover with a new technique; take control where you usually remain passive; reward him with a naughty new toy; try something in bed you've never tried before. Variety is *always* the spice of a successful sex life.

5) **Focus on quality, not quantity:** A 45-minute oral sex session means nothing if you're not enjoying yourselves. There's no prescribed time limit for foreplay, so go with what feels right for both of you.

6) **Pay attention to the *whole* body:** We all have sexual hotspots but foreplay shouldn't just be for these tried and tested areas. Discover new and exciting areas to stimulate to make it an all-over body-and-mind sexperience.

7) **Perfect your sexual signature:** When giving pleasure to your partner, perfect the technique you love to do the best (it tends to be one you're good at). Use this often, as, the more you enjoy doing something to your partner, the more enjoyment he'll get out of it.

8) **Ask for what you want:** Show him how, where and when you like to be touched and compliment him when he hits exactly the right spot. Sexual communication is a huge aphrodisiac.

9) **Delay the inevitable:** The longer you take to climax, the bigger the bang will be. Enjoy the build-up and learn how to stay on the edge for as long as possible. (That goes for him, too.)

'The best foreplay tip I ever got? Women want it for twice as long and half as hard as men do. That tends to work for me!'

Joe, 25, student

10) **And finally, throw out the rule book:** Anything goes when it comes to fabulous foreplay. Let your mood dictate the pace, passion and power of every sexual encounter.

FRENULUM

See also: masturbation for him, penis

Did you know?: The little seam of skin that joins the head of the penis to the shaft on the underside, called the frenulum, is the most sensitive part of the penis.

Try this: Flicking it with your tongue when you give him oral sex or massaging it deeply with the pad of your thumb. He'll thank you for it.

GAMES

Game 1: Sexy Spin the Bottle
What you need: Some drinks (preferably champagne), an empty bottle, pen and paper, few inhibitions.

Object of the game: To learn each other's sexy secrets.

Raunchy rules: Divide the paper into eight pieces and place them in a circle around the empty bottle. On two pieces write 'question', on two write 'favour', on two write 'drink' and on the last two write 'admission'. Take turns to spin the bottle and see where it lands. If it points to 'question' you have to answer a sexy question from your lover. If it hits 'admission', you have to admit something raunchy you've never told him before. If it hits 'favour', you have to perform an instant sexual favour of his choice. And if it points to drink take another sip of champers – phew!

Advanced instructions: If you're extra-adventurous, play this game with a group of friends or other couples. You'll be amazed what you discover about each other.

Game 2: Sexy Simone Says

What you need: An up-for-it boyfriend and a bossy streak.

Object of the game: To make your lover your sex slave.

Raunchy rules: Start by facing each other fully clothed and take on the character of 'Simone'. She can be anything you like – sexy French maid, dominating schoolmistress, the choice is yours. Your man must now do everything that 'Simone' asks him. Start with simple commands to warm him up like 'Simone says unbutton your shirt.' or 'Simone says kiss my neck', and build up to more intimate instructions. The beauty of this game is that you get to tell your man *exactly* how and where you like to be touched. If you forget to say 'Simone says . . .' and simply ask for something (it's easy to get carried away!) it's his turn to be in control.

Advanced instructions: This game is perfect for phone sex. Call him at the office and tell the switchboard to put 'Simone' through. This time let him know what *you're* doing by saying something like 'Simone says I'm unbuttoning my shirt' or 'Simone says I'm wearing very high heels'. He'll be a quivering, gibbering mess in no time.

Game 3: The Name Game

What you need: To know how to spell your lover's name and an active imagination.

Object of the game: To use all the letters in your partner's name in a sexual context and be as creative as you can.

What to do: Take turns with this one. You go first. What you have to do is think up a sexual action that contains each of the letters of your lover's name, then act out each of the actions you've suggested, one by one, before moving on to the next letter.

For example if a couple called James and Mandy were playing, Mandy would go first. She might decide to: **J**uggle James's balls (then she has to do it). Stare with **A**we into his eyes while kissing him intensely on the mouth. **M**assage a part of his body of his (or her) choosing. **E**ngage in oral sex for a set number of minutes, then slowly **S**trip for him.

He might then choose to: **M**ove his hands slowly and seductively across her shoulders. **A**rouse his favourite part of her body. **N**uzzle that spot and lick it all over. Go **D**own on her in a sexy way. Then **Y**elp like a dog and be her sex slave (hmm: those Ys are tricky!).

Advanced instructions: Use your partner's full name, including his middle names. Take your time over each task and, if you can, make them get raunchier as you go along.

Game 4: The Lust List
What you need: A great memory and a wild imagination.

Object of the game: To act out a list of sexy actions in the right raunchy order.

Raunchy rules: Snuggle up and start with the phrase, 'In my wildest dreams my lover would . . .' Take turns to add a sensual, sexy or downright naughty action to this list. You then have to remember the action, add another to the list and act them both out. For example, you'd start by saying, 'In my wildest dreams my lover would kiss me on the cheek,' and kiss him on the cheek. He then says, 'In my wildest dreams my lover would kiss me on the cheek and stroke my hair.' He does both actions. You continue with raunchier and raunchier suggestions until someone makes a mistake. Use specific words and details to try to catch him out. If he performs the wrong action or forgets the sequence he has to pay a sexual forfeit of your choosing.

Advanced instructions: Experiment with unusual props to create erotic recall fantasies. For example, if you say, '. . . seductively stroke my wrist while twisting my silver bangle', next time you wear the bracelet, you'll remember all the other actions, too. (Great for naughty work-time day-dreaming!).

GENITAL WARTS
See under: sexually transmitted infections

Nasty little lumps and bumps in and around the vagina or around the penis and scrotum caused by the human papilloma virus (HPV), a common virus that is spread by sexual contact.

GENITO-URINARY INFECTIONS
See also: sexually transmitted infections

Some infections such as thrush and cystitis aren't necessarily sexually transmitted but they can be passed on or made worse by sexual contact, so if either you or your partner has one, you'll *both* need to be treated. Here are the most common genito-urinary infections and what you can do about them.

Bacterial Vaginosis (BV)
What it is: A common infection leading to inflammation of the vagina and caused by rapid growth of natural vaginal bacteria.

Caused by: Anything from using perfumed bathing products in and around the vagina through having an IUD fitted, to having lots of sex. Some women carry BV without any symptoms, so it can sometimes flare up for no apparent reason.

Symptoms: An unpleasant fishy-smelling discharge from the vagina with a yellow–greyish watery tint, which can cause itching or burning around the vagina.

Treatment: Antibiotics or vaginal cream from your doctor's surgery or local GUM (genito-urinary medicine) clinic.

Prevention: Avoid highly perfumed bath or soap products. Can flare up if tampons are left in for too long so change them every four to six hours.

Cystitis

What it is: An inflammation of the bladder often caused by bacteria that usually live in the bowel and anus, spreading to the bladder.

Caused by: Often known as 'the honeymoon disease', because it can be caused when the urethra (the channel that links the bladder to the outside world) is bruised during energetic sex. Sometimes it occurs if you become dehydrated, as the bladder needs to be flushed out regularly to get rid of the bacteria.

Symptoms: Intense burning sensation in the bladder and urethra and the need to pee more than usual. Peeing is often painful and difficult.

Treatment: Antibiotics from your doctor if symptoms persist for more than 48 hours, or over-the-counter medication (this isn't as strong as the antibiotics you get from your doctor).

Prevention: As cystitis is often recurrent, prevention is often better than cure. Try drinking lots of water at the onset of an attack, as this can help flush out the germs (the bacteria that cause cystitis double in number every twelve minutes, so the quicker you tackle them the better). Cranberry juice contains a mysterious ingredient that helps prevent the bacteria from sticking to the bladder wall. Urinating before and after sex can also help flush out the bladder. Avoid rough sex and rear-entry positions, as these can bruise the urethra or cause small tears in it, making it easier for the infection to take hold.

Thrush (Candidiasis)

What it is: An inflammation of the vagina and vulva caused by an overgrowth of yeast naturally found in this area.

Caused by: Anything from a course of antibiotics (so if you're taking them for cystitis you may end up with thrush), through stress, high-sugar diets, and soaps, to wearing tight jeans or other tight-fitting clothes.

Symptoms: Intense itching and a thick cottage-cheese-like discharge. Can be transmitted to men and appears as an itch at the head of the penis or under the foreskin.

Treatment: Over-the-counter antifungal medications in the form of pessaries, pills or creams. Treatment usually works within a week but, if one type doesn't work, try another, as they have different active ingredients. Natural yoghurt applied to the vagina can calm the area.

Prevention: Always wear cotton underwear rather than artificial fibres such as nylon, and avoid tight clothes, which give the infection a warm, healthy environment to grow in. Avoid heavily perfumed soaps and bubble baths and avoid washing your hair in the bath (as shampoo can be just as harsh). If thrush recurs, see your GP for advice.

SAFETY INFO: If you have any form of unusual symptoms, it's best to get everything checked out by a doctor or at an STI or genito-urinary medicine (GUM) clinic, as symptoms of genito-urinary infections are very easily confused with STIs.

GONORRHOEA
See also: sexually transmitted infections

A sexually transmitted bacterial infection passed on through penetrative or oral sex.

GROUP SEX
See also: threesomes

Group sex involves sexual contact between more than two people. This could happen anywhere from a private party, a fetish club, a swingers' event, a deserted car park, or a hotel bedroom to the beach or even on a specially designed cruise ship holiday.

Advantages of Group Sex
- Watching other people have sex can be a huge turn-on.

- Being watched by others while *you* have sex can be a turn-on.
- Group sex can offer sexual gratification without the hassle of commitment (i.e. no strings).
- It can be a way to explore your sexuality or sexual identity or live out a fantasy.
- It's a way to have sex with someone else without lying to or otherwise deceiving your partner.

Disadvantages of Group Sex

- Unless you're in an extremely secure relationship, it can feel uncomfortable or upsetting to see your partner with someone else.
- Many people fantasise about having group sex but find that, in practice, it doesn't live up to their imagination.
- Often one partner is more into it than another, so the balance of power (and enjoyment) in the relationship is upset.
- If your relationship is insecure in the first place, bringing in another partner is often destructive.
- The more partners you share, the higher the likelihood of contracting an STI.
- Even if you're into it at the time, emotions such as guilt, jealousy, shame and insecurity can creep in afterwards.

Know Your Lingo

Swinging: Where couples swap partners or watch each other having sex with someone else. Mostly happens at private parties or between two consensual couples.

Orgies: Often known as group sex, this is where a group of people get together and have sex, either at a private party or club.

Threesomes: Where a couple invite another partner to have sex with them, either a man with two women or a woman with two men. Often works better if the same-sex partner is genuinely bisexual.

Dogging: Having sex in a parked car while being watched by other people who sometimes join in.

Think Before You Act

If you're thinking about taking part in any group sex activity, think through these questions very carefully:

- What impact will it have on your relationship?
- How will you feel with someone else touching, tasting or making love to your partner?
- Do you really enjoy the *idea* of group sex rather than the actual reality?
- Are both of you equally into it or is one partner doing it out of obligation to the other? (Think very carefully about this one.)
- Do you want to watch or be involved yourself?
- Do you trust the people you are going to be involved with?
- What ground rules do you want to decide on? What's allowed and what isn't?
- Are you both capable of having sex with other people without getting emotionally involved?
- Can you handle seeing your partner enjoying a different side of their sexuality, such as being turned on by someone of the same sex?

Go ahead only once you've both reached satisfactory (and truthful) answers to all these questions. If you do want to go for it, websites, invitations and personal ads are probably the best way to find suitable partners – but remember always to practise safer sex. Try typing 'group sex' or 'swinging' and the name of your town into an Internet search engine and see what happens.

SAFETY INFO: As with all penetrative sexual activities, condoms are a must. The more partners you have, the higher the likelihood of contracting an STI.

Fantasy Fun

Often it's the *idea* of group sex or a threesome rather than the reality of actually doing it that's such a turn-on. You can actually have more fun just playing around with these ideas than actually going the whole way and acting them out. Here's how:

Sexy sounds

Try having sex while a porn film is playing. Turn the volume up and face away from the screen so you just hear the sounds of other people getting it on (rather than being distracted by the wobbly sets and dodgy hairstyles).

Mirror magic

Bring all the mirrors you have into one room and place them at different angles. Dim the lights and start to slowly, and sensually remove each other's clothes before having sex. By catching reflections of each other in the mirrors, not only will you see yourselves having sex from a load of interesting angles, you'll also create the impression that you're surrounded by other people enjoying themselves as much as you are.

Toy story

Using more than one sex toy or being penetrated by a sex toy at the same time as your partner can give the impression that there's more than one penis in the room. Close your eyes and let your imagination run wild while he runs his tongue or his penis over one hotspot and a vibrator or dildo over another. (Remember not to put anything that's been in the anus back in the vagina as it can cause an infection.)

G-SPOT — FEMALE
See also: female ejaculation, orgasm

The G-spot is a controversial issue. Discovered in 1950 by the German gynaecologist Dr Ernst Gräfenberg (1881–1957) (hence the 'G'), it is a small sensitive patch of tissue on the front wall of the vagina around 3–5 cm up (that's roughly around a third to three-quarters of a finger or around 1–2 inches). Around the size of a small bean (think broad bean rather than baked bean), it swells when you're sexually aroused and may feel ridged or textured in comparison to the rest of the vaginal canal.

For some women stimulation of the G-spot is G-orgeous and G-ratifying. Women who respond to G-spot stimulation report that orgasms feel 'deeper' and often more intense than clitoral orgasms.

For some women, stimulation does nothing or very little. For others, it can feel positively G-ruesome or uncomfortable.

What is a G-Spot?

The controversy doesn't just centre on whether women have a G-spot or not. What it is and why it's so sensitive is another hotly debated issue. Here are five current theories:

1) That it's a patch of clitoral tissue buried deep in the vaginal wall that's actually attached to the clitoris, so, like the love button, feels great when stimulated.

2) That it's made of cells similar to those of the male prostate gland (see **G-spot – male** below). Its development is possibly due to slightly raised levels of testosterone during foetal development (hence some women have one and some don't).

3) That it's actually just erectile tissue surrounding the urethra (the tube connecting the bladder to the outside world) so it's rich with nerve endings. This might be why some women experience a 'need to pee' sensation when it's first stimulated.

4) That it's actually a series of glands around the urethra that can be felt 'through' rather than 'on' the vaginal wall, which is possibly where female ejaculatory fluid comes from.

5) That in order to access it, some part of your hand actually stimulates the clitoris, so it's this clitoral stimulation you're responding to rather than a special internal spot at all.

Whatever the science behind it, basic rules of lust apply: if it feels good, go with it. If it doesn't, don't worry about it. Some women have a G-spot or derive pleasure from being stimulated in that general area and other women don't. Simple as that.

SEX FACT! *Even the Kama Sutra refers to the G-spot and mentions a spot in the vagina 'wrinkled or rough like a cow's tongue' that when touched 'makes her eyes whirl round in a circle'.*

How Do I Find It?

Having a generally sexy exploration in your nether regions is great but don't feel you're in any way sexually incomplete if you don't hit a G-spot.

If you fancy an intimate exploration, here's how to go about it. You need to be sexually aroused to discover your G-spot, so don't try anything until you've had a bit of build-up. Try squatting or lying backwards, then insert a finger into the vagina and push it against the front wall (towards your tummy rather than your back). Now make a gentle 'come hither' beckoning motion with your finger. If you have a G-spot this motion should now be rubbing against it. Expert advice varies on whether the sexy little spot prefers firm pressure, finger waggling, concentric circles or gentle up and down motions, so try them all and see what feels best. When you first touch the spot, it may feel as if you need to pee possibly (yup, the science bods are still arguing over this one, too) because the same neural pathways connect the G-spot and the bladder to the brain. If you keep stimulating this area, this feeling will pass. Have patience: G-spot stimulation takes longer than clitoral stimulation but the end result can be just as, if not more, impressive.

> *'The only time I've experienced female ejaculation was with a bisexual woman. I was amazed at first but, thinking about it afterwards, I felt quite flattered: I must've been doing something right!'*
>
> Gary, 37, Marketing executive

Eek! What's with the Wet Patch?

Some women find that a G-spot orgasm is sometimes accompanied by a sudden rush of fluid, which can be slightly alarming the first time it happens. Again, those bods in white coats are arguing about what's going on here. Some say it's urine and that you're losing control of your bladder at the moment of orgasm. Other scientists dispute this by saying that this fluid isn't the same as urine and contains a substance much more like semen (but without the sperm), which might support the mini-prostate theory. As more lubrication tends to be released at the moment of orgasm anyway, many women don't even notice that they've 'ejaculated' in this way while others are immensely proud of their fluid-producing abilities. See **female ejaculation** for more info.

G-Spotting Hands-On Homework
Toy with it
Some vibrators are specially designed for G-spot stimulation. They usually have curved tips that make it easier to rub against the front vaginal wall. It may be easier to sustain a rhythm with a sex toy than with your fingers (or his).

Front-on fun
Rather than squatting you may prefer lying on your front and extending your hand downwards. This may make it easier to access the front vaginal wall than the other way up.

Palm Sunday
Try laying a flat palm over your clitoris while inserting your middle finger into the vagina to stimulate the G-spot. Use your other free fingers and thumb to explore the sensitive erectile tissue around the vaginal lips. (Feels great if it's not your own fingers, too.)

Oral plus
He won't be able to reach your G-spot with his tongue but a combo of tongue action on and around the clitoris, and firm finger action around the G-spot, can be a powerfully orgasmic combination.

Perfect Positions for G-Spotting
Any position where the penis hits the front wall of the vagina on the way in or out will help stimulate your G-spot. Failsafe favourites are:

Cosmo tip:
Empty your bladder before any G-spot exploration or stimulation so you'll be able to relax and enjoy yourself.

1) Rear entry
Any position where he enters you from behind is good. Try kneeling and leaning slightly forward while he kneels behind you. Your hands are now free for clitoral or breast stimulation as well.

2) The sofa dive
Try leaning over the arm of a sofa while he penetrates you from behind. You may have to play around with how far over the sofa arm

you go for the perfect angle (just resting on it with your lower arms maybe enough).

3) Table-top tension

Lie back on a flat surface such as a desk or table while he penetrates you from the front. Hook your knees over his shoulders or rest your bottom on a couple of cushions to get the best angle.

4) Missionary manoeuvre

From the basic missionary position, lift your knees up to your chest while he places his hands under your bottom to raise it up a little. He then leans backwards slightly, arching his back so his penis is tilted slightly upwards as it pushes in and draws back.

SEX FACT: *G-spot confirmation and female ejaculation are more common among gay or bisexual women. This may be connected to higher levels of testosterone in developing foetuses of gay women. Then again, they may just spend more time bothering to explore the area.*

G-SPOT — MALE

See also: masturbation for him, orgasm – his, perineum

The male G-spot is the prostate gland, a walnut-sized gland situated directly under the bladder and in front of the rectum. It produces about a quarter of the fluid he ejaculates when he climaxes and is packed with nerve endings, so is very sensitive to the touch.

'I'll tell you what really does it for me: a finger up the bum. I'm totally heterosexual but the first time my girlfriend did that to me I nearly exploded! I'd recommend any straight man to try it at least once: it's amazing.'
Ron 33, retail manager

How To Access It

You can massage the male G-spot in two ways: first, through the perineum, the patch of skin between his balls and his anus. Try using your knuckle gently in this area or using one hand on his penis while rubbing the perineum gently with the other. The second way (giving you more direct access) is by inserting a well-lubricated finger into his anus and pulling it forwards (towards his balls) in a 'come here' motion.

SAFETY INFO: Never put a finger that's been in or near the anus into the vagina as it can cause infections.

Be warned: putting your finger up his bottom is something that some men love and other men hate, so, just because you know there's a secret sex organ near there, it doesn't mean you can just go for it. It's only polite to ask first.

SEX FACT: *Although the existence of the G-spot is controversial in Western culture, in other civilisations it's been referred to for years. In Chinese culture, it's known as the black pearl. The Japanese refer to it as 'the skin of the earthworm', possibly because of its slightly ridged texture.*

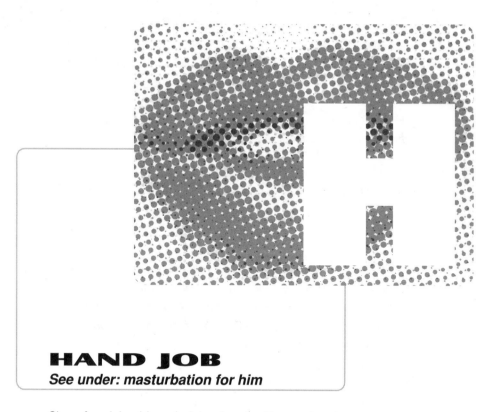

HAND JOB
See under: masturbation for him

Slang for giving him a helping hand with your hands.

HEPATITIS
See under: sexually transmitted infections

A viral infection that can cause serious liver damage that is sometimes sexually transmitted.

HERPES SIMPLEX
See under: sexually transmitted infections

A highly contagious virus that can be sexually transmitted. It also causes cold sores.

HIV
See under: sexually transmitted infections

A sexually transmitted virus that causes AIDS. Full name: human immunodeficiency virus.

HOLIDAY SEX
See also: condoms, quickies, one-night stands, outdoor sex

Pack for Pleasure
You don't want to be caught with a suitcase full of sex toys by security at the airport, but there are plenty of oh-so-innocent things in your hand luggage that can, with a little imagination, cause no end of sexual delights. Here's what to pack and why.

Arousing aftersun – turn your post-beach routine into a sensual sex fest by rubbing after-sun into each other's naked body.

A do-not-disturb blindfold – take turns to blindfolding each other and ravish each other's body.

A sinful sunhat – each write down five sexual sins you want to act upon on this holiday and pull them out at random; they're likely to be cheaper and more exciting than any excursions your hotel is offering.

An electric toothbrush – becomes a versatile vibrator without the airport embarrassment factor: use it against your clitoris (the handle, not the bristles – doh!) for a brrrrilliant buzz.

A bad-girl belt – use it to tie your lover's wrists to the bed so he's completely at your mercy. Fabric belts, bandanas or even the straps of your bikini also work well for this, but don't tie the knots too tight.

Once You're There
Get adventurous with these sun-soaked suggestions:

- For a frozen thrill, buy a lolly (or an ice cream), nip back to your apartment before it melts and get your lover to rub it all over your naked body and then lick it off.
- Go out to dinner for a romantic meal and reveal halfway through that you're not wearing any knickers. Make him wait through dessert (eaten slowly and lustfully obviously) until you let him have his wicked way with you.

• Find a secluded dune or hidden cove and make love in the open air. See the **outdoor sex** section for more saucy alfresco ideas or the **quickies** section for super-speedy suggestions.

'I had a fling with the man who fixed the light bulbs in our apartment in Tunisia once. All I wanted was a bit of attention and a couple of smooches but he asked me to marry him and take his virginity. I ran!'

Gloria, 23, receptionist

• Stay naked: once you're in the seclusion of your apartment/hotel room, forget about clothes and spend all your time naked. Order room service and serve each other up an erotic feast.

Holiday Sex Safety

If you're hooking up with someone new for a bit of holiday raunch, follow these rules:

• Always let your friends know where you'll be and when you'll be back. Don't let a stranger lure you to a secluded spot, however attractive he seems.

• Condoms. Condoms. Condoms. More people pick up STIs on holiday than at any other time, so take precautions.

• Be careful with alcohol: you're likely to be drinking more on holiday than you would at home, so don't go further than you want to or forget to use condoms in the heat of the moment.

• Look after each other: if your female friend's being chatted up by a local man, check out his reputation in your resort to find out if he does this to all the girls. That way, you can clue her in and she'll know what to expect.

• Enjoy flirting but don't give out mixed messages. If you're up for a fling, great. But, if you're not, let your holiday Romeo know the score.

• Have realistic expectations: the best holiday flings are just that – short term, no-strings fun. Although it is possible to turn vacation lust into long-term love, it's not that common. If things do carry on once you're back home, it's an unexpected bonus.

HORMONES
See also: adrenaline, afterplay, arousal

The Science Bit . . .
In a nutshell, hormones are chemical messengers released in one part of the body that stimulate activity in another part. Once you start thinking sexy thoughts, hormones are released into the blood and, along with a load of neurological messages that zip down the spine from the brain, cause the physical feelings of arousal all over your body (OK, it's not quite as simple as that but this isn't a biology textbook and those are the basics).

The Psychological Bit . . .
Although hormones undoubtedly affect sex drive and libido levels, how you're feeling emotionally also has a huge influence on your desire for sex. Regardless of your natural hormone levels, during the first three months of a relationship, you're likely to have a lot more sex than you have after thirty years of marriage. Libido and hormonal levels wax and wane but knowing the effect they have on your body can help you make the most of them.

Testosterone: The Sexual Stud
Testosterone is commonly known as the male hormone because, although it's found in women, it is between twenty and forty times higher in men. During puberty it's responsible for the development of male characteristics such as body and facial hair, muscle growth and the onset of sperm production. Produced in the testes and adrenal glands in men (and the ovaries and adrenal glands in women), it has a huge effect on sex drive, genital sensitivity and lust levels in both sexes.

Testosterone levels peak in the morning, dip mid-afternoon and crash just before bedtime, so take advantage of this by having sex in the morning. Levels are also thought to peak in the autumn (hence all those June/July babies!).

SEX FACT: *Some women feel ultra-sexy just before their period. Testosterone levels peak at this point, which might explain this.*

Low testosterone levels = lower sex drive. Testosterone levels dip dramatically if you're depressed, causing your libido levels to register zero on the sexometer, but it's unclear which comes first, the drop in desire or the drop in the hormone. An excess of testosterone can also cause other male characteristics such as excessive aggression.

SEX FACT! *Testosterone for girls? As it's known that testosterone has such a huge effect on sexual desire, it is currently being used as a treatment for increasing desire in both men and women. It's not a quick fix and is not prescribed if you're depressed, stressed or having trouble with your relationship.*

Oestrogen: The Confidence Builder

Oestrogen is produced in the first half of the menstrual cycle and peaks just before ovulation. It gives you a feeling of attractiveness, energy and a general overall feel-good factor (which is why you often feel great just after your period). Why not try being sexually adventurous during the first half of your cycle? This is the point where you'll have most confidence, feel most comfortable in your body and are likely to experience orgasms more easily. Physically, oestrogen affects your genitals, too, causing greater blood flow to the area and maximum lubrication. Many women feel ultra-sexy mid-cycle, as oestrogen levels peak at ovulation, causing a boost of desire. Oestrogen production stops at the menopause, causing vaginal dryness and sometimes a dip in mood or feelings of sexual attractiveness.

Progesterone: The Killjoy

After ovulation, progesterone levels start to rise. Progesterone suppresses the effect of oestrogen (and suppresses your immune system) so can cause a dip in sexual desire or lack of energy. Some women find the effects of progesterone relaxing, others find it depressing. At the end of your cycle, levels of both progesterone and oestrogen flat-line, which can lead to classic PMS symptoms of bloating, moodiness

'I always feel really sexy just before my period. My body feels fuller somehow, which makes me want to show it off. As I don't like having sex when I'm actually having my period, it also feels like my last chance for a while.'
Gabby, 25, TV researcher

and depression. You could try to alleviate these with a sensual massage, but, as progesterone also dulls your central nervous system slightly, you may take longer to become aroused. Make a rule that you can touch each other anywhere except your genitals to take the pressure off the thought of orgasm or penetrative sex.

Cosmo tip:
Don't demand a full match analysis after you've orgasmed. Basking in your rosy glow and drifting off to sleep is a much better idea. Make sure you wake him up for Round Two later in the evening after your hormones have had time to settle.

Oxytocin: The Cuddle Hormone

Known as the 'cuddle hormone', oxytocin is produced after orgasm in men and women. It causes women to bond more closely with their partners and men to fall asleep. Oxytocin is also produced during breastfeeding and childbirth, and is thought to create a bond between new mother and baby. The more sex you have with your partner, the more oxytocin you produce, causing you to demand more cuddles (the bonding bit) and him to feel relaxed enough to fall asleep more quickly.

Cosmo tip:
Every woman and man experiences hormonal highs and lows differently. Try keeping an arousal diary rating your feelings of desire for sex on a scale from one to ten throughout the month to discover when you feel the sexiest. (Bonus: just thinking about sex every day should make you feel sexier!)

On the Pill?

Hormonal contraceptives work by preventing ovulation and/or thickening the cervical mucus so that it is impenetrable to sperm. Many women find that, on their Pill-free days, they feel sexier than the rest of the month, thanks mainly to the break from progesterone. Others find that going on the Pill kills their sex drive. Different brands of the Pill have different levels of hormones and a subtle shift can make all the difference. Ask your doctor to swap brands if you find your libido levels dropping significantly.

HOUSEHOLD OBJECTS
See also: food, masturbation, toys

Here's One I Made Earlier
If you don't want to venture into a sex shop or get caught on the Internet at work ordering a Rampant Rabbit, you can use plenty of at-home props as fantastic sex toys. Just remember the same basic rules apply, as with the plastic variety: keep at-home-toys clean; don't use anything that hurts or could break inside you; don't let go of them; and don't put them back in the fruit bowl without washing them first.

Hairbrush handles
Handy plastic dildos in disguise.

Electric toothbrushes
Yup, many a girl has experimented with the vibrations an electric toothbrush can offer (just remember to use the non-bristled end!).

Shower head
Next time you take a shower, adjust the temperature so it's tepid rather than hot, and direct the water so it sprays on and around your clitoris (but not into the vagina).

Feathers
Deliciously sensuous, use them to tease and tantalise your lover with feather strokes around his genitals (and yours).

Pearls or beads
Try covering a string of pearls with massage oil or lubricant (fake ones work better) and sliding it around his penis or between your vaginal lips: luxuriously decadent!

Rubber gloves
Experiment with the different sensations a rubber or leather glove can give you or him. Play naughty doctors and nurses for an 'examination' with a difference.

Blusher brushes

Sweeping a big fat makeup brush all over your body is a sensuous sensation not to be missed.

Fruit 'n' veg

Popular choices include courgettes and bananas (obviously), ripe mangos and strawberries for squidginess and melons for him (yup: you could be twisting his melon, man . . .).

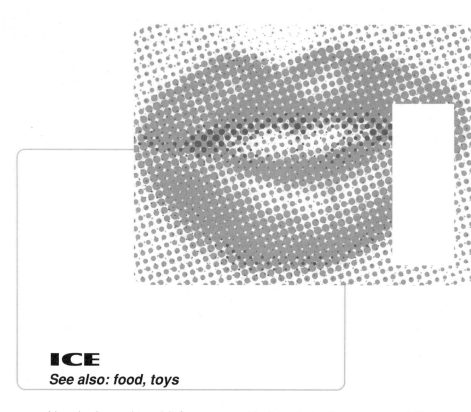

ICE
See also: food, toys

You don't need to wait for your next holiday to try these super-chilled thrills . . .

The (n)ice trail
Run an ice cube down your lover's spine all the way to the point at the base where his butt cheeks start (in most people, this is a particularly sensitive spot). As you run the cube down his body, blow on the ice trail you've left behind. The combination of hot and cold is irresistible.

Icy oral
Try giving your partner oral sex while sucking on an ice cube. The shock of the cold on his warm genitals is extremely arousing. Alternatively, try oral sex while holding ice cream in your mouth.

Frozen assets
Get your partner to rub an ice cube s-l-o-w-l-y around your hairline, down the side of your neck and around your nipples. Make sure he spends loads of time around the areola (the darker part of your breasts) before gently rubbing your nipples.

SAFETY INFO: *As ice numbs the skin, it's unsafe to insert more than a tiny piece of ice, which will melt quickly inside someone. Ice can also have sharp edges, so be careful.*

Fire and ice
Alternating any hot and cold sensations will feel good: try rubbing a sensitive part of your lover's body with ice, then dropping candle wax on to the spot. Keep him guessing as to whether it's fire or ice that's going to hit him next.

Grape-fully received
Select ten grapes and put half of them in the freezer. When they're frozen, mix them with the other five. Take it in turns to line up the grapes behind each other and pick a number from one to ten at random. You have a 50/50 chance of a frozen or unfrozen thrill. Use the grapes he chooses anywhere on his body. (The anticipation involved in this guessing game will raise your adrenaline levels, which increases your arousal.)

Freezing frenzy
Try putting your favourite sex toys in the freezer. Better still, have one in the freezer and one outside. Blindfold your lover so he can't see which toy you're reaching for. He'll be abuzz with anticipation, and, because his sight is restricted, it'll heighten all his other senses.

IMPOTENCE
See also: erectile problems, performance anxiety

Technical term for a man's inability to maintain an erection long enough to have sexual intercourse.

SEX FACT *All men will suffer from impotence at some point in their lives and the occasional case of a no-show erection is nothing for him – or you – to worry about.*

INDECENT BEHAVIOUR

It's a funny thing: one person's indecent is another person's arousing. Set your own boundaries as to which is which in your sex life.

INFIDELITY

It's an age-old question: what is infidelity? Is it:

a)   Kissing someone who isn't your partner?

b)   Having oral sex with someone who isn't your partner?

c)   Having full penetrative sex with someone who isn't your partner (so all other 'sexual relations' *à la* Bill Clinton don't count)?

d)   Emailing someone who isn't your partner?

e)   Being in a chatroom with someone who isn't your partner?

f)   Fancying someone who isn't your partner?

g)   All of the above?

Cosmo tip:

Infidelity doesn't have to mean the end of your relationship but it usually means there's something you're not happy about. Happy couples in successful relationships tend not to look elsewhere for sex, love or affection.

Remember that people have different ideas when it comes to straying, flirting or remaining faithful. Make sure you and your partner think along the same lines.

SEX FACT *Over 75 per cent of people who die during intercourse are being unfaithful. Now that's something to think about before you stray . . .*

INITIATING SEX

Statistically, men initiate sex more than women and it often makes a pleasant change for him if it's *you* who sets the sexual ball rolling. Stuck for ideas on how to make the first move in bed? Try these . . .

The technological
Send your lover a series of emails during the day, describing what you'd like to do to him when he gets home, then following through with your step-by-step suggestions as soon as he walks thorough the door (this is not one to do if your emails are monitored by the IT department!).

The romantic
Set a trail of rose petals or chocolate from your front door leading to the bedroom. When he opens the bedroom door, be lying on the bed wearing nothing more than a come-hither smile.

The subtle
In bed, lean back against your partner and squiggle your bottom against his semi-erect penis. Use your hand to grab his hips and stroke behind you until he's fully aroused and knows exactly what you're after.

The brazen
Tell your man in your strictest sexiest voice that he is now your sex slave for the evening and has to do exactly what you say. Make him perform a series of sexual favours on you, spanking him if he gets anything wrong.

The oral
Kiss him all over, starting from the top of his head, lingering over his mouth and neck, then moving down across his chest and other parts of his body, finishing off with fantastic oral sex: he'll soon get the message.

The not-so-subtle
Grab his crotch and drag him to the bedroom saying, 'I want you and I want you *now*!'

INTERCOURSE
See under: penetration, positions

Posh name for penetrative sex, a.k.a. what happens after foreplay (lots of . . . if you want intercourse to be good!).

INTERNET SEX

Reasons To Go For It
Fantasy: Online you can be anyone you want to be, explore your wildest fantasies, desires and personas, all from the comfort of your own home.

Self-expression: You can express yourself freely and will probably be less inhibited in a chatroom or in an email than you would be face to face.

Safety: So long as you follow a few basic rules (see box below), online sex can be safe and satisfying and a great way to develop parts of your sexual identity that you might not be able to express in real life.

Identity: You can discover communities of like-minded people who all share the same sexual interests.

Porn and passion: You can look at images that turn you on, read erotic stories that make you melt or pick up steamy sex tips or ideas that can enhance your offline sex life.

Information: You can discover information on any form of sexuality or sexual practice and find the answers to embarrassing sexual questions you wouldn't dare ask a 'real' person.

'I met my husband online through a dating site. We've now been married for five years and have a one-year-old. Although a lot of net dates don't work out, I'm living proof that it's worth giving it a go!'
Juliette, 34, writer

Shopping: The discretion of Internet companies beats the embarrassment of walking into a high street (or back street) sex shop any day.

Love: you could meet the man of your dreams, as Internet dating gives you access to a world of potential lovers and soul mates far wider than your social circle will ever be.

Reasons To Hold Back

Fantasy: The people you meet online can also be anyone they want to be too. If you're lying about your age, gender, height, vital statistics or salary, they can too.

Self-expression: Chatroom members can be harsher, more insulting, filthier and more direct than they ever would be in real life and Net rejection can feel just as hurtful as real-life waiting-for-the-phone-to-ring.

Porn too far: You may inadvertently discover sexual images or sites you really didn't want to look at or have a record of on your computer. Visiting sex sites can also generate tons of unwanted spam in your email in-box.

Reliability: Anyone can publish sexual information or advice on the Web, so you may not know how reliable or accurate the info you're reading is.

Spending: Adult sites are often expensive. It's also pretty hard (nay, impossible) to return low-grade sex toys you've bought from disreputable sites online.

'Within twenty-four hours of posting my profile on a dating site I had eighteen replies, which made me feel really special. I flirted with one guy for six months, we exchanged photos and eventually met up. In the end the email spark we'd had just wasn't there in real life, but I don't regret meeting him for a second.'

Jo, 33, IT sales

The real world: The chances of meeting the man of your dreams, realistically, are fairly slim.

Love lost: Spending too much time on the Net could affect your chances of meeting a real-life flesh-and-blood lover. Having an online affair could jeopardise your current relationship.

SEX FACT *Beware: one in ten of the 90,000 couples who contact relationship counselling organisation Relate each year blame their relationship problems on the Internet.*

The bottom line is: the Internet has a lot to offer from a sexual point of view. As when trying to book a holiday online, you'll probably find some sites more interesting and useful than others. Have fun and stay safe. Here's a quick rundown of what to expect:

Online Dating

There are thousands of Internet sites that aim to match you up with your ideal partner or to set you up with a string of potential lovers to chat and flirt with. You'll usually be asked to complete a questionnaire or set up an online profile, which is then either posted on the site (sometimes accompanied by your photo) or matched with men you might have something in common with. Email addresses are then exchanged (often via the site) and you can chat and flirt with your new-found friends all you like and maybe meet up.

'Online sex is even better than phone sex. You can be as raunchy as you like and it's easier to write dirty than talk dirty.'
Rachel, 23, hairdresser

Safety on the Net

1. Don't give out your real name or personal details such as your email address, workplace or contact number in any profile you post online or in a chatroom.

2. Set up an anonymous email account (such as a new Hotmail address) that will be easy to shut down or ignore if you get bombarded with spam or unwanted emails.

3. Never use your work computer for online sex play. (Even if you think you've deleted all the sites you've visited there'll still be a record on your computer.)

4. If you plan to meet an online lover in person, take all the precautions you would on an ordinary blind date, regardless of how long your e-affair has been going on or how well you think you know that person. Arrange to meet in a public place for a coffee first. Tell friends where you'll be and when to expect you back, take a cab fare and your mobile phone and, if it's going that far, practise safe sex.

Web dates

Online services such as MSN's Instant Messenger allow you to chat in real time with friends (or lovers) while you're both online. You can go on a 'web date' together by both visiting the same sites and checking out the same information. This can be as fun and fulfilling or as dire and disastrous as a regular blind date but could be a good dry run if you're thinking about meeting up outside cyberspace.

'Internet chatrooms have changed my life. I've chatted to all sorts of people across the UK, who I'd never have come across otherwise. After splitting up with my ex, chatrooms gave me my confidence back.'

Nicola, 22, student

Chatrooms

Chatrooms are a great place to meet new people, discuss topics you're interested in (anything from celebrity gossip or gardening tips to your favourite sexual positions) or to get down and dirty. You'll usually start by chatting to a group of people and then, if you feel a particular affinity with (or attraction to) one person, you can go off for a private chat together, which will probably get quite steamy, quite quickly.

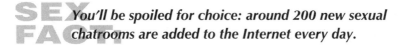 **SEX FACT:** *You'll be spoiled for choice: around 200 new sexual chatrooms are added to the Internet every day.*

Webcams

It's relatively cheap and simple to set up a camera in your own home, connect it to your computer and project your everyday activities (sexual or otherwise) on to the World Wide Web. There are also plenty of commercial sites that offer 'real-life girls' pottering around their real lives or getting sexual for the cameras. Stripping sites, where you pay for every layer of clothing that's taken off, are extremely popular. Although the majority of commercial sites are aimed at men, there are a few out there for women, too, and it can be fun to watch someone acting on instructions that you give them ('stroke your left thigh' etc.), although it can also be expensive (at around £2 a minute or more). Webcams can also be used on a more intimate, personal level to project images of yourself only to your lover. If the idea of interacting with strangers and performing in front of an audience appeals, or even if you're just checking out other girls' sites for inspiration, type 'camgirl' into any search engine for a selection of sites to appear.

SEX FACT: *According to the Cosmo Internet Sex Survey 50 per cent of Cosmo readers have used a chatroom to meet men, 40 per cent of those go on to meet the men they chat to online and a* *feisty 38 per cent have full cyber-sex (writing raunchy messages while masturbating).*

E-fidelity?

Does flirting online or having an email relationship count as infidelity? Yes. And no. The world is divided into two camps: those who think that hooking up with someone other than your partner in any shape or form, whether that's in person, in a chatroom or via email, is totally unforgivable; and those who think that a bit of email banter is as harmless as chatting to someone in your local bar (with absolutely no intention of going home with them at the end of the night). It's up to you where you set your own boundaries. Generally, if you spend more time with your online lover than the flesh-and-blood version or have more sex online than you do in real life, and your nonvirtual lover doesn't know you're doing it, then you're probably cheating. And it's up to you and your partner what you do about that. If you're open about what you're up to and both happy about it, type away.

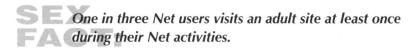 *One in three Net users visits an adult site at least once during their Net activities.*

INTIMACY

Intimacy is . . .	Intimacy isn't . . .
maintaining eye contact while you have sex.	squeezing your eyes shut and imagining he's someone else while you have sex.
sharing fantasies with your partner.	sharing fantasies with your partner to shock, shame or embarrass them.
enjoying watching your lover's orgasm face.	laughing at your lover's orgasm face.
appreciating the whole of their body (and yours).	appreciating just their genitals as if they were your personal sex toy.
learning more about your own sexual responses so you can teach your partner what turns you on.	knowing nothing about your sexual responses and expecting your partner to work miracles.

IRMA'S RULES FOR GREAT SEX

The legendary Irma Kurtz has been *Cosmopolitan*'s agony aunt for over thirty years, receiving thousands of letters a week from *Cosmo* girls the world over. No A–Z would be complete without a snippet of her frank, forthright sex advice. If you forget everything else you read in this book, take away these wise words that'll make your sex life sizzle, not just tonight but for the rest of your life.

Great Sex Rule #1: Stop Thinking, Start Feeling

Irma says: Think before you have sex, think after you have sex, but, while you are having sex, stop thinking! Concentrate on every touch and tingle, every mounting breath; set your entire self free of opinions and worries and vanity so it can follow where physical sensation leads.

Great Sex Rule #2: Romance = Raunch

Irma says: Though the word 'romance' is so little used these days that it sounds a little dirty, it also remains eternally attractive for both sexes. Plan a nostalgic evening full of a few of your favourite shared things; then, when bedtime comes at last, dim the lights, play *your* song, chill the bubbly, and wear something silky that is more suggestive than revealing. Like whipped cream and chocolate (which have their erotic uses, too), corn is sickening as a steady diet, but perfectly delicious once in a while.

Great Sex Rule #3: Beware Bedroom Boredom

Irma says: Enact your fantasies if they are shared, but beware of repetition, especially if the scenario works for only one of you. The same S&M routine over and over, for example, stops being about sex and starts being about itself, and bedroom boredom is the result.

Great Sex Rule #4: Ring the Changes

Irma says: Kitchen, shower, sofa, car, secluded beach or garden – change the location and change the sensation.

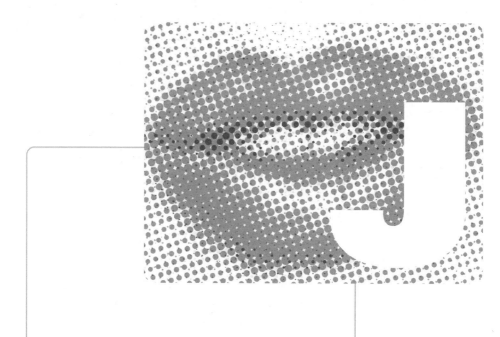

JACUZZI SEX
See also: water play

Sex in a Jacuzzi is the stuff of seventies porn movies but, despite that (or even because of it!), it can be bubblingly good fun. Here's how to make the most of it:

- If you're into role play, pretend you're millionaires and this is your mansion or you're porn stars rehearsing (or even filming) a scene.

- Use the jets to your advantage. Once you're naked, direct the water jets at different areas of each other's body starting with gentle non-erotic massages (backs, thighs, arms etc.), moving on to more sensitive spots such as nipples, buttocks, the penis and, of course, the clitoris.

- Experiment with combinations of hand touches and jet pressure on the extremely sensitive parts of your body such as the penis and clitoris. Have fun finding out what feels sexiest.

- Once you move on to penetrative sex, continue to use the jets to your advantage, angling them between your legs, over your breasts if you can, or over the perineum (the sensitive patch of skin between the testicles/vagina and anus).

- You'll have more room in a Jacuzzi than a regular bath, because your choice of positions is less limited: try him sitting against a water jet with you on top (with the spray between both your legs if possible) or try hooking your legs over the side with him straddling you with his feet on the floor of the Jacuzzi so his weight isn't resting on you.

SAFETY INFO: Water and condoms aren't a great mix, so penetrative Jacuzzi play is best for monogamous couples only.

JEWELLERY
See also: household objects, piercing

Accessories have never been so sexy. Here's how to turn your jewellery box into a treasure trove of sensual, sexual delights.

Chokers: Great for bondage play. Keep them on during sex and let him lick and kiss you all around them for a restrictive buzz.

Dangly necklaces: Anything that dangles down into your cleavage can be used to draw attention to this area. Fiddle absent-mindedly with a long necklace while you're talking if you want to show off your breast assets.

Pearls: Cover a string of pearls with lubrication (fake ones work better) and use them to massage each other's body. Pearls can be especially erotic when wound round the shaft of the penis or used between your legs (taking care not to get them caught in pubic hair – ouch).

Anklets: The ankle is an incredibly erotic area. Anything that rubs against your ankle bone or the soft spot directly below the bone will heighten the sensation you feel here during sex. Keep anklets on during sex and clasp your ankles against his skin so you can feel the sensual tension.

Dangly earrings: Again, great for twiddling with when you're flirting in an oh-so-coy manner. It's a form of preening that men find irresistible. Dangly earrings also give you an excuse to stroke the area just below your ear lobe, which is packed with nerve endings.

Rings: Twiddle your ring round and round while maintaining eye contact. Or, even less subtly, pull it up and down your finger. He'll spot the penis/finger analogy straight away! Rings can also be worn during sex play if you want to vary the sensation of your fingers on his body.

Belly rings: A chain round your tummy accentuates an incredibly sensual area and draws his attention downwards. Let him run his tongue under the chain for a great warm-up to oral sex.

Dress Up Downstairs

Jewellery especially designed for the penis, clitoris and nipples is available from sex shops. Many of the designs just clip on so you don't need to be pierced to enjoy the thrill of dressing up downstairs. Often these adornments heighten sensation, too – bonus! Of course, if you are pierced, that opens up a whole new box of delights. See **piercing** for details.

JUDGING THE MOOD

Sex is a wonderful thing: you can tailor-make your session to suit the exact mood you're both in, particularly if you're the one setting the pace. Before you choose a quickie over a slow-sensual session think about:

- how you're feeling emotionally: do you want intimate love making or a lustful romp?
- what location you are in: a swanky hotel room will set a much more lingeringly luxurious mood than a deserted alleyway.
- how generous you are feeling: do you want to pamper your lover or are you in the mood to lie back and be worshipped?
- how adventurous your mood is: is now the right time to try that new trick/position/role play?
- how lazy you are feeling: do you have enough energy to get on top and control the show or do you want to snuggle up and have lazy sex spoons-style?

Cosmo tip:
Unless you're masturbating, sex is a two-way process, so be considerate and receptive to the moods and emotions of your partner.

- what kind of build-up you are up for: are you in the mood to light the scented candles, dress in your sexiest underwear and strip for your man or will that have to wait till the weekend?

JUGGLING
See also: ball play

Definition #1: using both hands during sex
Why is it that during foreplay people tend to diddle and fiddle with only one hand, letting the other hand lie forgotten and dormant? Each time you have sex and are using one hand (on yourself or on him) think about what the other hand could be doing: stroking your breasts, caressing his cheek, clinching his buttocks, holding on to the bedposts . . . You are blessed with two hands: use them both.

Definition #2: fiddling about with balls usually in the air
This is a sex book: of course we're not talking about the beanbag variety. See the **ball play** section for more details.

Definition #3: having more than one partner and hoping never the twain shall meet
Tricky. Very tricky. Whatever you do, don't juggle their names, fantasies or favourite sexual positions.

Definition #4: trying to have a fantastic job, intimate relationship, sizzling sex life, fulfilling social life and enlightening spiritual life all at the same time
Also tricky but great regular sex can help. Honest.

JUST DESSERTS

What you'll get if you're selfish in bed: you have been warned!

KABAZZAH

See also: Kegel exercises

No, it's not another magic word like 'shazam!' It's a spiritual sexual technique in which both partners stay totally still during penetration (preferably staring into each other's eyes meaningfully) while the woman 'milks' her partner's penis using just her abs and her vaginal muscles.

- Try it while you're on top (pin his arms down with your hands if you fancy taking control).
- Try it in the missionary position for romance. Maintain eye contact throughout or wink cheekily in time with your muscle contractions to make him laugh.
- You can even try it while he has sex from behind. Do it in front of a mirror if you really want to enjoy the view!

SEX FACT *Although it takes years of muscle training to perfect this technique, doing a few Kegel exercises every day will strengthen your vaginal muscles and intensify your climax.*

KAMA SUTRA
See also: positions

What you already know: The *Kama Sutra* is the world's most famous sex manual, packed with positions, advice, tips and techniques.

What you may *not* know: It was written in India sometime before the fourth century and consists of seven different volumes. It praises the female orgasm and advises men to give their partners as much pleasure as possible.

What you probably *don't* know: Only one volume is about sex. The others contains 'life guide' info aimed primarily at young men. Funnily enough, that stuff hasn't proved as interesting to Westerners as the graphic descriptions of sex.

If you fancy expanding your sexual repertoire, get hold of a *Kama Sutra* translation or a book of positions based on those found in the ancient manual. (Alternatively, just look up the **positions** section in this book for more than a few ideas).

KEGEL EXERCISES
See also: orgasm, vagina

Limber up, ladies! Invented by the US gynaecologist Dr Arnold Kegel, these simple daily sexercises will tighten your PC (pubococcygeal) muscles, which increases blood circulation around your genitals, causes greater arousal and intensifies your orgasm. Your vagina will also feel tighter around your man's penis. What are you waiting for? Start your fitness regime today.

What To Do
1) Locate your PC muscles – they're the ones you use to stop yourself peeing mid-flow (you can find them when using the loo). Alternatively, insert a finger into your vagina and try squeezing on to it. These muscles form a kind of sling around your genital area and, together with other structures, are often

referred to as the pelvic floor. Lie on your back or sit down.

2) Tighten your PC muscles while breathing out. This feels like you're drawing all your muscles from your bottom to your vagina upwards and inwards. Concentrate on isolating your PC muscles rather than squeezing your buttocks, stomach and thighs at the same time. Relax completely on your in-breath.

3) Repeat fifteen to twenty times. After a few sessions, when you can do this easily, try to hold the contraction for three seconds, gradually building up to a full ten seconds. Next, build up your repetitions from twenty to around fifty.

4) Practise any time, anywhere – on the bus, in that boring sales meeting, at the dentist's (it may take your mind off the pain).

SEX FACT *Don't expect instant results: it takes around four weeks of twice-daily Kegel exercises to significantly increase your muscle tone. But it'll be worth it!*

Kegels for Him

This wonder-workout is not just for women. By strengthening *his* PC muscles, he'll benefit from stronger erections, more control and greater sensitivity. He can locate his PC muscles in the same way as you, by stopping the flow of urine. Next, he should try holding his contraction for three seconds, then releasing, gradually building up his repetitions.

'Doing Kegels turns me on, I guess because it makes me focus on my genital area. It can be quite distracting during meetings!'
Anthea, 38, human-resources director

Sex It Up

Kegelling while you're making love has some sexy hidden benefits:

• Contract your vaginal muscles in time with his thrusting (so you clench when he's deepest inside you) – it'll feel fantastic for both of you.

• Next, reverse this action so you're clenching when he's at the shallowest point of his thrust – you'll be clenching around the head of his penis, the most sensitive part.

- If you're on the verge of orgasm, try a few Kegels – the contractions can bring on your climax. Alternatively, try Kegelling through your climax – it'll intensify all your sensations.
- After you've climaxed, try some squeezes: if you're lucky, they can bring on another orgasm (or three . . .)
- To delay his climax, when he's on the edge, get him to squeeze his PC muscle while you lie still (i.e. stop thrusting or moving). With practice, he should be able to use this tactic a number of times until you're both ready to blast off.

> **Cosmo tip:**
> Try using a vibrator on or around your clitoris next time you're doing your Kegels. If you're getting some pleasure in return, it'll be easier to stick to your fitness routine.

KISSING
See also: oral sex for him, oral sex for you

'You can't beat a passionate snog. If they're a good kisser it is usually a sign that they'll be good in bed. For me, there's no point in taking things further with someone who doesn't know how to kiss.'
Dominic, 33, interior stylist

Romantic, passionate, intense, animalistic, caring, confident, shy, sly, sneaky, sexy–kissing can suit any mood, any occasion or any state of mind. So why don't we do it? Lustful lip-locking is an excellent foreplay technique that most adults tend to forget about after the first few love-struck months. It tends to be just the entrée, a passionate precursor for much more interesting things to come. We kiss our relatives and children. We kiss people goodbye or hello. If kissing for you has become routine rather than romantic, use the techniques below to loosen up your lips.

Lip-service Fact #1: When anticipating a kiss (that slow-motion heads-moving-towards-each-other movement) our lips, which are packed with nerve endings, swell in size and darken in colour just as our genitals do when we're aroused.

Lip-service Fact #2: Passionate kissing releases endorphins, the brain's feel-good chemicals, which dull pain and heighten arousal.

Lip-service Fact #3: The phrase 'kiss it better' has some medical currency, as saliva contains natural antiseptics that help clean a wound. The psychological benefits of kissing also help to dull both physical and emotional pain.

Lip-service Fact #4: Lips are the important part, *not* your tongue. Yes, tongues are great for sexploration but the packed-with-nerve-endings orgasm-inducing powerhouses are actually your lips, so they're the bits that need the most attention.

SEX FACT *Ancient sex manuals claim that nerves run directly from the upper lip to the clitoris and that a man's lower lip is directly connected to his penis – the perfect excuse to suck 'em and see . . .*

Kiss Me Quick (or slowly . . .)

Decide on your mood or the carnal connection you want to create and choose from the tongue-tingling techniques below . . .

> **Tongue-Tingling Techniques #1: Light and Intimate**
> **The gorgeous graze**
> With soft pursed lips, just slightly open, try grazing the surface of your lover's mouth so your lips barely touch his skin. Do this all around his face. Getting him to close his eyes will enhance the intensity of this experience.
> **Butterfly kisses**
> Try kissing his naked body with your eyelashes. It's a floaty fluttery feeling that's divine and intimate. The places where his skin is thinnest (such as his wrists) will be the most sensitive.
> **Sensitive spot search**
> Plant light, tender kisses all over his body, starting with his head and face and working your way down. Particularly sensitive spots will be his hairline, his ears and ear lobes, the skin around his neck (just below his ears is particularly hot), around his nipples and along his inner arms.

Tongue-Tingling Techniques #2:
Sexy and Seductive

Erotic explorations

Take turns to explore each other's mouth with your tongue so that, rather than fighting for tongue space, one person kisses while the other remains passive.

Suction seduction

Try sucking and gently nipping his lower lip, followed by his upper one. It's animalistic and sexy, as if you can't get enough of him. Alternatively, gently suck on his top lip while he nibbles on your bottom one, then change places. Suction draws more blood to your lips, making them even more sensitive.

Foxy flavours

Try kissing with different foods or drinks in your mouths, for example a glass of champagne or a mouthful of chocolate ice cream. Allow a little of the liquid to escape into his mouth or swap a piece of chocolate or fruit backwards and forwards.

> **Cosmo tip:**
> Don't forget to use your hands while you're kissing. A tender touch on the cheek or a naughty squeeze of the bottom can add to your enjoyment of the moment.

Tongue-Tingling Techniques #3:
Down and Dirty

Naughty nibble

Gently nipping the fleshy areas of his body can be naughty but nice.

'We started off kissing with a mouthful of ice – then we discovered iced fruit: melon, strawberries, kiwis – peeled grapes are hysterical, not to mention delicious.'
Joanne, 29, stylist

His buttocks, inner thighs and down the sides of his neck are perfect places. As you both become aroused, pain receptors are dulled slightly so the more turned on he is, the more he'll be able to take.

Sweet circles

Try circling his oh-so-sensitive spots with the tip of your tongue or drawing circles with your tongue on different parts of his body. Round his nipples, up and down his inner thighs and around the tip of his penis are all great places to try. (Ditto your clitoris and nipples.)

Thrusty work

Don't forget to kiss while you're having penetrative sex. The missionary position is excellent for mouth-to-mouth and can be incredibly intimate. Even in other positions where you're not face to face, try licking or kissing the body part that's closest to you: his ankles, hands, chest or neck. It keeps you connected body *and* soul.

Slave to the rhythm

Try mirroring your mouth action to your thrusting when you're having intercourse so your tongues are imitating the action of his penis. You can use the technique to subliminally set the pace of your love making: if you want him to slow down his thrusts, slow down your tongue action; if you want to up the pace, speed up.

SEX FACT! *Kissing during sex makes it last longer, enhances orgasm, boosts arousal and creates intimacy. (Need any more excuses?)*

KITCHEN TABLE SEX

See also: food, household objects, positions

Try this naughty kitchen table position for a little dirty dining: lie backwards on to the kitchen table and lift your legs in the air. He then stands in front of you and penetrates you while you hook your legs over his shoulders. He can hold your buttocks for support. (You may need a cushion under your back.) Try this at breakfast time for a morning thrill or as an after-dinner aphrodisiac.

KNICKERS

Try going on a date wearing no knickers. Even if you don't reveal your saucy secret, it'll give you a naughty glint and keep you amused even if the date is dire. If it's not, choose your moment carefully to let him know what article of clothing you've accidentally forgotten to put on.

LABIA
See under: vagina

Correct term for vaginal lips. You have two sets: the inner labia and the outer labia.

LAUGHING IN BED

Essential.

SEX FACT: *Sense of humour is cited over any other quality as the number-one attractiveness factor in sex surveys the world over.*

LEGAL STUFF

Legal Facts You Should Know

1)   The age of consent for heterosexuals in the UK is 16 (17 in Northern Ireland). Any man who has sex with a girl under the age of consent is breaking the law. Women can also be

charged with sexual assault if a male partner is under 16.

2)   The age of consent for homosexual males is also 16 in the UK (17 in Northern Ireland).

3)   Sex outdoors is currently legal so long as you can't be seen or heard by anyone else. If you can, you could be charged under the Public Order Act with behaviour likely to cause a breach of the peace, or in common law for outraging public decency or being a public nuisance.

4)   Necrophilia (sex with a dead body) is illegal.

SAFETY INFO: Be careful on holiday, as things that are perfectly legal in this country may not be legal or may be offensive or deeply frowned upon elsewhere. Be respectful of religious and cultural traditions while you're away.

LIBIDO
See also: aphrodisiacs

Dictionary definition: life force, craving, especially in relation to sex.
Cosmo **definition:** Sex drive, lust level, urge to merge, desire to get down and dirty, carnal craving.

Libido myth #1: Men's libido levels are always higher than women's
False: Everyone's libido levels fluctuate. Some people, both men and women, have a naturally high libido and crave sex often, while others have naturally lower levels. Your sex drive is likely to be higher at the beginning of a relationship, because being in love (or lust) creates a potent mixture of I-want-it chemicals in your body.

Libido myth #2: The more sex you have, the more you want
True: Having lots of sex and orgasms is one of the best ways to boost your lust levels. If your libido is naturally higher than your partner's, stop pestering them for sex all the time and start masturbating (in private). It'll give you the release (and relief) you need. If you're the one with the low libido, take yourself off and

give yourself a helping hand (See the **masturbation for you** section). Just because you masturbate while you're in a relationship (or your partner does), it doesn't mean you love or desire each other any less.

Libido myth #3: Men's libido levels peak much earlier than women's

True: to an extent. Young men generally want (and can handle) sex more often than older men while women tend to go through a libido-level peak around their thirties and forties. This could explain why older *Playboy* types tend to go for younger, less demanding models every few years. That said, sex drive, like any other character trait, is a very personal attribute, so there's nothing to worry about if you don't fit this general model.

Common libido killers
- stress, pressure and anxiety
- pressure to perform in bed
- physical ill health or tiredness
- having children or a new baby
- depression
- some medications such as antidepressants and some versions of the Pill
- hormone levels (particularly low testosterone levels)
- alcohol and some illegal drugs
- boredom in the bedroom, with your relationship or with life in general

Common Libido Lifters

1) Communication

Acknowledge your differing libido levels, then talk about what you love about your sex life and what you don't enjoy so much. Listen to your partner, then work out five things each that would

Cosmo tip:
If your libido levels take a nose dive when you go on the Pill or start taking any kind of medication, mention this to your doctor. It's a common side effect and often just switching to a different brand can make a huge difference.

improve sex for both of you. Introduce these activities gradually into your sex life. If you find it hard to talk directly to each other, a sex therapist or couples counsellor can be a great help.

2) Masturbation

Doing it on your own doesn't mean you don't fancy your partner any more. It's just a quick and easy way to boost your lust levels. The more orgasms you have, the more sex you'll want. (See **masturbation** for more info.)

3) Imagination

The brain is the biggest sex organ and, without engaging it, your sexual responses won't function. Try fantasising (see the **fantasy** section) before, during and after sex. Try reading some erotic fiction to get your juices flowing or writing an erotic story. As with actually doing it, the more you think about sex, the more you'll want.

4) Experimentation

If you're in a same-every-time sex rut, your brain will be numbed by the scenario you repeatedly go through. Eventually, you'll end up equating boredom with sex – a prime passion killer. Spice things up by trying a little **role play**, getting naughty and playing around with power games (see **bondage**) or by investing in a new sex toy (see **toys**). Even just deciding to take turns as to who is giving and who is receiving pleasure can be all you need to pep things up.

5) Abstention

Instead of focusing on orgasm or penetrative sex as your ultimate goal, shift the focus away from your genitals to ease sexual pressure. Try **erotic massage** for an indulgent treat or create a rule where you can't touch each other's genitals for a month (yes, that long). This forces you to become more creative in bed and should make the bonus sex session at the end of your month totally explosive.

6) Romance

Yup, those hearts, flowers and romantic dinners for two may be a cliché but they really do work when it comes to lust-lifting. Spend time wining and dining each other, going on dates, complimenting each other on your outfits or choice of venue. Men: flowers are *always* welcome! (This works particularly well if you're bringing up small children, as you've probably ignored indulgent just-us time for a while.)

7) Drug therapy

If low hormone levels are to blame, drug therapy can help. Testosterone is currently being used to treat low libido levels in both men and women, often with positive results. Your doctor will need to test your hormone levels and rule out any other causes of low libido before it's prescribed so it won't be the first solution on offer.

Cosmo tip:

If you don't fancy sex tonight ask yourself, 'Am I really not up for it or just being lazy?' If there's a teeny part of you that thinks, 'Hmmm, an orgasm might be nice', go for it: the body can easily be persuaded if even the smallest part of the brain is willing.

LIGHTING
See also: bedroom to boudoir

Good lighting is essential for great sex. The right lighting can set the mood, boost your confidence and flatter your figure. Bad lighting, on the other hand, can make you feel uncomfortable, show up your least favourite attributes, or even totally kill the mood. Here's how to get it right:

Cosmo tip:

If you're normally a lights-off girl, try opening your eyes and maintaining eye contact while you make love. As you're staying eye-to-eye, you know he won't be checking out your wobbly bits, so you should feel less self-conscious.

Go for	Avoid
Floor lamps and low lighting: your body looks thinner and sexier when lit from below. It'll improve your skin tone, too.	Harsh overhead lighting: the shadows cast downwards will make you look sallow and droopier than you really are.
An infusion of red light: either use a red bulb or drape a red scarf over the lampshade. Red is the colour of passion so it'll make you both feel raunchier and give you more in-bed energy.	High-wattage white bulbs: the harsher the light, the more wobbly bits and wrinkles will show. You'll also look washed out and grey.
Blue light, which is soft and flattering: invest in a blue shade or lava lamp.	Yellow lighting, which makes you look ill. Avoid yellow lampshades or curtains that reflect yellow light back into the room.
Candles on the floor and low surfaces, which are sexy and romantic and throw off subtle flattering light.	Tall candelabra as these light the room too high up and are easy to knock over in the heat of the moment.

Cosmo tip:
Experiment with different types of lighting. If you always have sex with the lights on, try doing it blindfolded or in pitch darkness: it'll make you concentrate on different sensations.

LITTLE DEATH
See under: orgasm

A euphemism for orgasm. Some cultures believed that you lose brain cells when you climax or that vital energy is lost by ejaculating. Others would say you'd just died and gone to heaven.

LOVE TRAIL

This is the sexy patch of skin from the belly button to the pubic bone. In men, it's usually accompanied by a trail of hair from the belly button downwards (hence 'love trail'). It can be an incredibly arousing spot in both sexes. Try:

- Rubbing his abdomen with a flat palm in the direction of his penis or stroking him in the direction of the hair growth (a great warm-up for sex and incredibly loving and comforting).
- Trailing your finger gently along the trail of hair all the way down to the genitals but not quite touching them.
- Doing the same with your tongue.
- While masturbating, try tracing your own love trail with a fingertip down from your belly button to the tip of your pubic bone, ending up just above the clitoris.

LUBRICATION
See also: vagina

SAFETY INFO: Never used oil-based lubricants (that includes all massage oils and vegetable oils) with latex condoms or latex sex toys as they rot them, causing small holes within sixty seconds of contact. Use a water-based lubricant like K-Y Jelly instead.

Cosmo tip:
Have fun applying shop-bought lubricants. Try pouring them on to his body from a great height so he can see what you're doing, using the other hand to rub his penis (a novel sensation for both of you), or putting lubrication on the insides of your arms and rubbing his penis between them. Get him to dribble it over your breasts or down your belly, then rub it in with his hands or his penis.

Sexual lubricants come in a huge array of colours, flavours, textures and price ranges. Some are oil-based (as are most massage oils), so shouldn't be used near latex condoms; some are designed for external use only, so shouldn't be placed on the genitals; others are water-based and are fine for use on the genitals or with condoms.

Your Top 10 Lube Facts

Lube fact #1: Lots of lubrication is essential for great sex. If you're dry it can be uncomfortable or painful for both of you. The phrase 'the wetter the better' applies to most sex acts.

Lube fact #2: Just because a women gets wet, it doesn't mean she's ready for intercourse. Lubrication *is* a sign of sexual arousal but this doesn't necessarily mean 'penetration now, please'.

Lube fact #3: A small amount of lubricant called 'pre-come' (or, more scientifically, 'pre-ejaculatory fluid') is released from the head of the penis. The rest is produced inside the vagina and released from the base of the vaginal opening.

Lube fact #4: The clitoris doesn't produce natural lubrication, so some will need to be taken from the base of the vagina and spread around the clitoris.

Lube fact #5: The amount of natural lubrication you produce will vary depending on where you are in your menstrual cycle. You'll be most lubricated on the run-up to ovulation as this is when oestrogen production peaks.

Lube fact #6: Medication such as antidepressants, antihistamines and cold cures can dry up all your natural lubricants (the ones in your nose and elsewhere).

Lube fact #7: Anything that dehydrates you can dry up your natural lubrication such as alcohol, black coffee and smoking. Stress, the Pill or a yeast or bladder infection will also all reduce your natural lubrication levels.

Lube fact #8: Using additional shop-bought lubricant does not mean you're a failure or aren't turned on: it just means you fancy getting a little more slippery. It can be great fun when used on you and him.

Lube fact #9: Lubricants designed specifically for sexual pleasure are available from sex shops and sex toy websites. You can also use natural lubricants such as light vegetable or mineral oils. Some people say egg whites are the perfect consistency.

Lube fact #10: The anus does not produce natural lubricant at all so additional lubrication is essential for any anal play (that's with fingers, toys or a penis).

Always read the label to see what you're getting and how and where it can be used. The best way to find one you like is just to experiment. If you're the sensitive type go for flavourless, colourless, odourless products. Start with one brand and see how it goes. If you don't like it, try another. They really can have a revolutionary effect on your sex life.

Cosmo tip:
If you're using a water-based lubricant and it gets a little dry and sticky, just add a few drops of water and it'll return to it's normal consistency again.

MASSAGE
See under: erotic massage.

This is a sex book, not a massage manual so you'll find all the hands-on tips you need under **erotic massage**.

MASTURBATION
See also: clitoris, masturbation – mutual, orgasm

Reasons To Have Solo Sex Tonight
1) It increases your levels of desire: the more sex you have (even if it's just with yourself), the more you want.
2) It relieves stress, tension, muscle cramps and period pain, helps you sleep better *and* elevates your mood.
3) It's the best way to learn about your personal pleasure spots . . .
4) . . . so it's easier to teach your partner about them, too.
5) It boosts your confidence when you know how your own body works.
6) It's totally safe sex.
7) You get to be utterly selfish, focusing entirely on your pleasure.

8) It's fun and free (and you can't say that about many good things in life).

Your Masturbation Masterclass

Don't have orgasm as your ultimate goal. Most women can teach themselves to climax very quickly but the longer you hold back from it, the more powerful the end result will be.

'The first time I masturbated I was about fifteen and I'd read a novel that had a couple of raunchy scenes in it. I had no idea at the time what a clitoris was but I knew after reading those passages over and over and touching myself in a certain way it felt naughty but nice.'
Clare, 24, student

Step one: Set aside some quality time when you know you won't be disturbed. Have a relaxing bath and slip into your favourite lingerie or a sexy silk dressing gown.

Step two: Start by touching your body all over, avoiding your obvious erogenous zones. Sensual massage oil can feel sexy. Rub it up your legs (the area round the ankle bone usually feels good), thighs and across your arms, shoulders and belly.

Step three: Get your brain engaged: physical sensations alone are not enough so think about a sexy scenario that turns you on. Try recalling a particularly raunchy sex session with your partner or imagining it's your favourite celebrity who's touching you.

Step four: Once your whole body becomes sensitised, reach down between your legs and start touching your vagina and clitoris (See the **clitoris** section for more hands-on details). Try pressing your feet together while tensing your thigh muscles, as this causes pleasurable tension in your vaginal area.

Step five: Explore the entire area to discover what strokes you like the best. The head of your clitoris is likely to be the most sensitive part and for most women, stimulation of this area is the quickest route to orgasm. Try varying your strokes here from up and down, to small circles, to side-to-side motions. Start with a light touch, becoming firmer and stronger as you get closer to orgasm.

Step six: If you can, hover at a highly aroused state and hold back from orgasm. Try touching yourself somewhere slightly less sensitive (like your vaginal lips rather than the clitoris directly) if you're on the edge.

Step seven: Let yourself go. At the point of orgasm you may want to ease off clitoral stimulation as it may become too sensitive to touch. The muscles around your entire vaginal areas will contract and you'll feel waves of pleasure running through your body as feel-good chemicals are released into the blood stream. Try squeezing your vaginal muscles in a 'sucking-in' movement just as you climax. This will increase the pressure inside, meaning you can ride the wave of orgasm for longer.

Step eight (only for the greedy): If you fancy more than one climax, as soon as you feel your first waves of orgasm flow through your body, stop clitoral stimulation but keep yourself highly aroused. Try touching your vaginal lips (parts of the clitoris are hidden behind them) or your breasts and inner thighs. Alternatively, try keeping your fingers still and swaying your hips for sexy but indirect stimulation.

Step nine: Keep your arousal level at a high point for a few minutes and then try touching yourself closer and closer to your clitoris, as it should be a little less sensitive by now. You should be able to bring yourself to another climax by stimulating yourself again in the way you love best.

> **Cosmo tip:**
> Your brain is the biggest sex organ in your body. If you're tense, stressed or distracted you may not be able to climax during masturbation. Think sexy and you'll feel sexier.

Step ten (only for the *really* greedy): Repeat steps eight and nine. Unlike men, women are biologically blessed with the ability to climax over and over again without necessarily needing a break.

Different Strokes for Different Folks

Not everyone chooses to focus so much on the clitoris. Experiment with these fancy masturbation moves for even more fun. Your partner can use any of these tips on you, too.

Palm pressure

Try resting a flat palm on top of your pubic bone and pressing down firmly. This stimulates the clitoral shaft (the bit behind the head that stretches back into your body). Try pushing forward and pulling backwards or moving your palm in tiny circles. This also feels great if you use the fingers of your other hand either inside your vagina to stimulate your G-spot (5 cm/2 inches up the front wall) or around your clitoris so you're receiving pressure from above and below.

SEX FACT! *According to scientific research, no two women masturbate in exactly the same way. You can read all the techniques you like, but, when it comes down to it, you'll be adding your very own unique-to-you touch. How original!*

Three-finger fun
Rub your outside fingers down the edges of your vaginal lips and use the third finger to stimulate your clitoris. Gently pull the clitoral hood up and down if you don't want to stimulate your love button directly. (Great for after your first climax if you're hungry for more.) Try tapping the clitoris from the top while using the other fingers to massage your lips from the sides.

Two-handed tricks
- While one hand is on your clitoris, run the other over different areas of your body: try your breasts, inner thighs, pubic bone and perineum (the patch of skin between your vagina and bottom).
- Use your other hand to massage your vaginal opening (rich in nerve endings) or the extremely sensitive area around your anus (also a nerve-centre hotspot). Try inserting a finger into your vagina at the point of orgasm to give your muscles something to contract around.

'Friends of mine bought me a vibrator for my 21st birthday. I can't thank them enough. I'd never had an orgasm before and now – there's no stopping me!'
Lucy-Ann, 23, PA

Vibrating fun
Vibrators are often the quickest way to climax and can be used anywhere on the body. Experiment with speeds and locations (see **vibrators** for more info). Try using one vibrator around your clitoris and another (or a dildo: a non-vibrating toy meant for penetration) inside your vagina. Try penetrating yourself from different angles to find out which parts of your vagina are particularly sensitive. (You can use this knowledge during penetrative sex to choose a position that hits the very same spot.)

> **Cosmo tip:**
> Using a vibrator on a high speed on dry skin can make you sore afterwards. Go easy if you're not used to it.

Public pleasure

Place a hand between your closed legs and squeeze them tightly together over and over again while surreptitiously rubbing the seam of your trousers or knickers against your clitoris. (Try it at work or on a bus: no one will ever know what you're up to!)

Pillow passion

On your front, try moving a pillow or the edge of a blanket against your clitoris while keeping your body still. (Many women discover masturbation this way in their teens so it becomes a firm favourite in later life.)

SEX FACT: *Eighty per cent of women say they masturbate; 94 per cent of men admit to it.*

MASTURBATION FOR HIM

See also: ball play, masturbation – mutual, penis

Show us a man who doesn't masturbate and we'll show you a liar (or an alien with no penis). Masturbation for men is seen as an integral part of sexual development and most men have been pleasing themselves with their hands since the dawn of time (OK, since before they did their GCSEs, anyway). This is great news for you because he'll be an expert on the exact techniques he likes best.

'You can't beat a great hand job. Although you could do it to yourself any time, women don't seem to realise how much better it feels if someone else does it for you.'
John, 29, architect

Back to Basics: Your Hand Job Masterclass

1) Sit in a comfortable position where you can use both hands (so you don't need to rest on one) – between his legs with him either sitting or lying usually works well. Alternatively, straddle his chest while he's lying down, facing away from him, so he can't see what you're doing.

2) Use some kind of lube. A lot of men use something when they're in the bathroom – either baby oil or something from the bathroom shelf (probably not toothpaste). If you're using latex condoms later, remember to use a water-based lubricant like K-Y Jelly, as all oils will rot them. Any form of massage or vegetable oil is great if you're not using condoms.

3) The key to a great hand job is the build-up: you're here to extend his pleasure rather than make him climax ASAP, so start by massaging his not-so-obvious erogenous zone, working your way closer towards his genitals. As you see him becoming aroused, move away from his genitals on to a less sensitive area. Do this over and over again before you touch his penis: the more build-up you give him, the bigger his climax will be.

4) Once you head south, ask for a helping hand. Place both your hands round the base of his penis and get him to place his hands over yours, guiding you as to what pace and pressure he likes. As a general rule, men can take more pressure than you can on your clitoris, but all men are different, so asking for a demo is the best way to get your technique right.

> **Cosmo tip:**
> When asking for feedback use one-word questions such as 'faster?' 'harder?' 'stronger?' so he has only to grunt yes or no rather than process a whole sentence.

5) With a curved hand, start with gentle pressure, running your hands up and down his shaft, never losing contact with his skin. The idea is to create a fluid movement rather than anything jerky. Gradually move faster and harder as he becomes more aroused.

6) When he's nearly at orgasm, stop all movement and stay still for a few seconds. This allows him to enjoy a high level of arousal without climaxing, which will eventually enable him to last longer when you're having penetrative sex.

7) Vary your strokes. Try twisting your hands in opposite directions while you go up and down (one hand clockwise, the other anticlockwise). Try moving one fist from the base to the middle of his penis and the other from the tip to the middle so they meet and then go back in opposite directions.

8) When you feel his arousal peaking, continue with a firm regular stroke (rather than playing around with a fancy moves). When he's about to come, the head of his penis will darken and his testicles will lift towards his body. Most men will like you just to hold tight during ejaculation but some like a few more strokes while they're climaxing, so ask him what he prefers.

9) When he's climaxed, stop all sensations – he'll be too sensitive to take any more.

Cosmo tip:
When you grip his penis, try to have the join of your fingers to the side rather than at the back of the penis (like a belt tied at the side rather than the front). Fingertips on the frenulum can be uncomfortable.

Advanced Hands-On Tricks

Brrrrrrrilliant!
Vibrators aren't just for your fun. Try using one on a low setting over his lower belly, inner thighs and balls while you masturbate him with your other hand. Start very gently (and somewhere less sensitive) at first to give his body time to get used to the new sensation. Resting a vibrator on the underside of his penis at the point where the head meets the shaft can be arousing. Try wrapping your toy in a piece of cloth (your undies are ideal) if the sensation feels too intense at first.

'The best masturbation is when a woman builds up to a fast rhythm, then slows down dramatically. If she does this three or four times, never taking her hand off me, it's incredible.'
Michael, 31, sub-editor

It's a ring thing
Use a silk scarf or even a string of pearls to make a ring around the base of his penis. Move this ring up and down for a novel sensation (remember lots of lube and keep those pearls away from his pubic hair!).

Slap 'n' tickle
While you're running one hand up and down his shaft, position the palm of your other hand the top of his penis so the tip (the most sensitive part) slaps against the palm of your hand on your upstroke.

Get juicy

While one hand is working up and down the shaft, use the other with a flat palm over the head of his penis and smooth it around as if you were juicing a lemon. Try closing that hand up (like closing an umbrella) and opening it again in the same rhythm as your up-and-down stroke.

Milk it

Just using an upstroke, pull a well-lubricated hand up his shaft and off the end. As soon as you lose contact with one hand, start at the bottom with your other hand, pulling it off the top with a flourish. Continue over and over in a regular rhythm, getting harder and faster.

> **Cosmo tip:**
> The more turned on you are about touching his manhood, the sexier the hand job will be. Try fantasising while you're doing it so the pleasure doesn't seem so one-sided. You could be a famous porn star in the middle of a show or a high priestess conducting a pleasure ritual.

MASTURBATION – MUTUAL

See also: masturbation, masturbation for him

Fancy a little hands-on fun for both of you? Follow these his 'n' hers hands-on tips . . .

1) It's showtime

Men love watching women touch themselves. Not only are you putting on a private sex show for your lover, you're also instructing him to pay attention to the exact strokes you like. If you're feeling self-conscious, dim the lights and pretend he's not in the room. Alternatively, start off by touching yourself while you're having penetrative sex to get used to doing it in his presence. If you're super-confident, maintain eye contact with him the whole time or talk him through – move by move – exactly what you're doing (very, very sexy!).

2) Sexy silk

Leave your knickers (your best silky satiny ones, naturally) on for as long as possible. He should touch you through the fabric, feeling you getting wetter and wetter the whole time. Vary the touch from long teasing strokes down the whole length of the vulva, to a specific fingers-on-the-clitoris touch (small circles feel great) to pushing the silk aside and varying material/skin contact. Once you've removed your knickers (it's a challenge to keep them on for long!), try wrapping them round the shaft of his penis and rubbing it up and down to show him what all the fuss is about.

> **Cosmo tip:**
>
> Give him a clue if he's getting it right! Arch your body, tense your thigh and vaginal muscles, moan, sigh, grip his hand – anything to let him know you're enjoying what he's doing.

3) On my command . . .

If he climaxes first, try masturbating yourself to orgasm while he talks you through it: he tells you exactly how and where you're allowed to touch yourself and you are totally at his mercy. His job is to delay your climax as long as possible by commanding you to stop or touch somewhere else if you're getting too aroused. Try swapping roles, too, so you're the person in command while he touches himself.

4) Two-person touch

Try stimulating your clitoris with your own hand while your lover uses a dildo or his fingers to penetrate you. Maintaining eye contact the whole time will heighten the sexual tension and increase both your lust levels. Alternatively, try using his erect penis to massage your clitoris and vaginal lips: it's a touch-sensitive turn-on for both of you.

'I find concentrating on her pleasure at the same time as mine too difficult, so I like to make her climax with my hands before she starts on me. That way, I know she's happy and afterwards I can lie back and watch her go to work without feeling guilty.'

Jason, 28, financial controller

5) Slick tricks

Experiment with different types of lubrication. Try pouring shop-bought lube into your open palms so he can watch the show. Delay touching his genitals for as long as possible by spending time warming the lube between your hands, then letting it drip slowly out of your palms and on to his belly and penis, finally using up and down strokes on him. Get him to repeat the process on you afterwards, so you're both super-sticky. (Remember, oil-based lube and latex condoms don't mix, so use water-based lubricants or plastic (polyurethane) condoms if you're going on to penetrative sex.)

Secret Seduction Moves for Both of You
TV quickie
Try watching an erotic movie together and, with your eyes glued to the screen, let your hands wander over to each other's genitals. The distraction of seeming to concentrate on the action on screen is arousing for both of you, as you're 'pretending' nothing is happening.
Blanket move
This is a great secret seduction move for any boring coach, train or plane ride. Simply slip his hand under a travel blanket and into your knickers. Get him to gently massage your whole genital area, sliding his hand backwards and forwards across the length of your vulva, finally concentrating around the clitoris. The trick is to perform the whole move without the blanket moving so no one else notices. The adrenaline rush of getting down and dirty with other people around adds a naughty buzz.

SEX FACT *Many people in relationships still carry on masturbating in private. It usually has no bearing on the state of your sex life. Think of it like treating yourself to a new lippy or a cream cake: you don't have to share those with your partner, do you?*

MIND TRICKS
See also: confidence, initiating sex, libido

Want to have more confidence in bed? Too shy to make the first move or take on a more dominant role? Use these sexy mind-tricks to fool your body and soul into sex-goddess status:

Imagine you're the man

Swapping gender roles in your head is a kooky, kinky way of tricking your brain into behaving in a more confident, dominant or demanding way. Imagine you're him and you're seducing your lover for the very first time. Your brain will trick your body (hands, tongue, fingers) into behaving differently. Don't tell your lover what you're thinking to make it even more surprising.

Be a seductive star

Imagine your favourite star in their most alluring scene/video. Think about how they move, how they flirt, how they talk. Next imagine your normal self having sex or being seduced and think about how you'd usually react. Play the same scene over in your head, this time imagining how your sexy star would act differently. This is a technique actors use to get into a role, and is called 'seeing through the character's eyes'. Now *become* that character: everything you do should now be in the role of the star you've picked, as if you're doing everything their way. It has an amazing effect on everything from your body language to the tone and pitch of your voice and has the power to boost your confidence and change the way you behave in any sexual situation.

Act as if

A great psychological technique for any situation where you need a bit of oomph: the principle is to 'act as if' you already had the quality you're trying to achieve. For example, if you want to be more assertive or sexier in bed, simply act as if you already were. You can also act as if you were extremely experienced in bed, very naughty, slightly kinky or incredibly seductive. Sure, you start off faking these actions and emotions but this forces your body to behave in a certain way. This behaviour is then reinforced by people around you (e.g. your boyfriend becoming incredibly grateful/submissive/pleased/turned on), which then reinforces this quality in your personality. Eventually, you'll find you're not acting at all any more.

MIRRORS

A mirror is an extremely versatile sex toy that doesn't even need to be hidden away at the back of the knicker drawer. For some lustful looking-glass ideas, try these:

Masturbation masterclass

If you're too shy to go for full-on mirror action with your partner, try masturbating in front of a mirror on your own. Look at yourself in the eye as you touch your body and let your imagination go wild: those could be anyone's hands all over you. Watching a sex toy on, in or around your vagina and clitoris can also be extremely arousing. Enjoy the visual show you're putting on for yourself.

Phone-sex sensation

Try having phone sex while you're in front of a mirror. Take your clothes off and start to masturbate while telling your partner exactly what you're doing. Don't forget to let him know you're watching, too. Describing what you can see, as if you were looking through his eyes, is incredibly powerful. And, as men are visual creatures, he'll be able to 'see' exactly what you tell him. Use an urgent whispering voice as if you can't wait to have him talk you up to orgasm.

'I'd never seen myself having sex until I stayed in a hotel room with a huge mirror in front of the bed. It felt really sexy to see how flushed and tousled I get during a frantic session!'
Lorna, 32, care worker

Big-screen action

Try having sex in front of a mirror with your partner. Imagine that what you're watching isn't just your reflection, but actually a porn film in which you're the stars. Pose for the camera, exaggerate your moves, invent a script and 'talk to camera' or take on a naughty new porn-starlet persona. This allows you to live out your exhibitionist fantasies without actually committing yourself to video. It's also a great way to try out camera angles if you *are* into the whole filming scenario. (See **movie making** for more details).

Strike a pose

Try out different sex positions in front of a mirror to see which ones you enjoy watching best. Being penetrated from behind directly facing the glass allows you to watch him in action and make eye contact with him at the same time. The same position but turned to the side allows you both to see the penis slide in and out of you (very arousing). Having him kneel while you straddle his lap allows you to look over his shoulder and, as you see only his back, makes him quite anonymous (he could be anyone!). You on top (both from the side and facing the mirror) allows you to show off your body in all your glory.

> **Cosmo tip:**
> Whatever you're doing in front of a mirror, try to catch your lover's eye and give him a cheeky grin or wink: it shows you're both enjoying the show.

MISSIONARY POSITION

See also: CAT position, positions, X-rated positions.

The most popular sexual position the world over: it's intimate, comfortable, sexy and adaptable. Lying back and thinking of England has never felt so good! For variations on the missionary theme see the **positions** section and for an orgasm-inducing alternative, see the **CAT position**.

MOOD ENHANCERS

See also: aphrodisiacs, fantasy, libido

Mental Mood Boosters

- Relive your sexiest lust encounter ever. Go through every raunchy detail in your head: the tastes, textures, sights and sounds. Slow down the action or speed it up; add an extra element of arousal to the story to boost its effectiveness. Visualise yourself back there: this tricks the body into responding as if you really were in the middle of the action.
- Let your fantasies run riot before, during and after sex.

Physical Mood Boosters

- Ask your partner for a massage to relax the body and energise the soul. Make it clear he's not allowed to touch your genitals but he can 'play' everywhere else. Your body will soon be tingling all over and the ban on genital touching will actually focus your brain on that area (particularly if all his strokes head in that direction!).
- Hot spicy foods get your pulse racing and send more blood to your genitals. Cook up that chilli now.
- Imagine all your favourite erogenous zones filling with blood and getting larger and more sensitive. This tricks the body into starting off the arousal cycle, giving you a kinky kick-start.

Emotional Mood Boosters

- Think back to the beginning of your relationship (or even back to your teenage years) when a slight brush of skin against skin set off an electric charge between you. Recreate those early days by going on a 'first date' again.
- Sit in front of each other naked and start to gently stroke each other's body. Take turns to be the leader, with one of you leading the action and the other mirroring those strokes and caresses. It's incredibly intimate and creates a strong mind–body connection.

MORNING-AFTER PILL
See under: emergency contraception

Another name for emergency contraception. In fact the so-called morning-after pill lasts up to 72 hours but is most effective the sooner after sex you take it. Be prepared, keep a pack handy, just in case of accidents.

MOVIE MAKING
See also: dressing up, photography, porn, role-play

Get ready for lights . . . camera . . . satisfaction.

> **Movie Making Rules**
> • Agree together that this film is for your eyes only and will *never* be shown to a third party.
> • Work out how far you want to go so you don't find yourself being required to do things on film you're really not into.
> • Label the tape (and hide it). 'Emma and Steve at it, Ibiza 2004' may attract the attention of anyone who checks out your video shelf and you really don't want to be confusing *Toy Story* with your own version, *(Sex) Toy Story*.
> • Make sure both of you are totally into what you're doing. There's no point if either one of you is uncomfortable with it.
> • Agree to destroy the tape if you ever go your separate ways. Using a sex tape as blackmail is totally unforgivable (and illegal).

Your Step-by-Step Movie-making Masterclass

Step 1: The inspiration

Watch as many raunchy or erotic videos as you can to decide what you like. These don't have to be porn videos (although they could be): anything could give you inspiration, from the classic food scene in *9½ weeks* to the spanking in *Secretary* to your favourite episodes of *Sex and the City*. Think about the exact scenes that turn you on and what it is about them (the character roles? the lighting? the language?) that you really like. Also think about your own fantasies: there may be a particular scenario that floats through your head that you wouldn't mind putting on film. Discuss the things that turn you both on.

Step 2: The equipment

You could just use your regular video camera, either hand-held or set on a tripod. Sophisticated video cameras combined with computer software often allow you to edit together your shots to form a sequence. Practise your filming skills and the type of shots you want to use on a non-sexy subject (e.g. a birthday or family party) to get used to the camera and work out which shots look best before you get raunchy. Alternatively, you could hire professional cameras or even set up a webcam. Investing in these options can be pricey so start off with the basic gear until you know you're into it.

Step 3: The plot

The best homemade films have some kind of storyline. Maybe he's your boss and you're the sexy secretary who's helping him with more than just his shorthand. Or you could be a naughty nurse giving him an intimate examination. You don't have to write down your script word for word: just have a basic idea of what you'd like to happen in your film and think about the different shots you want to use. Decide who'll be holding the camera for which shots and when you'll need it on the tripod. Realistic sounds such as panting and moaning often sound better on screen than cheesy lines.

> **Cosmo tip:**
> If you're using the camera on a tripod, position it at around five feet high so you get a good overview of the action.

> **Cosmo tip:**
> Take things very slowly: the longer you string out the action and build up the tension, the better your film will be. (And you can always edit out the boring bits.)

Step 4: The costumes

Dressing up is all part of the fun and deciding on your characters and costumes can be a turn-on in itself.

Step 5: The music

Does your film need a soundtrack? The tone of your music can radically change the feel of your film. Decide which music suits your mood and your theme and either have it running in the background or edit it over your shots afterwards.

Step 6: The lighting

This is crucial and can make all the difference to your finished movie. Use lots of bright but low lighting that flows upwards towards your face rather than overhead lighting that casts unflattering shadows. Use lamps on the floor with the highest-wattage bulbs you can get and check your shots first to see what looks good on screen: you'll need more light for your film than you'd normally want in the bedroom.

Cosmo tip:

Get a professional fake-tan treatment before you film: it'll boost your confidence, and tanned skin always looks better on film. Smearing yourself in baby oil can also make your skin glisten sexily on screen.

Step 7: The camera angles

The best films use a combination of shots. Mount the camera on a tripod first, look through the viewfinder to angle it so it covers your main area of action (e.g. your bed). Vary these static shots with hand-held action. One tip: don't use your camera's zoom button, as it's easy for the action to go out of focus. Zoom in by hand if you want a close-up. Either partner can hold the camera themselves to film the action. Check your location for minimal background noise if you want your lines to come out clearly. Clear your set of all unnecessary clutter such as bedside glasses of water or overflowing laundry baskets. They'll only distract your 'audience'. Practise looking straight into the lens: it'll look great in the final film.

Step 8: The run-through

Have a trial run where you test out everything – your location, your props, your costumes, your plot, your camera angles – but without turning the camera on. Just pretending to film each other can be a huge turn-on and it's great practice for the real thing.

Step 9: Lights! Camera! Action!

Save your best performance for the reel-deal. The more you get into it, the better your film will be, so really let yourself go. Have patience while you're filming, as you may need to film certain shots or scenes more than once to get them exactly right. Once filming is over, you may want to edit your film. Take time putting the shots together and choosing the sequence you like best. Hot tip: if only one of you does the editing, the final cut will be a sexy surprise for the other one!

SEX FACT *One in five British couples like to film themselves having sex, and 36 per cent enjoy sexy videos together.*

Step 10: The premiere!

For the first viewing of your sexy film, imagine you're going to a real-life movie premiere. Dress up and get the champagne on ice. Take a snap of yourselves as if you really were stars being photographed by the paparazzi. (When anyone sees the snaps they'll think you were just going to a party, but the two of you will know better.) Celebrate your 'stardom' with a few glasses of champagne, then settle down to watch your on-screen action.

'My boyfriend filmed me masturbating once. I pretended I didn't know he was filming (he watched me through an open door) which gave the whole thing a Peeping Tom-type feel – watching it back was amazing.'
Belinda, 35, journalist

MULTIPLE ORGASMS
See also: arousal, ejaculation, orgasm

Both men and women are capable of multiple orgasms but the techniques needed and sensations felt are subtly different (it's much easier for us to have them than it is for him). In both cases, the key is getting to know how your body responds to different levels of arousal. The best practice is usually masturbation on your own at first so you can learn about your body. You can then teach each other your techniques and exactly what feels right. Good luck – may the multiple-force be with you!

> **Cosmo tip:**
> Female levels of desire fall much more quickly than male levels. If you stop stimulating a man, he'll remain aroused for much longer than you will if your stimulation stops. Bear this in mind when you're attempting multiples.

	Your Multiple Orgasm: The big bang followed by little starburst	**His Multiple Orgasm: Little starburst building up to the big bang**
What is it?	Usually involves coming to a climactic peak (your first orgasm, usually, though not always, the strongest), then holding your arousal at a high enough level to be able to peak back up again (causing another orgasm and another).	Usually involves being able to delay ejaculation (coming) but experiencing the physical sensations of orgasm, i.e. riding a high enough wave of orgasmic pleasure over and over again without getting right up there to the big bang.
Difficulty rating	8/10 – but it depends on the woman. Some find it easier than others.	9/10 – most men are satisfied with just the one climax and don't have the time or patience to separate ejaculation from the feeling of orgasm in order to go multiple, but it can be done (with a lot of practice).
The theory	After your first orgasm, rather than just cuddling up with your lover/vibrator/cup of cocoa, you need to keep your body and mind focused on keeping your arousal up there so that it becomes possible to peak again.	He needs to have tremendous control over his arousal levels in order to be at a high enough peak to be able to experience orgasm (rhythmical contractions, extreme senses of sexual pleasure) without tipping himself over the top into ejaculation (propulsion of semen out of the penis). In other words, he needs to be able to surf the wave of extreme sexual arousal without giving in to the end result.
The practice	Try masturbating yourself to orgasm once. Your clitoris may feel too sensitive to the touch at first, so try playing	Masturbation on his own is usually the best way for him to get the hang of controlled arousal. He should practise getting to the point of

around with your breasts, vaginal lips or perineum (the patch of skin between the vagina and the anus). Keep your breathing even and focus your mind on your favourite fantasy. If you're with a partner, try good old-fashioned passionate snogging while he uses his hands away from your clitoris. Build up a steady rhythm of whatever feels good, getting closer and closer to your clitoral head. Some women find using different strokes around the clitoris works well, others like breast or inner-thigh stimulation. If you're having penetrative sex, try keeping your legs together rather than apart (try the missionary position with his legs apart and yours together – the reversal of the traditional position). His thrusting will cause more tension on the vaginal lips, which pulls the clitoral hood, indirectly stimulating the clitoris. Build up a steady rhythm with whatever technique you choose until your arousal peaks again.

extreme arousal (say nine on a scale of one to ten), then stopping just short of ejaculation. All his senses need to be focused on how this feels, what's going on at this point inside his genitals, pelvis and PC muscles (the ones he uses to control his pee), and what exactly he needs to do to get to this level, then come back down again. He needs to play around with different types of stimulation – short sharp strokes, long steady ones, every time stopping at a high point, taking himself down to a lower level, then coming back up again. Once he's familiar with his own levels of arousal, you can join in using a scale of arousal from one to a hundred. He needs to be able to learn to hover around the 85 mark in order to experience waves of orgasmic pleasure without ejaculating.

The payoff

Waves or orgasmic pleasure either one after another or a few minutes apart, either starting with a larger climax or building and building and building . . .

Although this takes extreme control and a lot of practice, the finale (i.e. ejaculation, when he eventually lets himself go) is a fantastically big bang with orgasmic sensations being felt across the whole of his body.

SEX FACT: *Taoist and Tantric teachers believe that, for men, being able to orgasm fully while withholding ejaculate is one of life's greatest sexual highs. He'll need a professional teacher if he fancies training himself up for this as it's an extremely advanced technique.*

NAILS

Use your talons to your advantage with these naughty tricks:

- Try giving him a scratch massage where, instead of a relaxing stroke, you use your nails to tempt and tease.

'Girls with long nails – they really do it for me. I love to be scratched all over my neck and shoulders!'
Louie, 35, builder

- Use the intensity of your nail movements as a sign you're about to climax (or really enjoying what he's doing to you and well on your way!). If he's giving you oral sex, dig your nails into his shoulders as he brings you to orgasm or scratch your fingers down his back if you're having sex in the missionary position to up the passion for both of you.
- Try the zig-zag: if you're running your nails down his back, move them in a zig-zag pattern rather than a straight line. This fires more nerve endings than a straight line, as he won't know where he's going to be touched next.
- Try running your nails across his buttocks and over his balls – be gentle but passionate. The idea is to get his adrenaline pumping with the hint of harder strokes to come.

SAFETY INFO: If either of you is inserting fingers inside the other, nails should be kept short and clean, as long nails or straggly cuticles can cause infections.

NAMES
See also: talking dirty

Name Rule #1: Using his name while you're having sex can be extremely erotic. Just make sure you (a) know what it is and (b) get it right.

Name Rule #2: Although it's perfectly acceptable to have kooky names for your private parts (especially ones you can play around with quite innocently in emails or texts), it is unacceptable to reveal his naughty name to any other party.

NECK

Kissing isn't called 'necking' for nothing, as the neck is one of the most sensitive spots on the body. Make the most of yours with these saucy suggestions:

Naughty nipping
Get your man to kiss you all the way around your hairline (front and back) and then continue the kisses all the way down your neck and around to the hollows at the front where your neck meets your collarbone. Try alternating kisses with naughty little nips.

Saucy stroking
While you're having sex, get your man to stroke both his hands gently up and down the sides of your neck. He can also hold on to your throat (very loosely) – the sensation of having something round your neck when you're on the build-up to orgasm can be extremely arousing.

⚠ *SAFETY INFO: Never do anything during sex that restricts your breathing in any way. It's extremely dangerous and can be fatal.*

Head rush central

Try having sex with you on the bottom with your head thrown back over the edge of the bed, exposing your neck for him to stroke and kiss. This sends all the blood rushing to your head, which creates an amazingly erotic sensation. Your nipples will feel extra sensitive, too.

Penis play

For a sexy build-up to oral sex for him, kneel in front of your man while he stands, and kiss and lick his inner thighs. Once he's aroused, gently take his penis and stroke it all around your face and neck. Let it lightly brush your lips, give it a little lick, then take it away to your neck again. Next, hold it in your mouth for a few seconds then take it away. Do this for as long as you both can stand.

NERVE ENDINGS
See also: erogenous zones

Want to know where you're likely to be the most sensitive? It's where your nerve endings are closest to the surface of the skin, which means anywhere you can see veins near the surface, such as your inner elbows, wrists and backs of knees.

Nerve-tingling Trick #1: To discover new erogenous zones, take an old-fashioned hairpin and run it along your body. In most places you'll be able to feel just one of the prongs of the hairpin, but in the places where you're most sensitive you'll distinctly feel both prongs as different sensations. Erogenous zones exist where nerve endings are closer together, so that's why you're more sensitive to the hairpin in your hotspots.

Nerve-tingling Trick #2: To stimulate the most tactile nerves in your body, use gentle stroking rather than firm pummelling. Use a flat, gentle hand or a soft brush and concentrate on those thin-skinned sensitive spots. Avoid the genitals and obvious erogenous zones such

Cosmo tip:
Don't use these nerve-tingling techniques merely as a precursor to sex. They can be an erotic ritual in their own right, bonding you together emotionally as well as physically.

as thighs and nipples, otherwise your nerve receptors will be swamped and you won't feel these subtle sensations.

NIBBLING
See also: spanking

Nipping and nibbling can be intense and sexy, and a little pain in the neck (or elsewhere) can be incredibly arousing.

SEX FACT! *Eighty per cent of Cosmo readers say a mischievous little nibble drives them wild!*

Try:

- Biting the strong muscles that run down the sides of the neck after kissing your lover tenderly around that area: it'll be a strong sexy surprise.
- Nibbling his ears, particularly the fleshy lobes.
- Biting his fingers after sucking them seductively.
- Nibbling (with your lips, not your teeth) along the shaft of his penis as if it were a corn on the cob.
- Biting his inner thighs on the way up (or down).
- Giving his bottom a few sharp little nips – his fleshy parts can take more punishment than the bony ones.
- Nipping him gently up either side of the spine, culminating on the shoulders.
- Biting down (gently) on his wrist bone or fingers while he gives you oral sex – you'll nibble harder as your sexual pleasure intensifies.

SAFETY INFO: Never break the skin when you're nibbling your partner. It's too painful and could cause an infection.

SEX FACT! *When you're aroused, endorphins, the body's natural painkillers, which dull pain and increase pleasure, are released into the body.*

NIPPLES
See also: breasts

Your nipples and his engorge with blood and become erect when you're sexually aroused. They can swell up to three times their normal size. His nipples can be just as sensitive as yours and probably deserve more attention than you're currently giving them. Try licking, flicking, sucking, stroking or slapping them (a plastic ruler is great for this). Alternatively, straddle him and run your hair down the length of his body so it just glances over his nipples for a sexy tickly sensation.

Sex shops sell nipple-enlarging machines, which work on similar principles to penis pumps (and are, in our opinion, just as daft). They are usually a little suction pump used to pull the nipple upwards and outwards. Be careful if you use one, as too much pump action can be harmful.

Chest for Him . . .
For tantalising techniques to stimulate your nipples, see the **breasts** section. For some nipple action for him, read on . . .

Hands on
Start by making large circles around the whole of his chest area with flat oiled palms, getting closer and closer to his nipples. As you feel his nipples hardening, spread your fingers and take his nipples between them, squeezing your fingers shut as he becomes more and more aroused. Try rolling each nipple between your fingers or take it between a finger and thumb and squeeze it hard.

Get imaginative
It's not just your hands that will feel sexy on his chest: use your imagination and try different fabrics or props for different sensations. Leather, silk and rubber will appeal to some men. Your undies (dirty or clean!) will appeal to others. Ice can feel nice, and a soft make-up brush or a piece of fake fur can also feel sexy. Try blindfolding him so he concentrates on his feelings rather than what he's seeing. (This game works well for both of you and you can gradually draw the props further and further down each other's body.)

Magic mouth action

Kiss and lick from his neck down to his chest area. Take his nipple into your mouth and suck on it quite firmly until you feel it enlarging. Try flicking it with your tongue and biting gently on the nipple. (Your hands can be paying attention to another erogenous zone at the same time for extra stimulation.)

NO
See also: bondage, libido, yes, yes, yes!

No Rule #1

That oh-so-important two-letter word *always* demands respect. No should always mean no, regardless of when it's uttered. Got that?

No Rule #2

It's OK to say, 'No, not tonight darling' if you really don't feel like any bed action, but if you say it too often your **libido** levels can drop. See the libido section for ideas on how to get revved up again.

No Rule #3

During fantasy games, no can sometimes mean 'ooh yes please'. Always have a neutral safe word that means 'stop' to avoid confusion. See **bondage** for more details.

NO-TOUCH SEDUCTION
See also: blindfolds, talking dirty

You don't have to be hands-on to get turned on. Try these sensual no-touch seduction tricks for the ultimate build-up (if you can keep your hands off each other for long enough).

The hoverfly

Try running both your hands over each other's naked body without touching the skin. You should aim just to brush the hairs on each other's body, which stimulates the nerve endings in a new and exciting way.

Voice your desires

Your voice is one of the most versatile sex toys you own. Try blindfolding your lover, then telling him exactly what you'd like to do to him once you are allowed to touch each other. Don't forget to tell him what you'd like him to do to you as well – it's a great way to communicate what you love in bed. Hot tip: you may find this easier if you're both blindfolded.

Touch and tease

Just because you can't touch *each other*, it doesn't mean you can't touch yourself. Whether you're at a romantic meal or he's watching you apply sun cream on the beach, make touching yourself an erotic ritual by intensely holding his gaze. Touch your hair and neck; gently stroke your finger across your mouth; linger on all the places you'd like him to touch you. The fact that he's not allowed to will drive him wild.

On my command

Sit on the bed naked with a little distance between you (so your bodies can't touch) and take it in turns to give out some touch-yourself-there instructions. Start off gently by saying, 'Stroke your neck and shoulders', and build up very slowly, including more and more intimate places. Watching him follow your orders and being in control of exactly how, where and for how long he touches himself can be highy arousing. This is an extremely erotic visual treat for both of you, so make sure it lasts for as long as possible.

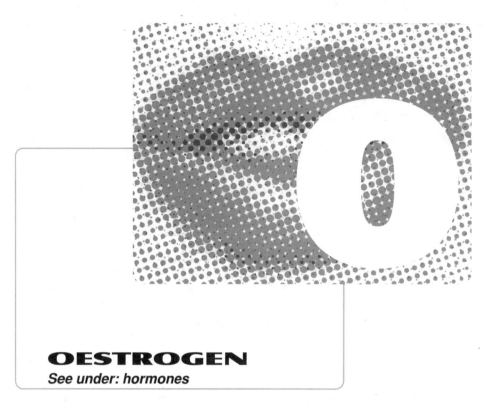

OESTROGEN
See under: hormones

Uplifting female sex hormone that peaks just before ovulation.

ONE-NIGHT STANDS
See also: alcohol, condoms

'If I'm serious about someone, I tend to wait longer before I have sex with her. If things progress too fast you can burn out the passion and lose that fairytale feeling. I'd always be upfront about my intentions so there's no confusion whether it's a one-off or not.'
Darren, 27, recruitment consultant

Disastrous or delectable? Most of us have had our fair share of both types (and if we haven't, then they're simply not our thing and we'll probably never experience the good, the bad or the ugly). Here's how to get the best from one night of passion . . .

Do:	Don't:
Flirt outrageously for the whole evening. The chase is sometimes more fun than the actual sex, so enjoy this bit as much as you can.	Stalk someone who really isn't interested: spotting someone across the bar, flirting with them until they're too drunk to care, *then* taking them home is not acceptable.
Carry and use condoms.	Go back to someone's house if you really don't know anything about them or if alarm bells ring in your head. Your gut instincts are usually right.
If you're going back to his, let your friends know where you're going, who you're with and when to expect you back. No point in putting your safety at risk for a quick fling.	Pretend this is something it's not. Sitting by the phone expecting it to ring is hell. As a general rule, having sex on the first night doesn't tend to result in a life-long relationship. There are exceptions, but in general, a bit of getting to know each other on a more than just physical level tends to take place first.
Be clear from the start about what you both want. The most successful one-night stands are the occasions where you both know this is no-strings sex and that's all there is to it.	Expect the sex to be super-spectacular. Sometimes it can be hotter than hell and your bodies fuse in all the right places. Other times (thanks to the influence of alcohol, mainly) your flirting can fizzle into nothing as soon as you hit the sheets.
Sexperiment. One night of passion is often an opportunity to try things you'd find difficult to introduce with a longer-term lover; be as liberated as you want to be.	Do anything you really don't want to do. Being sexperimental is one thing. Finding yourself in a torture chamber when you're more the romantic hearts-and-flowers type is quite another.
Have something to do the next day. Even if it's a fake shopping trip, having somewhere to go gives you an excuse to get	Give out your phone number unless you're convinced he'll call. If you've not enjoyed yourself and you're put on the spot, giving out

out of the house (his or yours). If he wants more, make him wait.

a fake number is fine (but remember that he can do the same).

Use the experience as an ego boost. If you're likely to feel guilty in the morning, it's really not worth the hassle (even more so if you're in a relationship already). This should be a pleasurable treat rather than an act of desperation or revenge.

If you do swap numbers, don't be tempted to send sloppy texts next time you get drunk. There's a fine line between stalker and sex kitten when it comes to telecommunications.

Cosmo tip:
If you really want to enjoy yourself, take control in the bedroom. Remember that, although it takes a little more work, your orgasm is just as important as his.

SEX FACT: *According to the* People *newspaper, women from Yorkshire are the most likely to have sex within 24 hours of meeting a new lover.*

ORAL SEX FOR HIM

See also: ball play, masturbation for him, penis, spit or swallow

The holy grail of great sex for most men is receiving amazing oral attention. The key to awesome oral? The more you enjoy yourself down there, the more he will. Enthusiasm and confidence combined with some stunning technical secrets is your key to success. Read on for all the tips, tricks and tongue-tingling techniques you'll ever need.

Back to Basics: Your Blow-by-Blow Guide to Fabulous Fellatio

1) Begin with him sitting or lying on a chair or bed with you between his legs, so you're both comfortable.

2) Keep the lights on: men love to watch while they receive oral. Close your eyes if you feel self-conscious – from his angle he'll think you're gazing adoringly at his penis.

3) Start by kissing and licking his thighs and belly to warm you both up. Don't put his penis in your mouth until it's fully erect. Move on to kissing his penis, then moving your head away to tantalise him further.

4) After a couple of minutes take the first two inches or so of his penis in your mouth, covering your teeth with your lips. Keep a bottle of water to hand to keep your mouth lubricated – the wetter the better.

'Although I love getting blow jobs, I'd never force a girl to go down if she really didn't want to: you can tell when a girl's into it and when she isn't. Enthusiasm is the biggest turn-on.'
Mark, 28, accountant

5) Gently brush the top and underside of your tongue across the head of the penis, which is the most sensitive part. Find the frenulum (the little ridge of skin on the underside near the top of the penis and flick this with your tongue: it's supersensitive. Lick up and down the shaft sustaining a regular rhythm. Rest your elbows just inside his thighs if it helps you keep your balance.

6) Next, make a ring around his penis with your thumb and first two fingers, which extends the tunnel made by your mouth, giving him the sensation of deeper penetration. Form an 'O' shape with your mouth and, along with your hand, run your mouth up and down his shaft. Use your hand, not your mouth, to control how far in he goes. If you become tired, stop with your mouth but keep your hands going.

7) Don't suck his penis like a lollipop, which can cause an uncomfortable vacuum – lick it like an ice cream, then try moving up and down the shaft while twisting your mouth from left to right.

8) The secret to great fellatio is to vary what you're doing as much as possible, but, once you feel he's nearing his climax (a few appreciative groans plus faster, harder breathing indicate it's imminent), stick to what you're doing: usually one simple repetitive action.

9) When he's about to come, ask him to give you a signal so you

Cosmo tip:
To minimise the taste of semen, have his penis at the back of your throat rather than the front when he climaxes. There are fewer taste buds at the back of your tongue than at the tip.

can finish with a flourish. It's totally up to you whether you spit or swallow. If you don't like the taste of semen pull his penis to one side when he climaxes.

Advanced Oral for Him
Once you've mastered the basics, try these tongue-twisting techniques.

Lovely lip work
Close your mouth and let him push gently to part your lips with the tip of his penis, bit by bit – this mimics the feeling of his penetrating your other lips.

Upside-down lust
Turn yourself around so you face his feet rather than his head. The direction of his erection is now in line with the curve of your throat, *and* he gets a great view of your bottom.

Hot to trot
Take a cup of hot tea and a glass of ice-cold water into the bedroom. When you go down on him alternate with a mouthful of the hot, then cold, drink – it's a sensual treat he'll love (and works on your bits, too).

Hum a tune
Humming causes sexy vibrations to travel from your mouth across his penis – try his favourite team's football song (or even 'Happy Birthday' if you go south only once a year!).

A taste sensation
Mints, mint tea or toothpaste will create an unusually zingy sensation on his bits (and can help disguise the taste of semen).

Come hither
Instead of going down on him, let *him* come to you. Lie on your back with your head on some pillows while he kneels in front of you. Allow him to gently pump in and out of your mouth while you remain still. This position requires a lot of trust (as he's really in control) but leaves your hands free to masturbate, so can be a turn on-for both of you.

While You're at it: Turn-ons for You

To up your what's-in-it-for-me factor try these tricks:

- Before you take his penis in your mouth rub it across your nipples. Once you're in the middle of the action, with your free hand stroke or pinch your nipples and if you can reach (and are coordinated enough!) reach between your legs.

- Instead of resting your whole body between his legs, shift across to the left or right so one of his legs is between yours. From here you can rhythmically rub your clitoris against his knee or leg while you pump his penis in and out of your mouth.

Cosmo tip:
The food he's eaten beforehand will affect the taste of his sperm. Curry, garlic, beer and any strongly spiced food will produce what *Sex and the City*'s Samantha delightfully called 'funky spunk'. Strawberries, kiwi fruit and vanilla ice cream will all improve his flavour. The same goes for your bits, too.

SEX FACT *The average mouth is 9 cm (3.5 inches) long and the average penis is 15 cm (6 inches) long, so, no matter what he thinks, you can't possibly get it all in (unless he's teeny-tiny!).*

- Don't underestimate the power of your brain: imagine it's Brad Pitt/Robbie Williams's bits you're sucking or that you're performing on stage in front of an excited audience.

- If your mouth gets tired, continue with one hand while masturbating yourself with the other. Kneel up and show him what you're doing while looking him in the eye – fantastic!

- Remember, she who giveth also receiveth. Yippee! It's your turn next . . .

SEX FACT *Although giving oral sex is not considered a hundred per cent safe sex, it's a low-risk activity. You can lower your risk of infection further by not letting him climax in your mouth. You could also use flavoured condoms.*

ORAL SEX FOR YOU

See also: masturbation for you, oral sex for him, orgasm, sixty-nine

For awesome oral for you, just let this book casually fall open at this very page.

SEX FACT: *Eighty-seven per cent of men say they enjoy giving a woman oral sex, according to* Cosmo's Male Mind *Survey.*

Back to Basics: Make Your Man a Cunnilingus Champ

1) Get comfy. The easiest position for you is to lie back on the bed and raise your knees. Your man then kisses and licks his way down your body to warm you up.

> **Cosmo tip:**
> Run your hands through your pubic hair to get rid of any loose ones before he goes down there. Hair in mouth = not pleasant.

2) Let him tease you with his tongue before he heads for your bits. Kissing your hip bones, abdomen and inner thighs, then gently brushing his lips oh-so-lightly across your nipples, then your vagina, creates a great build-up.

3) Although most women climax from direct clitoral stimulation, he shouldn't head straight there. It can feel uncomfortable if he hits your love button before you're fully aroused.

4) Get him to start off by licking and kissing your genitals in the same way as he'd kiss your mouth, varying closed-mouth kisses with long up-and-down or side-to-side licks. His tongue can be hard if it's taut and pointy, or soft if it's flat and relaxed. Get him to experiment with different techniques so he can get used to his new tool. Hot tip: the slower he goes at the start, the faster you'll climax.

5) Once you're aroused he can head for your clitoris. Each woman enjoys different types of clitoral stimulation and you may find you enjoy different strokes depending on what kind of mood you're in or the time of the month. It's up to you to let him know what you like.

6) He can try licking across the clitoris from side to side or top to bottom or gently flicking it with his tongue. Alternatively, try the suction pump: his mouth forms a seal over the top of the clitoris and then sucks rhythmically. He can use his tongue inside the seal at the same time.

7) Get him to vary what he's doing until you feel yourself building up to a climax. The key here is lubrication: keep a glass of water by the bed so his tongue doesn't dry out.

8) Gradually he should build up into a steady rhythm or pace. When you feel yourself close to the edge make sure he knows it and carries on with exactly what he's doing. Men often take orgasm-ahoy signs to mean 'increase pressure and speed, please', which is probably what he'd want *you* to do if he were on the receiving end.

Cosmo tip:
Vaginal lubricant is produced from tiny ducts inside the vagina. If you're getting dry during oral sex, get him to put his finger or tongue inside you to release some more fluid.

9) When you do climax, let him know whether you want him to stay where he is or stop right there: some women like to be licked through their orgasms, others like to be left alone. Squeezing your pelvic floor and vaginal muscles rhythmically can intensify your climax.

10) Your clitoris will be extremely sensitive afterwards, so, if you fancy another orgasm, he may need to ease off the pressure for a while or concentrate on a different part of your body.

Cosmo tip:
A healthy vagina shouldn't smell strong or unpleasant. A strong or unusual smell can be the sign of an infection and should be checked out by a doctor.

Make It Easy for Him

Communication is your greatest oral-sex tool. Teach him better tongue techniques with these subtle tricks:
- Show him exactly how you liked to be licked by licking his palm before he heads south – just thinking about what he's

about to do will turn you both on.
- Tell him what he's doing *right* rather than what he's doing wrong – it's hard enough for him negotiating his way round there without having his ego crushed in the process.
- Use one-word instructions such as 'harder', 'softer', 'slower' and 'left'/'right', which sound like commands rather than criticisms.
- When you're close to a climax, your pulse rate quickens and your breathing will become fast and shallow. You'll probably tense your leg muscles, too. It'll be useful for him to pick up on these signals, so don't hold back.
- If you love what he's doing, squeeze his shoulder or press down on his head if you want a little more pressure (not hard: you don't want to suffocate him).
- Raise your hips up to meet his face and pulse rhythmically in time with his tongue – that way, he can take his lead from you.

Advanced Lick Tricks

Spell it out

Let him sign his name across your vulva with his tongue. Make sure he uses his most elaborate, flourishy signature!

'My boyfriend is fantastic at oral. Right at the beginning of my climax we switch to penetrative sex, as I like to feel him inside me as I come.'
Jemma, 28, TV researcher

The long hello

Get him to lick your vulva with a flat tongue from top to bottom very, very slowly. This whole extended kiss should take around sixty seconds and is absolutely heavenly.

Digit heaven

Tongues and fingers are an orgasm-inducing combo for many women, particularly when you're extremely aroused. He can stroke you while licking or insert a finger or two inside you while his tongue's busy elsewhere. The perineum – the area between the vulva and the anus – is packed with nerve endings, so he can play here, too, either with his fingers or his tongue.

SAFETY INFO: *Never blow directly into the vagina: it can be dangerous.*

Use your mind

When he inserts a finger inside you, imagine you're having a threesome with one man giving you oral sex and the other penetrating you. Because you can't see what he's doing, it's easy to let your imagination run riot.

Good vibrations

Get him to use a vibrator across your vaginal lips while he's licking your clitoris. Some women like to have a dildo or vibrator inserted into their vagina or anus while receiving oral sex.

'I love giving oral and I think I'm quite good at it but it doesn't come easily: you have to practise to get it right. My ex was a brilliant teacher and she made me try loads of different techniques. My advice to women is, if you like what we're doing, show some appreciation. That way, if you're totally unresponsive, we know to change tack.'
Marcus, 32, architect

Perfect Positions for Oral for You

Basic: You lie back and he rests between your legs. To lift yourself up, rest your feet on his shoulders or hook your legs over them. Alternatively, resting on your arms, lift your hips up to meet his face.

Intermediate: Try standing up while he kneels before you. It's a harder position for him to maintain but you get a great view. Alternatively, sit on the edge of a table or worktop while he crouches down.

Advanced: Sit on his face. He lies on the bed, then you lower yourself on to him either facing the wall in front of you (so your bottom's away from him) or the other way round (so you're both facing the same direction). You'll need strong thigh muscles for both these positions.

ORGASM

See also: arousal, clitoris, masturbation for you, orgasm –
his

You Know You've Had an Orgasm When . . .

- your heart rate, breathing and body temperature peak.
- your nipples and breasts swell up to 20 per cent bigger than their normal size.
- you experience involuntary contractions around the clitoris, vagina, pelvis, anus and sometimes uterus (womb).
- your clitoris retracts slightly while your vaginal secretions peak.
- your body arches and your facial muscles twitch involuntarily.
- contractions speed up to a steady rhythm for 10–60 seconds, at intervals of four-fifths of a second.
- your face and chest flush.
- you experience intense feeling of release, relief, release of tension and extreme joy and satisfaction.

SEX FACT: *Women generally experience between three to fifteen contractions on average during each orgasm.*

A gentle word of caution

As every sex therapist worth their training will tell you, great sex is not all about the big O. There's plenty of fun to be had without having orgasm as your ultimate goal. By not making your orgasm the full focus of your sex sessions *every* time, you're likely to be relaxed enough to have more of them, more often. As with a first-class Eurostar trip to Paris, you'll have the most fun if you enjoy the journey as well as the final destination. That said, what girl could resist the promise of bigger, better and more frequent climaxes? The more you know about your body, your timings and your sexual hotspots, the more likely this will be. Take your pick from the different types of orgasms below:

'Men are success junkies and are results-orientated. Knowing the woman you're with has come gives you an amazing sense of achievement, however you make it happen.'
Davey, 38, garden designer

Top Six Female Orgasms

No. 1: Clitoral orgasm

Holding the number one-spot is the clitoral orgasm – a climax achieved by clitoral stimulation. This is by far the most common climax, and a record 85 per cent of women need clitoral stimulation to climax. In fact, it's now thought that even the lucky few of you (fewer than 30 per cent) who climax during penetration, are getting there through indirect clitoral stimulation thanks to the angle of his pubic bone and his thrusting against your love button.

You can stimulate any area around the clitoris, from the clitoral head (the nubby bit you can see and feel at the top of the vagina) to the clitoral wings, which run down behind the vaginal lips (see **clitoris** for more info). The sensations of a clitoral orgasm will centre on the clitoral area but it causes muscle spasms and contractions in other parts of your body, such as the vagina and anus.

Increase your chances of this one by . . .

- Focusing your attention (or getting him to) around the clitoral area. As it's much bigger than previously thought (around three-quarters of it is buried inside your body), this means the vaginal lips – the area above the clitoral hood (gently pressing down on the pubic bone often feels good) – and the area to each side should all be explored (see the **CAT position** for clitoral-climax-inducing intercourse).

SEX FACT: *The father of modern psychology, Sigmund Freud, has a lot to answer for after describing vaginal orgasm as the only 'mature orgasm'. Clitoral orgasm was considered 'infantile', i.e. not fully formed. Nice to know how wrong he was.*

No. 2: Vaginal orgasm

In at number two is the vaginal orgasm, caused by (yup, you've guessed it) stimulation of the vagina, mainly through penetration. This orgasm involves contractions of the vaginal canal and sometimes the uterus (womb). Contractions can sometimes be so strong that the penis (or vibrator) is pushed out. Often combined with the clitoral orgasm, it may be difficult to identify, particularly if you enjoy clitoral stimulation during penetration.

The difference between these two climaxes is subtle but scientists have discovered that the neural pathways to the brain (the nerves that carry the oh! oh! oh! messages) are different in a vaginal orgasm from those used in a clitoral orgasm. Vaginal orgasms are said to feel 'broader' than clitoral ones, and will be felt across the whole of the pelvic region rather than just round the clitoris.

Increase your chances of this one by . . .

- Pulsing your PC muscles (the ones you use to stop the flow of pee) just as you're about to come. This can set off contractions deep within the vagina.

> **Cosmo tip:**
> All orgasms are subjective experiences and it really doesn't matter if you're experiencing a clitoral, vaginal or all-over body shaker: the fact that you're enjoying yourself in bed is enough – try not to worry about the small print!

- Getting him to alter the depth and speed of thrusting as you're nearing a climax. Try three shallow thrusts (which stimulate the sensitive first third of the vagina), followed by two deep ones, which give you a sense of fullness. Get him to mix up the rhythm so you're constantly surprised.

- Rather than tensing 'upwards' as you're about to come, pushing your PC and vaginal muscles downwards when you climax for a more intense sensation.

Blend the Rules
A blended orgasm is a climax that combines clitoral stimulation with vaginal and G-spot fun. This three-in-one treat is said to cause a fantastic all-over climax as the oh! oh! oh! messages are sent to the brain along two different neural pathways.

No. 3: G-spot orgasm

Holding fast at number three is the G-spot orgasm, a climax brought on by stimulation of the G-spot, a super-sensitive patch of tissue on the front wall of the vagina about 3–5 cm (1–2 inches) up (tummy side). Not all women appear to have a G-spot, so don't worry if you can't find yours. See **G-spot** for info.

Increase your chances of this one by . . .

- Stimulating the G-spot with two fingers in a curved beckoning motion towards your tummy (if you feel the need to pee, you've hit the right spot). Some women say firm sustained 'pounding' action works better than soft strokes.
- Kneeling with your forearms flat on the bed while he stands or kneels behind to penetrate you, because any rear-entry position where his penis hits the front wall of the vagina is G-reat. Vary this by lifting up on to your knuckles, then bending back down again.
- Putting a cushion under your bottom during regular missionary-style positions to elevate the vagina, making the front wall easier to hit.

SEX FACT
Twenty-three per cent of women achieve their first orgasm by the age of 15; 90 per cent achieve it by the age of 35.

No. 4: Multiple orgasm

In at number four is the magical multiple, defined as a sequence of more than one orgasm in a single sexual session. Multiples can take different forms, most commonly (a) the rolling orgasm, which feels like a continual 'roll' of peaks and troughs of orgasmic pleasure (like surfing a wave) and (b) sequential orgasms in which you reach climactic peaks a few minutes apart (i.e. you're having distinctly separate orgasms one after the other). For some women, this happens almost automatically; others will never have the pleasure. The secret of multiple magic is not to let your arousal level fall too far after your first big bang. You don't want to go below the plateau level of arousal (see **arousal** for more info) in order to climb back up again. This usually works by keeping the vaginal and clitoral area sexually sensitised and keeping your brain tuned in to those sensations.

Increase your chances of this one by . . .

- Laying off direct clitoral stimulation after the first climax – it will feel too sensitive at first. Concentrate on other areas of your body such as your breasts and vaginal lips. Once your clitoris has calmed down, start paying it more attention to climb back up to another climax.

- If you're masturbating, trying to vary the actual hands-on technique you use for each new orgasm: try up-and down motions on the clitoris first, then turn to side to side or sliding your hand down past the clitoris so you're stimulating the wings rather than the head, then try circular motions for your final burst.

- Trying to switch to penetration after an orgasm through oral or hands-on stimulation. If he 'rides high' (i.e. in the missionary position, scooting himself over your shoulders a little), his thrusting will effectively pull on the vaginal lips, indirectly stimulating the clitoris via the clitoral hood.

Hours of Bliss?

The American husband-and-wife team of sex researchers, Dr Steve and Dr Vera Bodansky, have invented a sex technique called 'the one-hour orgasm', which does exactly what it says on the tin. The basis of this technique is that the woman is kept constantly at an orgasmic level for around an hour (or more) thanks to gentle yet persistent stroking techniques from her partner (yup: quivering contractions and everything). The technique is based on mental as well as physical discipline and takes a while to master but could keep a smile on your face for, oh, hours!

No. 5: Whole-body orgasm

This is the delicious advanced sensation in which the whole body becomes totally sexualised and turns into one huge all-over erogenous zone. Orgasmic waves feel as if they're being sent to the brain from nerve endings all over the body rather than from just the genitals. For example, if you're into S&M and have, say, a rubber fetish, the feeling of rubber anywhere on your skin can flood the brain with sexual sensations. It doesn't just have to be near or around your obvious sex organs. Practitioners of **Tantric sex**, which involves lots of ritualised body stroking, mental focus and nongenital touching, can train their bodies to respond intensely to all-over rather than genital stimulation.

Increase your chances of this one by:

- Focusing away from your genitals. Try mutual genital stimulation at first to get you both into a highly aroused state, then switch your stroking or licking manoeuvres to different parts of the body. Go back to the genitals if you feel arousal dropping, then back to the rest of the body (takes some willpower!). Continue with these peaks of nearly-but-not-quite arousal until your whole body feels sensitised.
- Trying a long session of **erotic massage**, during which any form of genital touching is forbidden. If you know you won't receive any genital stimulation, it'll sensitise the rest of your body.

No. 6: Simultaneous orgasms: come together – right now!

Right down at the bottom of our chart is the ever elusive same-time, same-place orgasm. Some lucky couples fit together so perfectly in bed in terms of timing, training, tallness and technique that his 'n' hers (or indeed hers 'n' hers or his 'n' his) at-the-exact-same-moment orgasms are a wonderful and regular part of their sex lives. Lucky them. They are the rare and extremely fortunate exception to the rule. For the rest of us, simultaneous orgasms should be thought of as an occasional and accidental treat. In other words, don't get too hung up on trying to achieve simultaneous bliss, as it simply doesn't happen that often. If it's any consolation, most people (particularly men, it seems) derive pleasure watching their partner climax, which is pretty hard to do when you're in the throes of it yourself.

Increase your chances of this one by . . .

- Slowing him down. The secret of simultaneous orgasm is usually to slow down his sexual responses so you can catch up. This involves a lot of clitoral stimulation for you and minimum hands-on stimulation for him until you're both extremely aroused.

- Trying to match your breathing to his while having slow, controlled penetrative sex (sitting opposite each other with your legs wrapped round the bottom of his back works well for this). On his in-stroke he should breathe out while you inhale as if you were inhaling his breath (or sexual energy, as Tantric devotees would call it). On his out-stroke, you breathe out while he breathes in. This takes time, practice and patience but, once it's mastered, you should both be in sexual sync as you feel each other's sexual intensity rising together. See **delay tactics** for more hands-on slow-him-down techniques.

Five Ways to up Your Orgasmic Potential

1. Relax: Enjoy the whole process rather than just the ten seconds at the end.

2. Masturbate: The better you know your body, the more you can teach him about it.

3. Communicate: He's not a mind reader and sometimes ahhs! of ecstasy are easy to confuse with eughs! of disgust.

4. Experiment: Just because you know oral gets you there the quickest, it doesn't mean you should go for that option every time. The body (not to mention the brain) loves surprises, so try sexperimenting with different sensations.

5. Think sexy: Don't reserve sex for twenty minutes in the bedroom – stay sensual all day long: think about sex at work, imagine sexy scenarios on the bus and rev up your responses in anticipation. The more you think about sex, the more responsive your body will become.

SEX FACT: *Have passionate sex or masturbate during your period. Orgasms alleviate the menstrual cramps that are due to contractions in the uterus.*

Other Orgasms You May Know and Love

Breast orgasm

Some women have extremely sensitive breasts and can climax through stimulation of the chest area alone. Get your man to focus entirely on your breasts and nipples while gently (almost carelessly) brushing a hand or his fingers across your clitoris, then removing them again. The combination of breast stimulation and the anticipation of clitoral stimulation to come is a climax classic.

Anal orgasm

It figures that if you enjoy anal penetration or anal play then orgasms can be had from this kind of stimulation. As your PC muscles cover the whole of the vaginal and anal area, you'll experience anal contractions through a clitoral or vaginal orgasm anyway – anal stimulation will just heighten this experience.

SEX FACT *Orgasms aren't just a physical bodily response: scientific research shows that brainwave patterns also alter.*

Fantasy orgasm

A few extremely lucky people have the ability to climax with nary a finger, vibrator or penis in sight. Fantasy is an extremely powerful force when it comes to bringing on a climax and many people use the power of the mind during regular sexual encounters anyway (nothing like dreaming of George Clooney while doing it doggy style). The fantasy orgasm is just an extension of this: by thinking about an extremely raunchy scenario – imagining every sense of an encounter – you can literally think yourself into a climax without touching any part of your body.

There may be a physiological reason why some women have the ability to do this at certain times of the month: for example just before you ovulate and just before your period, oestrogen and testosterone levels peak, heightening all your sexual responses.

SEX FACT *Between 10 and 20 per cent of women have been woken up by having an orgasm in their sleep.*

What's Stopping You?

Common things that might be preventing the big bang for you or him . . .

The Physical

1) Alcohol, drugs and smoking: Alcohol or drugs may help lower your inhibitions but a few glasses or lines too many also slow down your sexual responses, causes dehydration (making lubrication more tricky) and can inhibit your climactic potential. Smoking constricts the blood flow to genitals and may lower testosterone levels in both men and women.

2) Overeating: Feeling overfull makes it difficult for the body to respond as well as it normally does and may make some sex positions uncomfortable.

3) Medication: Many medications can affect libido, particularly anti-depressants and some versions of the Pill. Others (antihistamines, for example) cause dehydration. Talk to your GP if you're experiencing lacklustre libido side effects, as switching to a different type of medication (a different brand of the Pill, for example) can help.

SEX FACT! *About 50 per cent of women and 20 per cent of men will suffer from an inability to orgasm at some point in their lives.*

The Mental

1) Stress: Any form of stress or pressure outside the bedroom is going to affect your sexual responses between the sheets. As orgasm is a mind–body response, worrying about work, money, promotion or any pressure that's occupying head space will affect your ability to climax.

2) Performance anxiety: If your boyfriend expects you to climax every single time you have sex, this may build up as pressure in your head, which can turn into a mental barrier. The more it's expected of you, the harder it becomes. Try making everything other than orgasm the focus of your sex sessions.

3) Tiredness: Physical or mental exhaustion are bound to affect your sexual responses. Even if you're able to muster up the energy simply to lie back and think of England, the concentration and focus needed to achieve orgasm may be too much.

The Emotional

1) Embarrassment or shame: Deep-seated feelings of shame or a belief that sex is in some way dirty or wrong will affect your ability to climax. Sex therapy or regular psychotherapy can often help.

2) Self-consciousness: Worrying about the size or shape of your body in a particular position or during a particular sex act will inhibit the Big O. Remember, he's having far too much fun to be worrying about the size of your thighs.

3) Feeling uncomfortable: Never do anything in bed that makes you feel physically (or emotionally) uncomfortable: pushing sexual boundaries is one thing, feeling daft or embarrassed is quite another.

Cosmo tip:
Male alert! Stop expecting her to climax every time. The female orgasm is an elusive little creature that sometimes appears and sometimes doesn't. Yes, it's gratifying if she does climax, but, if you expect her to *every* time, she'll start faking. Not what you want.

'Sometimes when I feel really raunchy, my boyfriend just has to touch my breasts and I can feel myself near the edge. If he stays there long enough, as soon as he moves downwards I know I'm going to come – and quickly. Other days, nothing he does is going to push me over the edge – I know that; I just wish he did.'
Joanne, 34, mortgage advisor

ORGASM – HIS
See also: arousal, ejaculation, multiple orgasms

The Science Bit

His climax is pretty much down to hydraulics rather than any particularly complex internal moves or sensitive spots. At the peak of arousal, fluid from the prostate gland (see **G-spot – male**) pumps into the urethra, combines with sperm from the testes and is pumped out in rhythmical spurting motions accompanied by

Boys as young as seven can experience pleasurable sensations of orgasm without ejaculation. It's only when sperm production kicks in during adolescence that ejaculation begins, usually in the form of wet dreams.

muscular contractions in the pelvis, anus and abdomen. These happen at similar rates (0.8 seconds) to the female orgasm. His face and body may also twitch or contort and muscles elsewhere (legs, thighs, feet, buttocks) may contract. His face and chest may flush.

The average length a man can 'shoot' is 18–25 cm (7–10 inches). If he hasn't climaxed for more than three days, this may reach up to 90 cm (3 feet). The longer he waits, the more powerful his ejaculation will be.

Ejaculation v. orgasm

Ejaculation, the rhythmical expulsion of semen from the body, is the physical side of orgasm for most men. Orgasm is usually a combination of ejaculation, a response in the nervous system (the muscular contractions) and some sort of emotional (or at least brain-based) connection – the feeling of sexual pleasure rather than just the physical release of semen. It is possible for men to ejaculate (release sperm) without experiencing orgasm, and with some practice, to orgasm (feel distinct waves of sexual pleasure) without ejaculating (see **ejaculation** and **multiple orgasms**). Climaxing while holding back ejaculation is taught by Taoist and Tantric practitioners and can lead to male multiple orgasms. Most men aren't that bothered by the difference and tend to experience the Big O during, or, just before, the big E.

'Sometimes I can ejaculate but not have an orgasm. It's like my body's functioning without engaging any emotions. In order for both to happen at the same time, I need to be really into what I'm doing mentally as well as physically.'
Peter, 39, store manager

OUTDOOR SEX
See also: quickies, positions

....

Sex Outdoors and the Law

A plan to introduce a prison fine of up to six months just for doing the dirty in your own back garden or the privacy of your car, if you could be seen from the street, has been shelved (for the moment) but you still need to be *very* careful. Wherever you choose to get down and dirty, make sure you *definitely* can't be seen by anyone else. If someone takes offence at your behaviour, under current British law you could be prosecuted for 'gross indecency', 'outraging public decency' or 'causing a public nuisance' if you are seen by others.

....

SAFETY INFO: Be careful if you're planning sex on the beach in a romantic holiday location: some countries are very strict about what you can and can't do outside, so check local customs and restrictions first.

Lust Locations for Any Outdoor Occasion

The beach

Best for: Romantic rollicking in the sand dunes or *From Here to Eternity*-rolling in the surf.

Perfect position: The best thing about sand is that it's soft and pliable, which means you can mould it to almost any position to help you achieve your outdoor thrills. Try having sex with you on top (that way he gets most of the sand!) with his knees up so your back is resting on his knees. Lean back so he can enjoy the view.

Best to avoid: The traditional missionary position: sand in your cracks is never a pleasant feeling.

Passion prop: A large beach towel or blanket. Those funny sand flies that come out at night can feel mighty uncomfortable if you're lying on damp dunes.

Spice it up by: Using suntan lotion erotically during the day. Either rub it into your lover as sexily as you can (a few naughty words in his ear as you do it won't go amiss) or turn rubbing it on yourself into the ultimate sex show – erotic for you, unbelievably sensual for your audience. Make sure you're still oily when you come together later for a slip-slidey thrill.

SEX FACT! *Only 1 per cent of the British public thinks sex outside should be banned while 94 per cent think it's a great way to maintain a healthy relationship, according to a recent survey by* Mates *condoms.*

Your hotel balcony
Best for: Sneaky post-beach action while watching the sun go down.
Perfect position: Try leaning over your hotel balcony while your lover approaches you and penetrates your from behind. To the rest of the hotel complex, you're simply admiring the sunset together (just make sure his thrusts aren't too jerky).
Best to avoid: Balconies that are just see-through railings rather than solid brick, unless you have a very big beach towel that'll cover the whole area.
Passion prop: A gorgeous tropical cocktail – it's the ultimate in holiday decadence. If you can balance a cocktail in one hand, do a good impression of admiring the view *and* get a passionate seeing to from your lover all at the same time, you're an extremely clever girl.
Spice it up by: Taking turns to be the visible one on the balcony: let him go out first while you crawl out on your hands and knees and pay attention to his body from the waist down. Make sure he returns the favour on day two of your holiday.

Cosmo tip:
Although alcohol may give you the courage to try a new *alfresco* location, too much will impair your judgement and make you take unnecessary risks.

A picnic in the park
Best for: Satisfying your carnal appetite with sneaky naughtiness plus delicious food.
Perfect position: This extremely daring position requires a lot of guts plus a long, flowing skirt. Position your picnic blanket somewhere sexy and secluded. Sit on top of your lover and let your large skirt cover as much of him as possible. Slip his flies open and lift him out. Next, slip your knickers

to one side (leaving them at home altogether might be easier) and sit on top of your lover while he leans backwards a little and rests on his hands. Rock subtly backwards and forwards to keep your clitoris in constant contact with his pubic bone.

Best to avoid: Going anywhere near a children's play area. Cries of 'Why is that man giving her an extra big cuddle, Mummy?' are not what you want to hear.

Passion prop: A picnic basket full of sensual goodies.

Spice it up by: Feeding each other delicious morsels. Close your eyes and seductively lick food from each other's fingers.

'I once had sex in an open tent during an amazing thunderstorm in the South of France. The air was charged with electricity and every few minutes the whole tent was lit up by fork lightning. It was sexy and scary at the same time.'

Eleanor, 28, singer

Other Lust Locations to Try

- **The sea:** Are you just cuddling out there or is there more too it than that? Who knows?
- **The forest floor:** Pine needles are prickly but smell divine when crushed against two naked bodies.
- **Up against a tree:** Be his Maid Marion in your very own Sherwood Forest.
- **The bus stop:** Just because it seems as if buses never come, it doesn't mean you shouldn't.
- **On a swing:** Devotion in motion.
- **In an alleyway:** Sexily sordid, just the way we like it (occasionally!).
- **In a tent:** If the British weather lets you down, try making love under canvas for a campfire thrill.
- **Your own back garden:** The stars up above, the neighbours tucked up in bed, your toothbrush only twenty metres away . . .

'My boyfriend and I made love on an amazing beach in Northern Queensland. It was unbelievably romantic with the Great Barrier Reef in front of us and thousands of stars above us. Afterwards, while washing ourselves off in the sea, the water was full of millions of little glowing things that looked like water fireflies. It took my breath away.'

Macy, 23, gap-year student

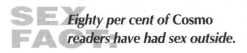

SEX FACT! *Eighty per cent of Cosmo readers have had sex outside.*

PC MUSCLES
See also: Kegel exercises

Your PC muscles, technically known as your pubococcygeal muscles, which make up part of your pelvic floor, are a band of muscles that form a kind of 'sling' around the whole vaginal and anal area. Strengthening and exercising your PC muscles, known as **Kegel exercises**, can improve the tightness of your vagina, making it feel stronger and firmer. This can also increase the strength and frequency of your orgasms.

PENETRATION
See also: positions

The secrets of great penetrative sex (in no particular order) are:

- **The build-up:** Penetration should never be painful or uncomfortable. Foreplay builds excitement, desire and lubrication. The longer you wait, the better the sex will be.
- **Lubrication:** The wetter the better. If you don't have enough lubrication of your own, there's nothing wrong with using some of the shop-bought stuff such as K-Y jelly or Durex Play.

- **The angle of the dangle:** Some positions will feel better than others because his penis will stimulate extra-sensitive spots inside you or cause indirect friction against the clitoris.
- **Comfort:** He may like the look of your legs stuck behind your ears but, if you're not comfy, you won't enjoy yourself. Cramp, back pain and discomfort for either of you are not great orgasm enhancers.
- **Variety:** Think speed, think depth, think pace. Now think of variations on all these themes. As with food, sometimes you fancy slowly consuming a twelve-course banquet. Other times only a McDonald's will do. Go on: surprise each other next time . . .
- **Safety:** Intercourse is considered a high-risk activity so condoms are a must. Nothing kills passion quicker than worrying about diseases or unwanted pregnancy.
- **Rhythm:** Getting in sync with your partner and mirroring each other's passion and pace will intensify the experience for both of you.
- **Expectation:** Thanks to a teeny design fault in the human body, men can climax through penetration easily while most women need clitoral stimulation to reach the big O, which doesn't usually happen without a little help during intercourse. Keep your expectations open and don't always have orgasm (yours or his) as your ultimate goal.
- **Communication:** Let him know what you love and what you loathe. If you're one of the tiny percentage of women who can climax through penetration alone, congratulations. If you're like the rest of us mere mortals, let him know that clitoral stimulation is what you really need to get you oh-oh-oh-so excited. Reassure him that it's nothing to do with him – it's the way most women are made.
- **Extra enhancements:** Sexperimentation is the name of the game. Use whatever you need for a bit of extra stimulation – a finger, a vibrator, a blindfold or a rubber glove will all make things more interesting. And don't forget the biggest enhancer of all: your imagination. Think sexy, feel sexy, be sexy.

PENIS

See also: arousal, ball play, masturbation for him

The Biological Stuff

A thorough inspection of a live specimen will aid the learning process immensely, as will a white coat, suspenders and a stethoscope. (OK, the stethoscope isn't strictly necessary but you may find it useful to check his pulse, which may rise considerably as you carry out your examination.)

Head: Also called the glans, this is the mushroom-shaped tip of his penis. It's the most sensitive part and is packed with nerve endings close to the surface of the skin. The penis contains 4,000 nerve ends. Sounds like a lot? The clitoris is blessed with twice as many. In uncircumcised men it's covered by a flap of skin, the foreskin, when the penis is flaccid. This pulls back when the penis becomes erect. (Circumcision – the removal of the foreskin – usually takes place in infancy or later for medical or religious reasons.)

SEX FACT: *Around half of the world's population are circumcised, including the majority of American men. The majority of British men are uncut.*

Urethra: The tube running through the penis that carries pee and semen to the small hole at the very tip. Please note: his hydraulic system is so sophisticated that internal valves shut off the flow of urine once he's fully erect. (In other words, he can't pee and ejaculate at the same time.)

Coronal ridge: This is the small ridge of skin that surrounds the penis, connecting the head to the shaft (it's also called the crown of the penis). Also super-sensitive, it generally likes to be stroked or licked.

Frenulum: A little triangular flap of skin on the underside of the penis (the side near his balls rather than his belly) where, in uncircumcised men, the foreskin attaches to the head of the penis. As the most sensitive part of his whole package, it usually likes to be licked, flicked and generally worshipped.

Shaft: This is the rest of his penis below the head. It contains three chambers of spongy tissue that fill with blood when he's sexually aroused, causing an erection. Although it's less sensitive than the head, it still likes plenty of hand or mouth attention.

Base: Much of the penis is situated inside the body with strong ligaments attaching it to his pelvis. (These ligaments can be cut in a penis-extension operation so the penis hangs away from the body, making it look longer – ouch!).

Cosmo tip:
His penis may not be the same colour as the rest of his skin. Some men have darker penises, some men are lighter down below. You need to worry only if his penis is the same colour as his favourite team's away strip. Especially if they play in stripes.

SEX FACT! *The average penis is 15 cm (6 inches) when erect. According to the Kinsey Institute 90 per cent of all erect penises are between 13 and 18 cm (5.1 and 7.1 inches).*

What Else is Down There?

Testicles: Those two balls that hang around at the base of his penis are housed in a sac of stretchy material called the scrotal sac.

Perineum: The patch of skin between his balls and his anus, delightfully called the 'tain't' in America (because it ain't his balls and it ain't is anus). Again, this area is rich with nerve endings and, in many men, responds to a firm massaging touch.

Male G-spot: Otherwise known as the prostate gland, which is situated at the base of the bladder about 4 cm (1½ inches). It can be felt inside the anus against the front wall (towards his belly). It's another highly sensitive spot and can be stimulated either by massaging the perineum or by inserting a finger into his anus.

Anus: The puckered hole at the end of his rectum. This area is also rich in nerve endings and often responds well to massage or pressure. It swells when he's aroused.

SEX FACT! *Because men get friendly with their penises at a young age, they tend to associate good sex with the penis, while women, because our sexual responses are subtler and slower to develop, associate good sex with relationships.*

The Controversial Bit

The male clitoris: According to Dr Andrew Stanway, creator of the Lovers' Guide range of erotic videos, men also have a clitoris which is 'situated deep in the head of the penis – underneath the little fold of skin on the underside'. Dr Stanway suggests massaging this spot (just where the frenulum is) with two firm fingers or a vibrator on a low setting, even if he doesn't have an erection. Hmmm. According to our extensive research, the male clitoris is a tricky little fella to locate, but hey, who cares? The fact that you can use the 'you find mine and I'll find yours' line is a good enough excuse for us. Have fun searching . . .

Penis Myths Explained

Myth #1: Bigger is better

False: It's not the size of the engine, it's how he handles it that counts. Scientific studies have proved that smaller men spend more time learning excellent foreplay techniques to make up for their lack of stature. Make sure Mr Big doesn't expect you to worship at the alter of his manhood while neglecting everything else.

'I went out with a guy whose penis was no bigger than a small gherkin. It wasn't really something we discussed. We just worked through the positions until we found something that worked for both of us: doggy-style was the best for me.'
Katie, 29, advertising executive

Myth #2: Bald men are well endowed

False: Increased testosterone levels cause hair loss, which can also elevate his sex drive. If he's follicularly challenged, he's likely to want sex more often and have superhero stamina rather than a supersized penis.

Myth #3: A circumcised penis is cleaner

False(ish): Glands around the frenulum secrete oils that lubricate and moisturise the head of his penis, which is why it's so soft and shiny. These oils can sometimes get stuck under a foreskin, so uncut men need to make sure they wash carefully underneath it. As long as the rest of his personal hygiene is up to scratch, there's no need to worry about his bits and whether he's circumcised or not.

Myth #4: Big hands, feet and nose = big penis

False: Absolutely no truth in this one whatsoever.

Myth #5: Black men are bigger

True: Yup, statistically, black men have larger penises. Asian men are the smallest with Caucasians coming (so to speak) in the middle of the scale.

'I used to hate having a big willy. At school everyone, even the girls, used to call me "donkey". It was humiliating. Now I don't mind so much: my girlfriend loves the way she feels so full when we have sex.'
Greg, 32, bar manager

Myth #6: If he has an erection he wants sex

False: All males, from day-old babies to ancient granddads, may have erections. It's their system's way of testing the hydraulics. These erections aren't necessarily stimulated by sexual thoughts or activities, so, if a man wakes up with a stiffy, don't expect him to perform straightaway. He'll need to be revved up in the normal way before he's in the mood.

Maximise *Your* Pleasure With His Plaything

His penis isn't just there for *his* pleasure. Here's how to get the best out of it for you. (Please note: he'll find these actions pretty arousing too):

1. Take control: Use his penis to stroke your nongenital erogenous zones. Try it on your nipples, the sides of your body or around your hairline and lips.

2. Get stimulated: Rather than going straight for full-on penetration, slide his penis through your vaginal lips and use its tip to rub your clitoris.

3. Shallow gal: As the first third of your vagina is the most sensitive, encourage him to use short, shallow thrusts. He can then surprise you with a sneaky deep thrust every now and again.

4. Toy-tastic: Vibrators aren't just for girls. Just before penetration, use a vibrator on his shaft and balls (the head of his penis may be too sensitive if this is new to him). When he penetrates you, switch the vibrator over to your clitoral area. He'll still be able to feel the vibrations so it'll arouse you both.

The longest recorded penis is around 30 cm (12 inches). The smallest, known as a 'micropenis', is just 1.8 cm (three-quarters of an inch) when erect.

PERFORMANCE ANXIETY
See also: erectile problems, orgasm

Both men and women can suffer from performance anxiety in bed. The result for him can be losing his erection, or in some cases being unable to climax and in others climaxing too fast. In women, too much pressure on the big O can prevent it from happening. Relieve performance anxiety by:

- Not having orgasm as your ultimate aim – for both partners. Enjoy lots of foreplay for the pleasurable sensations rather than just as a route to orgasm.
- Banning penetrative sex for a month. To build up your sexual confidence, start with a just-touching rule and take it in turns to give and receive pleasure. Give each other a sensual massage and focus on how each touch feels (whether you're the giver or the receiver). Touching each other's genitals should be banned to begin with (and for as long as you can bear it) so you can focus on arousing different parts of the body.
- Not doing anything in bed that makes you feel embarrassed or uncomfortable. Just because he wants you to dress up like a school girl, if you feel unsure of yourself it'll sap your sexual confidence. If you're both enjoying yourselves, you're far more likely to relax.
- Complimenting each other – not just in the bedroom. Often, the root of performance anxiety is in your self-esteem. If you can build it up outside the bedroom, then take those compliments between the sheets, you'll gradually feel less pressured and more confident in bed.
- Not expecting fantastic sex every time. Enjoy each sexual experience for itself rather than comparing it to others or

feeling bad/guilty because it 'wasn't as great as last time'.

- Switching your mindset. If you're focusing on your pleasure and you feel anxieties or worries creeping in, try switching the emphasis on to your partner for a while to allow your mind to become absorbed in what you're doing to him rather than worrying about yourself.

- Engaging your imagination and using fantasy to block negative thoughts during sex. It's impossible to think of two things at once, so, rather than worry about how and what you're doing, fill your mind with positive sexual thoughts instead. The more you focus on your naughty fantasies the more effective this technique becomes.

- Never faking an orgasm. Men: this means not expecting her to climax every time. Women: this means not pretending that something he's doing tips you over the edge when it doesn't. Both sexes sometimes fake orgasms if they feel under pressure, but giving out false I-love-that signals really doesn't help.

- Having fun. Sex is not a test or a trial. It's not about getting things right or wrong. It's about connecting physically, mentally and emotionally. Arrange a nonsexual date where you do something completely out of the ordinary. Go to a theme park, take a hot-air balloon ride – anything that's out of your normal routine. At the end of the date, kiss like chaste teenagers and go your separate ways. By shifting the focus away from sex, you'll be able to relax into it next time you're together.

PERINEUM
See also: balls, G-spot-male, masturbation for him

This is the soft patch of skin between his balls and his anus. It's packed with nerve endings and is extremely sensitive to the touch. Some men love having their perineum stimulated during masturbation or penetration; other men find it uncomfortable, ticklish or too sensitive. The other reason it's sensitive is that directly underneath the skin is the male G-spot, or prostate gland, which can be stimulated by massaging the perineum. Be warned: many people are unused to having this area stimulated and may even think that, if they enjoy stimulation here, it must mean they're gay. Utter tosh. Pleasure is pleasure and you simply can't argue with what your nerve endings are telling you.

Here are a few perineum-touching techniques to get you started:

- Start by gently extending your hand downwards to this area when stroking his penis and balls.
- Use your knuckles to knead the perineum as if you were gently kneading a loaf of bread.
- Massage firmly at the base of his balls until you feel the 'root' of his penis (if he's erect, it'll feel like a firm length of muscle going backwards into his body). Continue this massage firmly downwards across the perineum.
- With the pads of your fingers, massage this area firmly in little circles to stimulate his prostate gland under the skin.
- Some men love having a finger inserted into the anus (but some men hate it, so suss him out first). Try massaging upwards with a thumb or finger in his rectum (towards his balls). At the same time, with the pads of your fingers from the other hand, massage downwards on his perineum. This two-handed technique stimulates the prostate from the inside and out.

You've Got One Too . . .

Women also have this super-sensitive patch of skin between the vagina and the anus, which is packed with nerve endings and blood vessels that swell and enlarge when you're sexually aroused.

- Try massaging the base of your vagina, extending a finger downwards towards the anus when masturbating.
- He can rub your perineum while penetrating you with a finger, vibrator or his penis.
- A vibrator on a low setting placed on the base of the vagina, extending down the perineum, can be extremely pleasurable.
- Try getting him to lightly spank the base of your vagina and perineum during masturbation or penetration. It's an unusually arousing sensation.

SAFETY INFO: Never place a finger or vibrator that's been in your anus back into the vagina without washing it first, as this can cause an infection.

PHEROMONES
See also: hormones

These are unique odourless chemicals given off by animals (including humans) that send out signals such as sexual attractiveness or readiness for sex. Animal pheromones are much stronger than the human varieties and can attract a mate from miles around. Human pheromones are subtle in comparison but do have a genuine effect on attractiveness. Found in the armpits and groin, they are odourless but when mixed with sweat help to make up your unique-to-you smell, which both men and women find arousing. In scientific studies, women are most attracted to men whose unique smell subtly indicates a different genetic makeup from their own. Biologically, this ensures a woman's offspring will have as unique a set of genes possible rather than duplicating ones she already has. Females are thought to be more sensitive than males when it comes to human pheromones – both those given off by men and other women. Female pheromones are thought to be the reason why women working or living together have synchronised periods that all start within days of each other. Sex shops and novelty stores have tried bottling animal pheromones in the form of perfumes or wipes but, as yet, the mate-magnet potential of human pheromones has not been accurately reproduced in a lab.

PHONE SEX
See also: talking dirty

Thanks to the wonderful world of mobiles, you can make love to your man any time, any place. Here's how to perfect your turn-him-on telephone manner:

Flirt first

Start off your carnal conversation with some gentle flirting to set the mood. Think of your voice as a vibrating toy that can hum, sigh, sing, pause and give him exactly what he wants to hear. Lower your voice by several tones and speak more slowly than normal, using lots of suggestive pauses. If this is going to be a long, lusty, full-blown session make sure you're comfortable and won't be disturbed. Once the tone is set, you're ready to get raunchy.

Watch and tell

Start by describing exactly what you're wearing, paying particular attention to the environment you're in. (Feel free to elaborate – that's half the fun.) Try doing this after a warm bath so you're wrapped in little more than a silk bathrobe. Describe all the minute details: how your skin feels hot . . . and damp . . . (long pauses are great). How you're rubbing scented body lotion into your calves . . . your thighs . . . up your legs . . . Pace your voice to the rhythms of desire: speeding up, slowing down and using deliberate teasing silences, which give his imagination time to go wild.

'I'd never had phone sex before but when my husband went to work in Manchester it just kind of happened. We'd talk late at night and I'd nearly always be naked. He'd tell me to touch certain parts of my body and I'd have to describe exactly how I was touching them and how it felt – amazing!'
Lilly, 34, personal shopper

Ask for direction

Ask him what he'd like you to do next. 'Where should I rub the lotion in now?' 'Should I untie my dressing gown?' 'What am I wearing underneath?' Guessing games are good because they get him to subconsciously tell you what he wants you to be doing/wearing. Alternatively, tell him what you'd like him to be doing to you if he were in the room at that moment. Describe every detail, paying particular attention to all your senses – what you're hearing, smelling, touching, tasting.

Replay the past

If you're stuck for something to talk about, start by describing a particularly sexy session between you and your lover. Replay the past in as much erotic detail as you can, delaying the actual sex act for as long as possible. Embellish on the scene, adding a few extras such as someone watching you or another person joining in if you want to raunch it up.

Take control

Alternatively, command him to remove his clothes item by item or touch himself in various places. Make sure you take this process really slowly – don't let him touch his genitals until he's extremely aroused. Be firm and don't let him climax till *you're* ready. Tell him that you're going through a similar body-caressing routine at the other end of the phone and make him *wait*!

Oh! Oh! Oh!

The sound of your breath getting faster and faster, or the pauses you make while you masturbate, will be magnified by the distance between you. Make sure he hears you getting excited – exaggerate your breathing and moan, sigh and talk dirty to him as you near your climax. Listening to him becoming more and more turned on at the other end of the phone should be enough to topple you over the edge.

> **Cosmo tip:**
> Marilyn Monroe trained herself to talk during her outward breath, creating her sexy, soft, breathy voice. To achieve this, speak the words *through* your outward breath. Think '*Happy Birth*day, Mr *Pres*-i-dent' and you'll get it right.

Work-time fun

One of the best phone-sex games is to call your lover at work when you know he's surrounded by people and can't act on your demands. Describe, in sensual detail, what you'd do if you could crawl under his desk . . . unzip his flies . . . take him in your hands . . . in your mouth.

Video-phone fun

The video phone or webcam is an obvious choice for compulsive phone flirters: he can watch you doing exactly what he tells you to do (or you can watch him) and the fact that you're talking into a screen may make you even more sexperimental than normal. Use this fabulous piece of technology wisely: you don't want all his mates sharing your sexy striptease or the image of you fellating a banana shown to anyone but your lover.

Text sex

Texting is an excellent short, sharp way to flirt – it's quick, it's easy and it gives almost instant gratification. And, once you start, flirty banter will flow extremely quickly. Subtle double-entrendres are the way to go first, so you can gauge the mood of your text-mate. From there you'll soon graduate into full-blown filth! Enjoy . . .

PHOTOGRAPHY
See also: movie making, porn

Taking sexy snaps of each other can be extremely arousing so long as you follow these get-it-right tips:

Posing tips

- Choose your camera carefully: a Polaroid will give you instant results and there are no negatives floating around. A digital camera allows you to see and edit your snaps instantly. The downside of going digital is that the images you create can easily be emailed to other people or posted on the Web, so make sure you trust each other before you click the shutter.
- Semi-naked shots often looks better than full-on nudity. Leave something to the imagination by keeping on your favourite lingerie/shoes/jewellery.
- If you're too shy to take pictures of yourself, take a snap of your favourite accessory or sex toy and slip it into your boyfriend's work bag with the words 'You + Me + This = Tonight?' written on the bottom.
- Take a silly snap of you naked, *à la* Austin Powers, with only a couple of melons and a teapot covering your modesty, then get it made into a jigsaw and give it your man as a present. (Or he could do the same for you.)
- Raising your arms over your head makes your breasts look perkier. Leaning back over the bed and being snapped from above makes your body look longer and leaner. If you're

standing up, turn your elbows out and place one foot slightly in front of the other: it elongates your frame (Liz Hurley loves this trick – look at any picture of her posing and you'll see she's doing it).

- Keeping heels on (even if they're not actually in the shot) will make your body look more upright.
- If you don't feel comfortable committing yourself to film, try posing in front of a camera with no film in (take the batteries out to make doubly sure they'll be no evidence). Just playing model and photographer can be a turn-on for both of you.

PIERCING

Body piercing is often done for adornment or sexual excitement. Here are a few of the options.

Unisex Piercing
Nipples: Piercing of the nipples (usually directly through the nipple itself) can increase sensitivity of the area for both men and women. Chains, leads or clips can be attached to the piercing.

SAFETY INFO: Never attempt any body piercing yourself. Always go to a recognised body-art technician and don't be afraid to check out the safety procedures (use of sterile equipment, safety certificates/licences etc.) first. Follow aftercare advice carefully to avoid infection. Condoms should be worn while genital piercing heals.

Piercing for Women
Clitoral piercing: A ring or stud can be placed through the clitoral hood, just above the clitoris (not through the clitoris itself). This can heighten sensitivity if a weighted ring rests against the clitoris.
Labia piercing: Rings or studs through the vaginal lips are common. Again, said to heighten sensitivity. Sometimes just done for decoration.
Vaginal/perineum piercing: A ring or stud can be placed between the base of the vagina and the perineum (the patch of skin between the vagina and the anus).

Piercing for Men

Prince Albert: A ring is inserted into the urethra (the hole he pees through) and out through the underside of the penis. Said to heighten sensitivity for both partners during penetration.

Frenulum piercing: A horizontal barbell is passed through the underside of the penis, making it feel more solid. (This rod can also be passed through the penis above the urethra.)

The apadravya: A vertical piercing through the head of the penis mentioned in the *Kama Sutra*.

Scrotum piercing: Different piercings of the scrotum or perineum are also available.

SEX FACT: The Prince Albert gets its name from its popularity during Victorian times. Men would slip a ribbon through the ring to hold the penis flat to the leg so it didn't disturb the cut of popular flat-fronted trousers. Prince Albert himself was said to use another ring to hold back his foreskin.

THE PILL
See under: contraception

A hormonal form of contraception in pill form.

PORN
See also: movie making, photography

SEX FACT: The word 'pornography' comes from ancient Greek and means writing of prostitutes.

Hmm: controversial subject. What's all the fuss about?

Although looking at visual images for the purpose of sexual excitement has being around since Neanderthal man was able to draw on a cave wall, some people think it's degrading, disgusting or just plain uninteresting.

So porn is bad, right?

Not necessarily, although it does have its downsides: a lot of mainstream porn is at best low-budget and cheesy with wobbly sets and appalling acting; at worst it's exploitative, violent and/or degrading. Also, men who received their entire teenage education through mainstream porn may expect women to behave and look like the actresses they've seen in the movies: to worship the male genitals, to be submissive in bed, to have certain-shaped bodies.

SEX FACT: *According to the 2003* **Cosmo** *sex survey, 61 per cent of readers' boyfriends admit to using porn, while 76 per cent of these own an erotic video.*

So what are the plus points, then?

Watching porn together can be an erotic experience, turning you both on and giving you creative ideas to spice up your sex life. Scientific studies prove that women can find looking at pornographic images just as arousing physically as men, yet we often find it hard to admit (or even recognise) that we're aroused.

Right – so women could get just as much enjoyment out of porn as men, then?

Biologically, yes, but mentally it's a different story. Male adolescents are often brought into contact with some kind of porn when they discover and develop their sexuality: the dirty magazine down the side of the bed; the illicit images conjured up on someone's parents' computer. For women, porn doesn't play such a central role in our sexual development, so sometimes it's harder to find it acceptable (or even interesting).

> *'I watched a load of porn when I was growing up and dirty magazines were always passed around, but it's just something you grow out of. It just doesn't interest me now I have a regular girlfriend.'*
> Martin, 20, gas inspector

So what's with the impression that women are turned on by words and men by pictures?

There is something in this: the majority of erotica (i.e. words rather than pictures) is bought and read by women, while the majority of porn is bought and viewed by men. The benefit of reading an erotic novel is that you can superimpose your own image on to the characters and settings and let your imagination run wild. With a porn film involving bad hair and a dodgy script, that's more difficult. Maybe it's something to do with our sexual arousal taking longer than his: all he needs to see is a naked couple and he's ready for anything, whereas we have the patience to read through a story and become involved with the characters as our arousal levels build up slowly.

What happens if I stumble across a secret stash of porn my partner hasn't told me about?

First, although this can be upsetting, try to get things into perspective. Yes, you've discovered a sexual secret, which may not fit your moral or political point of view. However, enjoying porn doesn't mean he finds you any less attractive or wants you to be like any of the women in his magazines/films. Using porn or erotica doesn't mean he wants to be unfaithful, either. There's a huge difference between fantasy and reality – and porn is fantasy. Most couples continue masturbating in private even if they have extremely satisfying sex lives together, so using a few films or images doesn't reflect badly on him or your relationship.

Yes, but it's still upsetting

If you are upset by it, talk to him about it and let him know how it made you feel. Men often go through phases in their lives where they become more or less interested in porn, so you may find his stash actually isn't currently in use. Alternatively, have a look at it yourself and see what all the fuss is about. If it's not your thing, let him know you'd rather he kept it out of sight or perused it when you aren't around. Really, the use of mainstream porn (stuff that doesn't involve violence, children or animals) should not become a serious problem unless it's taking up a huge amount of time or money and is having a serious impact on the rest of his/your life.

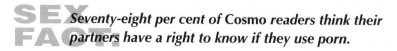

Seventy-eight per cent of Cosmo readers think their partners have a right to know if they use porn.

Right, we're over that hurdle. What happens if we want to watch some porn together?

It's quite difficult to tell good porn from bad, so it's best to get on to the Internet and look a few things up. Go to a sex-toy website (see the back of this book for suggestions) and look for their latest releases or recommendations. Some sites have customer reviews that are worth reading. Renting X-rated videos is also a good way to try before you buy, as buying porn can be expensive (don't get embarrassed: video shop assistants have seen it all before). Some of the instructional videos like the *Lovers' Guide* series can be a good place to start if you want to find out whether seeing explicit images turns you both on or not – although some couples find these too clinical. Personal recommendation is also

'I find watching sexy movies with my boyfriend incredibly arousing, especially ones involving two women together. Although I'm not bisexual, women's naked bodies are so much more attractive than men's. Touching each other to the same rhythm as the action on screen really gets us going.'
Fiona, 28, music teacher

another good route. Also, typing in a key word of something you find interesting like 'spanking' or 'threesomes' or even 'sci-fi porn' can throw up an array of options on the Internet. Look out for films or books recommended in *Cosmo*, too.

What about porn made explicitly for women?

Again, some of it's good, some bad. Female porn stars such as Candida Royalle are taking time out behind the camera to direct and produce female-oriented porn. On the whole porn made for or by women tends to have more developed plotlines, although there are no guarantees it's any better. Big studios or companies tend to have bigger budgets and certain 'stars' become cult figures. Internet sites marketed specifically at women tend to have long-haired Chippendale-type 'hunks' with huge penises flobbing about, which aren't to everyone's taste.

SEX FACT: *More than twice as many women as men enjoy reading erotica, according to Cosmo's latest sex survey.*

What about homemade porn?

Amateur films and images are a whole sub-genre of porn, which some couples find more arousing than scripted films, since the couples seem to be actually enjoying themselves rather than play-acting. (Wow, real orgasms!) The quality of these films is often poor and the lighting may not be as flattering as that of the professional high-budget productions. There are also plenty of Internet sites out there where you can watch other couples having sex via webcams – most sites charge a fee for this.

So it's all a matter of taste, then?

'I found watching porn with my girlfriend quite embarrassing. Neither of us knew where to look. I think it's a boys-only thing.'
Mark, 32, financial consultant

Totally. If it's your thing, go for it. If it isn't, don't. If you're not sure, have a look around and see what takes your fancy: there may be something out there that attracts your attention.

Love porn? Enhance your enjoyment by:

- Pretending to keep your eye on the screen while touching each other in all the right places. The pretence that you're not actually doing anything naughty can be a great turn-on.
- Acting out your favourite scene or using lines from your favourite movie when you're in bed together.
- Remembering the erotic images you've seen and conjuring up your favourite bits to take you over the edge, either when you're with a partner or while masturbating.
- Pretending you're starring in your very own film and putting on the performance of your life. It'll boost your confidence and make you behave completely differently in bed.

Hate porn?

If you hate rice pudding you just don't order it from the menu. Same goes for porn. No one's going to make you watch it/buy it/read it if you don't want to.

SEX FACT! *An estimated 30 per cent of all video rentals are X-rated tapes with 40 per cent of these aimed at the women and couples market.*

POSITIONS

See also: CAT position, quickies, penetration, X-rated positions

SAFETY INFO: *Don't forget the condoms. Penetrative sex is considered a high-risk activity, so always stay protected.*

Your Back-to-Basics Guide to Perfect Positions

Most sex positions are actually just a variation of five basic poses. These five can all be adapted to your own particular requirements and will enable you to achieve pretty much any position that takes your fancy.

SEX FACT *Remember that most women climax through clitoral stimulation, which doesn't occur naturally in most sex positions. Don't be afraid to add a little hands-on action to your lovemaking.*

Position #1: Missionary Magic

The basics: You lie flat on your back and he lies on top of you with his legs straight between yours. You can open your legs wide and tilt your pelvis up to meet him. He balances on his hands or elbows as he thrusts. By keeping your knees bent and your feet firmly on the bed you can push upwards towards him. Not the world's most common sex position for nothing, the missionary position is comfy, intimate (with lots of eye contact), relaxing and adaptable.

Why it works for you: Great for lazy girls, this position requires almost zero effort from you. Also, you both get full body-to-body contact. The disadvantage is that you don't get much control and it can feel a bit as if you were pinned to the bed, powerless to resist him (ooh, that actually sounds quite sexy!).

Why it works for him: He has total control of the speed and depth of thrusting. He can also reach your breasts or play with your clitoris with his hands.

> **Cosmo tip:**
> Don't forget kissing and talking to each other. The missionary position is perfect for whispering sweet nothings (or dirty delights!) into each other's ears.

231

Variations on Missionary Magic

1) **Flat-lining:** By stretching your legs out flat rather than raising them up, you narrow the vaginal entrance, causing more friction around the clitoris and making him feel bigger inside you. Try squeezing your legs together with his legs outside (rather than inside) yours for extra-sexy tension.

2) **Cushioning the blows:** Place a cushion under your buttocks to raise your pelvis. This causes more friction for both of you and makes the clitoris easier for you or him to touch.

3) **Change the angle:** Get your man to shift his weight on to one side, leaning on one arm for support. When he enters you it will be from a slightly different angle, so he'll hit parts inside you he wouldn't normally reach.

4) **Surrendering control:** Try the missionary position with your hands tied above your head or with a blindfold on. Because it's a naturally submissive position, playing with submissive and dominant roles will add to your excitement.

SEX FACT: *Six out of ten adults say the missionary position is their favourite. One in four prefers the woman on top.*

Position #2: Woman on Top

The basics: You sit, squat or kneel on top of him with your legs either side of his. He lies flat with his legs together while you lower yourself on to his erection (you may have to lean forward a bit to get the angle right). You then sit up and he watches the show. Getting into the right rhythm can take practice, so experiment with different speeds and angles to discover what works best for both of you.

Why it works for you: You get to control the speed and depth of thrusting while he lies back. It's also extremely easy for you to touch your clitoris or angle yourself to get as much clitoral stimulation as possible. (Leaning forward and rocking rather than thrusting often works well.)

SEX FACT: *'Woman on top' is the position in which you're most likely to climax as you're in control and can generate the most clitoral friction.*

Why it works for him: Men love this position because they get to watch your gorgeous body. It's also great for you to take control and, because he doesn't have to support his own body weight, he's likely to last longer as he can devote more energy (and brain power) to delaying his climax, so you're more likely to come together.

> **Cosmo tip:**
> Remember that the first third of the vagina and the head of the penis are the most sensitive parts, which means that shallow thrusting can be just as fulfilling (if not more so) than going deep, deep down.

Variations for Woman on Top

1) **Full-body contact:** Once you're on top, lie forwards on your man and straighten your legs so your whole body is in contact with his. Try rocking backwards and forwards for a position that's both intimate and sexy.

2) **Reverse cowgirl:** Sit facing his feet rather than his chest for an interesting twist. (If you can manage it, start in the basic position, then slowly swivel round so you're facing his feet without losing vagina-to-penis contact. It's an amazing corkscrewy feeling for him and you.) Experiment here with sitting up and lying down flat. Move slowly and sensuously to stop him falling out of you. In this position he'll hit the front wall of your vagina every time he goes in and out, so it's great for G-spot stimulation.

3) **The squeeze tease:** On-top positions are perfect for using your PC muscles (the ones you use to stop the flow of pee) to 'milk' his penis. Try squeezing hard as you bear down on his erection and releasing as you pull upwards.

4) **Squats:** Instead of kneeling, try squatting over him. It's a great toning position for your thigh and buttock muscles and feels primitive and animalistic. Try bouncing or rocking. If his penis comes out of you, use it to massage your clitoris before placing it back inside – it'll calm him down while revving you up.

> **Cosmo tip:**
> When you're on top, try pausing for a couple of seconds in the middle of your session before you slide down his penis again. The surprise and anticipation will drive him wild.

Position #3: Rear Entry (a.k.a. Doggy Style)

The basics: You face away from him on your hands and knees while he kneels (or stands at the edge of the bed) and penetrates you from behind. He holds on to your hips and thrusts into you. As he moves in and out, drop your head down as you push backwards against him. Alternatively, you both thrust together or he remains still and you use your body to move backwards and forwards on to him.

> **Cosmo tip:**
> If he's especially well endowed, be careful with rear-entry positions, as they can feel uncomfortable if his penis bashes against your cervix.

'When we were teenagers it was all about, "Have you tried this position or that position?" These days I stick to the ones that give me the most pleasure: doggy and the missionary position. I've tried others but these are my true faithfuls.'
Rebecca, 30, PA

Why it works for you: This offers the deepest penetration of all the traditional positions and because you have no eye contact you can let your imagination go wild. His penis is hitting the sensitive front wall of the vagina, which gives him direct access to your G-spot. Also, because you're facing downwards, all the blood rushes to your nipples, making your breasts extra-sensitive.

Why it works for him: He gets to watch his penis thrusting in and out and experiences deep penetration. He's in a dominating position here, which can be a turn-on for both of you.

Sexy rear-entry variations

1) **Lying flat:** From the basic position, move forward so the whole of your body is flat on the bed while he lies over you, resting his weight on his elbows (you may have to lift your buttocks a little). With the whole of his weight over you, you can feel totally enclosed and dominated, which can feel extremely intimate. You can also grind your pelvis into the bed for extra arousal.

2) **Sofa so good:** Try leaning over the arm of a sofa while he penetrates you from behind for a comfy twist on this classic position. Experiment with pulling your body up towards his or leaning right down over the arm.

3) **Slap 'n' tickle:** In any of the positions where he's entering

you from behind he can gently slap your buttocks in time to his thrusting, which can be a turn-on for both of you (you naughty girl, you!). A gentle slap brings the blood to the surface of the skin, making it feel more sensitised.

Cosmo tip:
Try turning your head round to kiss your lover in any of the rear-entry positions. It increases eye contact, ups your arousal levels and can be particularly passionate in the throes of the moment.

4) **Vibrator play:** Try lying flat with a cushion under your upper body. Raise your bottom upwards so he can penetrate you from behind. Now slip a vibrator between your body and the pillows and wind it down to your clitoris while he's pumping you from behind.

Position #4: Standing Up

The basics: Any position where one of you is standing up requires supreme leg strength, so be aware that you can both tire easily. That said, sex standing up is especially good for sex outdoors or in confined spaces (such as the stationery cupboard or toilet cubicle). For the basic position, you lean against a wall while he stands in front of you. You jump up and wrap your arms around his shoulders and your legs around his waist while he holds on to your thighs and penetrates you from the front. He then thrusts into you while you remain still.

What's in it for you: It's an extremely intimate position, because the whole of your upper body is in contact with his and, because he's supporting you, he's likely to last longer than usual.

What's in it for him: With you squashed against a wall, he has ultimate control. It can feel extremely naughty (and arousing) if you're trying this in a semi-public place or having a quicky while you're fully clothed.

Sexy Standing Up Variations

1) **Bending it like Beckham (well, kind of!):** He stands behind you and penetrates you from behind while you bend forward as if you're touching you toes (if you can't touch your toes just bend forward until you can hold on to the bed or a chair). He gets maximum penetration while his penis hits the sensitive front wall of the vagina. He has to hold on to your hips and do

all the thrusting, as you can't move much.

2) **Shower sex:** Try having sex standing up in the shower (the basic position works best for this). Although showers can be extra sexy, they may wash away your natural juices, so you may need extra lubrication.

3) **Both standing:** Depending on your height difference, both of you can have sex standing up (the shorter partner might have to stand on a box or sturdy low table). He can crouch down a little to reach you while you bend your legs outwards a little, tilting your pelvis upwards. Try this either facing each other or with you facing away from him. (Try facing towards a wall with him behind you: you can push against the wall to create even more friction between you.) Alternatively, stand on one leg with the other wrapped round his hips. This allows you to balance on one leg and use it to pump you up and down (be careful not to fall over!).

'A lot of women don't realise that men "performance masturbate" – if you make yourself climax on your own, when you have sex later, it'll last longer because it takes you more time to reach orgasm the second time around.'
Toby, 25, researcher

Position #5: Side by Side (Spooning)

The basics: With both of you lying on your sides, he lies behind you while you bring your knees upwards slightly. You then snuggle close as if you were two spoons in a cutlery drawer (hence the name). Lift your top leg upwards so he can penetrate you from behind.

Why it works for you: He can reach round and play with your breasts and clitoris. It's comfortable for both of you and neither person has to do much work. Try rocking backwards and forwards or reaching down and stimulating your clitoris with your own fingers.

Cosmo tip:
Crossing your ankles in any position helps tighten the vaginal canal, which makes him feel bigger inside you.

Why it works for him: The weight distribution is balanced evenly between you, so he doesn't have to rely on upper or lower body strength to keep things going. Penetration is from a slightly unusual angle, so may feel different (and therefore sexy) to him or you. It's also gentle, relaxing and intimate.

Side by Side Varieties

1) **Going face to face:** Instead of lying with your back to him, lie on your side facing him and wrap one leg over his, so he penetrates you from the front. You get to watch each other face to face and both of you can run your hands all over each other's torso and beyond.

2) **Delaying the inevitable:** In the spoons position, avoid penetration at first while each of you spends ten minutes stroking and touching the other's body. After your allotted time is up, let him penetrate you extremely s-l-o-w-l-y, inch by inch, to finish the sensual tease. Curl your upper body round to increase the depth of penetration.

3) **L-shaped lust:** You lie your on your back while he lies at a 90-degree angle to you on his side, so your torsos form an 'L' shape. You lift your legs over his hips while he penetrates you from underneath. He can easily use his top hand for clitoral stimulation. Great for slow sensual sex.

If you've whipped through all these positions in a flash, turn to the **X-rated positions** section for super-advanced versions of your favourites.

'I love being on top: it brings out the show-off in me!'
Betsy, 31, receptionist

PREGNANCY
See also: contraception

Congratulations! You're pregnant. Go and get yourself a pregnancy book that has the space to expand on your expanding horizons. In the meantime, here are a few basic sex-while-pregnant facts.

Sex while pregnant fact #1: Every pregnancy is different

As you've probably found out, some women feel incredibly sexual during pregnancy. Others don't and, although all pregnancies follow the same basic pattern, each one is totally unique, particularly when it comes to sex. Don't be alarmed if your sex drive goes through the roof or disappears entirely.

Sex while pregnant fact #2: It won't harm your baby

Sex – and especially orgasm – is actually relaxing for you and your baby. The little nipper is protected by a load of cushioning amniotic fluid, so a little rumpy-pumpy won't do it any harm whatsoever. You'll feel different at different times during your pregnancy, so may want sex more or less.

Sex while pregnant fact #3: Don't forget, he'll be emotional too

Being a potential father also stirs up a load of emotions in his head. He'll be watching your body (and moods!) change too, so his sex drive and desires may vary as well.

'My husband thinks my bump is really sexy – I catch him looking at it in awe when I'm naked. Pregnancy has made me love my body and feel incredibly womanly and turned on. It's the best thing to happen to our sex life for years!'
Marianne, 28, retail manager

Sex while pregnant fact #4: Find positions that are good for you

Depending on your size (and to some extent your body image), certain positions will feel better than others. So long as you're comfortable, the baby should be comfy, too. Spoons (lying side by side) is usually a comfortable and intimate position through most of your pregnancy.

Sex while pregnant fact #5: It's not just about penetration

There are hundreds of different ways to turn each other on (just look at the pages of this book for starters!), so if either of you doesn't feel like penetration try something else instead.

Sex-while pregnant fact #6: Orgasm can help bring on labour

As your uterus contracts during orgasm, it can be one of the most pleasant ways to bring on labour. Some enlightened midwives even suggest playing with vibrators during labour to help relax you and release the feel-good chemical oxytocin (see **hormones** for more info).

SAFETY INFO: *As every pregnancy is different, it's vital to discuss sex with your doctor or gynaecologist to find out what's suitable for you.*

And Afterwards?

Sex after pregnancy can be a tricky business (there's a little bundle of joy to distract you for starters) so take things extremely slowly and see how you go.

Do talk to your partner about how you're both feeling.

Do talk to your doctor about when is a safe time to think about sex for *you*, particularly if you've had a Caesarean.

Do make time for you and your partner alone once the baby is born: just a few hours together on your own is essential, regardless of how you spend them.

Do remember that you're a sexual being and not just a mum. Same goes for Dad, too.

Don't ignore the issue if you don't feel like sex. Turning your back and pretending to sleep won't help.

Don't put too much pressure on each other. All couples are different, so take things at your own pace.

Don't think of sex just as penetration. Masturbation, cuddling, touching and stroking should also be on the menu (when you're ready).

Don't forget about contraception. Although breastfeeding can prevent pregnancy, many women become pregnant during this time and another pregnancy straightaway is probably not what you need.

SEX FACT: *Only one in three women has penetrative sex in the first six weeks after giving birth. Around two-thirds have sex within three to four months.*

PREMATURE EJACULATION

See also: delay tactics, performance anxiety, orgasm

Kiss. Cuddle. Fondle. Ooops . . . it's all over. Technically, premature ejaculation means 'climaxing before you're ready' and for some men that can mean before the first kiss, before the first thrust or before the end of a three-hour marathon lovemaking session. It really all depends on your definition of 'premature'. Most men would like to last a little longer in order to (a) please you more (yey!) and (b) please themselves more (fair enough), and an occasional quick sprint to the finish line really isn't anything to worry about. But, if he climaxes superfast on a regular basis and it bothers both of you, there could be a problem.

SEX FACT: *It's estimated that around 30–40 per cent of men have a speedy-ejaculation problem at some point in their lives.*

Why does premature ejaculation occur?

There are a couple of physical reasons for it – a bladder infection or a lingering STI, which might make sex uncomfortable for him, in which case he should see a GP or go to an STI clinic. Most commonly, the reasons are psychological. Maybe he's stressed about work, anxious about his performance (very common at the beginning of relationships when he's trying to impress you the most). Maybe when he first started to masturbate he had to get it over and done with quickly for fear of getting caught or first learned about sex through quickies in the park or masturbating competitions to see who could climax first. Maybe he's suffering from depression, so finds it harder to connect emotional feeling with the physical sensations. Whatever the reason, usually the key to solving the problem is for him (and you) to know his body and his sexual responses better so he has more control over them.

What can you do?

Most sex therapists agree that overcoming premature ejaculation is a team effort: it requires time and patience from both of you.

- Be tactful and kind: his self-esteem is likely to be at an all-time low, so you need to handle the situation gently.

- Talk outside the bedroom rather than right before or after the problem has occurred.
- Be prepared to work as a team. He'll probably need to work on the techniques outlined below on his own first, then with you. In order to tackle the problem thoroughly, rather than temporarily fixing it, you'll both need to take things s-l-o-w-l-y.

What can he do?

Quick-fix solutions sometimes involve trying to dull physical sensations so that he becomes less responsive to sexual stimuli, for example by wearing two condoms (not recommended). This is tackling the problem from the wrong perspective: in order to have more control, he needs to become *more* sensitive to what turns him on and the way he's feeling rather than less aware of what's going on. Try the self-help methods below first but if the problem is long-term and persistent a few visits to a sex therapist or psychosexual counsellor can really help. These professionals look at all the reasons for the problem and try to tackle the root causes. A couple of sessions may be all it takes to get him back in the saddle so they really are worth it.

Self-Help Techniques for Him

Masturbation masterclass

First he needs to play around on his own to work out what turns him on, what his ejaculation triggers are and what he can do to stop them working so quickly. This focuses his mind on the nearly-there sensations rather than just letting everything go at once.

Clock watching

One technique involves masturbating to an alarm clock that is set at gradually longer and longer time intervals. He's not allowed to climax until the clock goes off. This can be useful but things might get tricky once you're involved and there isn't an alarm clock in sight.

The stop–start technique

This involves masturbating to an extremely high level of arousal, then stopping just before he climaxes, taking note of exactly how he's feeling: all the sensations in his body, his breathing, how his muscles feel etc. He then lets his arousal levels fall slightly, then builds himself back up again. This takes a while to master but he shouldn't move on to the next stage (where you come in) until he's truly got the hang of this. This technique is also useful for anyone who wants to have more control over their orgasms – men or women: staying in a highly aroused state increases the intensity of your orgasm whether you have a problem with premature climaxes or not.

Once he's really got the hang of this on his own, you come in to help, first with manual stimulation and eventually (don't rush it or the whole process will be pointless) with penetration techniques. He needs to be able to communicate with you to stop moving completely while his arousal goes down. You might want to invent a no-words code for this such as a squeeze on the arm, as having him shout '*halt!*' every time might be intrusive.

> **Cosmo tip:**
> As all of these techniques focus on his pleasure, don't forget to include yours in your training sessions. Pleasuring you in ways that don't involve intercourse or his climax (by, say, oral sex or touchy-feely stuff) will give him a much-needed in-bed ego boost.

The squeeze

A similar technique is the squeeze, whereby instead of stopping all movement at the moment before ejaculation, you reach down and squeeze just under the head of his penis, which causes arousal to subside. Start by just touching each other's body while getting gently aroused. You reach down and gently squeeze the penis to get him used to the sensation. Next you use the technique during mutual masturbation and finally (give it time) during penetration.

The final countdown

The final hands-on technique involves charting his arousal on a scale of one to ten, with ten being ejaculation. The aim is to learn to hover at around the sixish/sevenish mark rather than racing from, say, two to nine in one speedy step. Start by stimulating his genitals in a way you know he likes and getting him to tell you where, on the scale, your actions take him. At first he'll just be pretty much picking numbers at random but after a while he should be able to link them to exact sensations. If you get him up to, say, seven, start touching him somewhere else until his arousal goes down again. Have fun repeating this over and over until he can stay at a highly aroused yet not over-the-top level. Next, try the technique using your genitals to stimulate him (avoid penetration for now – that may be too much). It gets harder with your full body involved, so be patient. Finally, move on to motionless intercourse so he can get used to how it feels to be inside you and, then on to full intercourse when you're both ready.

Have patience: to work properly all these techniques take months rather than a few quick sessions, but they're worth it in the end. All of them can be used by anyone who wants to slow down their sexual responses, so you can both have more fun.

SEX FACT: *Men's sexual responses naturally slow down with age so the younger your lover, the quicker his climax is likely to be.*

PROGESTERONE
See under: hormones

Female sex hormone that peaks in the second half of the menstrual cycle.

PROSTATE
See under: G-spot – male

A highly sensitive walnut-sized gland that produces some of the fluid that makes up ejaculate.

QUESTIONS

The Five Essential Questions to Ask Your Lover that Lead to Better Sex

(Please note: although the explanations for these questions refer to *him*, as if *you've* asked the questions, they'll improve your lust life only if you *both* answer them.)

1) Which part of your favourite fantasy is the bit that really turns you on?

Why it works:

- You find out the *heart* of the fantasy rather than the irrelevant details.
- It lets you know the theme within the fantasy that turns him on, which should give you ideas you can use in the bedroom without necessarily acting the whole thing out.

2) What's the sex technique you use on me that you enjoy the most (and why)?

Why it works:

- You get to know what he enjoys doing to you, which should

boost your ego and your confidence.

- It gives you the opportunity to add sexy suggestions to improve his technique.
- If it's something you really don't like that much, you get to suggest alternatives you do like.
- It's a great way to inadvertently get him to talk dirty (or, if you're answering, for you to talk dirty without getting embarrassing, e.g. 'I really love touching you there because . . .').

3) Which area of your body is the most sensitive (excluding your obvious erogenous zones)?
Why it works:

- You'll know what parts to pay attention to on the warm-up to serious foreplay.
- It'll focus your lust play away from the genitals, making the build-up to sex even more exciting.

4) Is there anything I do that you really don't like?
Why it works:

- Usually this turns out to be something petty like 'using that stupid Austin Powers voice' or 'sticking your tongue in my ear', which can be simple to avoid but incredibly useful to know.
- You get to know what he really isn't keen on (and get to tell him in return).
- You don't waste your time doing something he gets nothing from.

> **Cosmo tip:**
> If you don't fancy asking these questions make up five of your own each – things you've been gagging to ask for ages – then put them in a hat and pull them out at random, taking turns to BOTH answer them (so you'll have to give answers to YOUR questions too. If you're clever, you can reveal things YOU want to tell him through your questions).

5) What's the one thing about any aspect of sex that you wish the opposite sex knew?
Why it works:

- This should reveal something that niggles him that you might be able to put right.

- It could bring up a discussion of techniques and timing that improves sex for both of you.

And the Five You Should *Never* Ask . . .
1. Does my bum look big in this position?
2. Did your ex do it like this?
3. Which one of my friends would you like to sleep with and why?
4. Have you actually heard of the clitoris?
5. Is it in yet?

QUICKIES
See also: outdoor sex, positions

Quickie sex, whether it's with a sexy stranger or your long-term lover, can be just as satisfying as a leisurely, lingering lovemaking session. It's all about mood and seizing the moment. Quickies are fantastically fulfilling because, if you're in a public or semi-public place or having sex at a time when you shouldn't, your body becomes flooded with adrenaline. This increases your heart rate, increases the blood flow to your genitals and heightens sexual arousal. Basically, you're body is screaming for a lust fix and fast! Spontaneity is at the heart of a good quickie and having one every once in a while will boost your sex life and self-esteem for months to come. So what are you waiting for? On your marks, get sex, *go*!

Quickie Essentials
Although the perfect quickie shouldn't take hours of planning (that really isn't the point), there are a few things that'll make the whole process a little easier:
1. Fast-release clothes: think Velcro and poppers, zips rather than buttons, skirts rather than trousers and easy-access underwear.

2. Guts: in order to seize the day you need to be willing to take a risk and go for it, right here, right now.

3. A willing partner in crime: it just won't be fun if one of you really isn't into it.

4. A condom: carry one in your purse or make-up bag rather than your handbag, as it's easier to slip away clutching a purse than an oversized shopper.

Quickie Positions

Maximise your pleasure by choosing the right position for the right location . . .

The Broom Cupboard Balance

What to do: Put your back against a wall (not the door, as it'll probably rattle) and raise one leg up and wrap it round his waist. You balance on your remaining leg while he holds the raised one and penetrates you from the front.

Great because: When you're standing up the pressure and weight of your vagina bearing down on him increases, which makes penetration feel deeper for both of you.

Also good for:

- **Love in an elevator** – just use your free hand to hold down the doors-closed button.
- **Joining the Mile High Club** – balance your leg on the toilet seat and remember to leave separately.

The Alley Cat

What to do: The beauty of a dark dingy alleyway is that, if it's narrow enough, you can use both walls to push against. He leans against one wall with his feet propped against the other. Facing away from him, you straddle his legs and lower yourself on to his erection, resting your arms on the wall in front of you and your feet on the wall behind you.

Great because: His penis should be hitting the front wall of your vagina – perfect for G-spot stimulation, plus you get to control all the action.

'I once had sex with a waiter in the wine cellar of a restaurant when I was out with my parents. We both climaxed extremely quickly but it was so exhilarating. Trying to hide my post-orgasmic flush was pretty difficult but I don't think anyone noticed!'
Deborah, 29, hotel manager

Also good for:

- **Train toilet cubicles** – you're confined but this position should be quite comfortable.

SEX FACT: *According to German research an unfortunate few suffer from blinding headaches at the point of orgasm if they indulge in quickie sex due to the sudden build-up and release of blood pressure.*

The Hall of Shame

What to do: On your way out of the house, forget to put your knickers on and ambush your man in the hall or near the front door. Lift up your skirt and wrap both your legs round his waist while he supports them with his hands. Lean against the wall (or door) while he pumps into you.

Great because: You get to walk into that party fashionably late and sexily flushed. If it's a narrow hallway, bring your legs right up and push them against the opposite wall. This shortens the vagina, making him feel bigger inside you.

Also good for:

- **Deserted hotel corridors** – just make sure there are no CCTV cameras.
- **Halls of residence** – in fact, anywhere with a hallway will do nicely, thank you very much.

> **Cosmo tip:**
> Don't get caught. You could be shamed, sacked or even arrested if you're in a public place so *be careful!*

> **Cosmo tip:**
> Remember that quickie sex doesn't have to involve full penetration. Oral sex, a bit of mutual masturbation or just a very passionate snog can be just as exhilarating.

Office Ecstasy

What to do: Working late is such a trial. Spice it up with naughty nookie in the boss's office. Sit on the edge of the desk while he sits or kneels in front of you (depending on the height of the work surface). Wrap your legs around his back and lower yourself on to his penis, crossing your ankles behind his back. Squeezing your thighs together narrows your vaginal canal, which enhances the friction you both feel. Alternatively, lean backwards on the desk and get him to hold your legs straight up while he stands in front of you and penetrates from the front.

Great because: You control the depth of penetration so you can hurry yourselves to a climax by pushing down. Also, the boss's office will never look as intimidating again.

Also good for:

- **Kitchen table shenanigans** – lie back and enjoy the naughty feeling of being 'below stairs'.
- **Living room lust** – if you can't quite make it to the bedroom, get him to sit in an armchair and wrap your legs around him in the same way.

SEX FACT: *Twenty-five per cent of* Cosmo *readers admit to having sex in the office.*

Stairway to Heaven

What to do: Having sex on a stairway is perfect if there's a big height difference between you. Bend over, holding on to the railings, and let him penetrate you from behind.

Great because: He's hitting you in all the right places and penetration will be deep, fast and furious. If you can balance, get him to hold your wrists behind your back for a bit of sexy bondage action.

Also good for:

- **Attic action** – those stairs that no one ever goes up are just begging you to try them (especially during a big family get-together!).
- **Club land classics** – use the same position in a crowded club: if you're leaning over a balcony in the semi darkness, he should be able to penetrate you from behind with no one noticing (but be very careful not to get caught: big bad bouncers tend not to like that kind of behaviour in their establishments).

'My boyfriend and I slipped away from my sister's wedding and had sex in a shed at the bottom of the garden. Something about the romance of the day, his sexy suit, the champagne and the fact that loads of boring relatives were milling round the garden and could discover us at any time made the whole thing extra exciting!'
Laura, 34, gas engineer

QUIET SEX

Sometimes you want to get down and dirty but you need to keep the noise down. Maybe you're sneaking into the spare room while staying at your parents'. Maybe you're trying not to wake the children sleeping next door. Maybe your roommate/best friend/real boyfriend is asleep in the next bed. Or maybe, just maybe, you fancy a change from your normal scream-the-place-down routine. When you're having sex somewhere you shouldn't, the fear of getting caught by parents/children/friends/ex-lovers etc. sends adrenaline coursing through your body, heightening all your senses and increasing your levels of arousal. Make the most of the restriction of being quiet with these keep-shtumm ideas:

Quiet Sex #1: The Best Positions

The CAT position
This is a spin on the usual missionary position where you're actually rocking rather than thrusting (so you'll make less noise). The benefit for you is that the clitoris and his pubic bone stay in constant contact, meaning orgasm for you is more likely than in any other position. See the **CAT position** for how-to details.

Downward dog
OK, this isn't the yoga position of the same name. It's actually a version of doggy style, where he penetrates you from behind (careful with his thrusts: they need to be slow and sensual to keep the noise down) while you're on all fours. Now, instead of staying on all fours, bury your head in the pillow in front of you. That way, the sound of your gasps will be muffled by those fluffy feathers. Try biting on the pillow if you feel the urge to scream with pleasure. Biting also tenses your muscles, which can help to bring on orgasm.

'I'm usually quite vocal in bed and my boyfriend loves it when I moan and pant, but one day he looked me in the eyes, put one hand over my mouth and the other holding my hands down over my head. I loved the fact that he'd become so dominant: it was a huge turn-on!'
Clarissa, 25, administrator

Quiet Sex #2: The Best Props

Your own hand (or his)

Anything you can bite down on will stop you screaming out in ecstasy. Biting on each other's fingers (or having a finger in the mouth) can be extremely erotic for both of you.

Some kind of gag

You can use anything to stop sound coming out of your mouth so long as it *never* restricts your breathing or is tied so tightly it can hurt. Being restricted in any way can be extremely arousing (see the **bondage** section for more info) but, whatever you're using, you must always have a safe word (or, if you're gagged, a sign like a tap on the leg or a click of the fingers) that means stop, so you can be released at any time. Also, keep a pair of scissors handy for quick release.

Quiet Sex #3: The Best Technique

Tension turn-ons

If you really can't move a muscle (say you're sleeping in the same room as other people or you're getting intimate in the back of a car while someone else is driving), try tensing all the muscles in your body and letting his fingers do the work on your genitals (a travel blanket helps if you're in a car). He can gently stroke your vagina and clitoris while you hold everything taut. You'll become much more aware of your breathing speeding up, your body temperature rising and your vagina becoming wetter. The fact that you can't make a sound makes the atmosphere sizzle.

'I once had sex under the stage at school while there was an assembly going on (we were in the sixth form and supposed to be on late-comers duty). We tried not to make anything creak and the excitement of doing it in front of all those people (and possibly getting caught) was amazing.'
Tania, 32, musician

QUOTA

See: masturbation for him, masturbation for you

Think you're not getting enough sex? Want to up your quota? Instead of making unreasonable demands on your partner, try masturbating. Most couples still masturbate while they're in a long-term relationship (usually in private). It'll keep you sexy and satisfied without pestering your partner every time you have the urge to merge.

RADIANT
See also: orgasm

The way you'll look after a great sex session. Energetic sex is great for the circulation and helps cell rejuvenation, keeping you looking younger for longer.

SEX FACT: *Orgasm causes your cheeks to flush as blood rushes to your head. Your post-orgasmic glow lasts between twenty and forty minutes.*

RELAXATION TECHNIQUES
See also: delay tactics, erotic massage, performance anxiety

Feeling a bit nervous? Need to calm down before you get all worked up again? These relaxation techniques will help you wind down and connect emotionally before you get down to the physical nitty gritty:

Breathe right

Get naked and sit in front of your partner. Start to breathe slowly and deeply, slowing your breathing down gradually. Coordinate your breathing so you're in time with your partner. Maintain eye contact and concentrate on nothing other than your breathing. Stay like this for as long as you can. This creates intimacy and a bond between you.

Feet-to-feet

Try the same exercise but this time lie flat on the floor with your feet touching his feet. Get into a rhythm with your breathing, but this time breathe in when he breathes out and out when he breathes in, as if you're breathing in each other's air. On your in-breath imagine a white light entering your body from your lover's body through the soles of his feet. Imagine it entering from your feet and travelling all the way through you, energising every part of your body. On the out-breath, feel the light leaving your body and entering your partner's. Again, a powerful carnal connection is created between you.

Stroke of genius

Try stroking each other's hair and body extremely gently. Use long, slow, repetitive strokes and concentrate on what you're doing. It will make you both feel calm, loved and cherished. For a more intimate touch technique see the **erotic massage** section.

Find your comfort spot

Everyone has a place on their body that feels incredibly comforting and relaxing to have touched or held. To find yours (and your partner's) try placing your hand over different parts of each other's body after sex. It could be the small of your back, your bottom, the top of your head or even a light cupped hand placed over your genitals (or his). It's the place that makes you feel safe, secure and loved. Once you've discovered your comfort spot, use it any time you need a bit of reassurance or relaxation.

REVERSE COWGIRL
See under: positions

You-on-top sex position where you face his feet instead of his head.

RHYTHM
See also: penetration, positions

Great sex is all about getting a good rhythm going and, as with learning to ride a horse or a bike, sometimes it's there and sometimes it isn't. Occasionally, you'll jump into bed with a near stranger and bang! thrust! bang! thrust! – you reach perfect rhythm immediately. Usually it takes a little more practice and will depend on other factors such as your mood, your energy levels and your concentration (thinking about what you'll wear to the office tomorrow really doesn't help).

> **Cosmo tip:**
> Don't worry if you aren't in perfect sync all the time: sex should be playful and fun, not a finely tuned military procedure.

To improve your carnal coordination, try:
- Experimenting to find the positions in which you both feel most comfortable, as they'll be the ones where you'll both be able to build up a steady pace.
- Experimenting with different thrust depths and speeds. Great rhythm doesn't just mean pummelling as furiously as you can. It's to do with being in sync with your partner.
- Matching your breathing to his. It's a subconscious way to set the pace and it'll focus both your minds on what your bodies are doing.
- On his in-stroke (when he thrusts deepest into you), lifting your pubic bone slightly to reach his body. On the out-stroke release back down again. This not only helps to build up a steady rhythm but

'Sometimes, when I know my boyfriend is going to climax I stay still and just let him pump in and out of me. I love to watch him go for it and feeling so passive is a turn-on for me.'

Rebecca, 31, administrator

you also get to crunch the top of your clitoris against his pubic bone, which is arousing for both of you.

RHYTHM METHOD
See under: contraception

A form of contraception that takes time to master where you use your natural menstrual rhythms to work out your fertile and non-fertile days. Requires training from a natural family planning consultant to perfect, otherwise it can be unreliable.

ROLE-PLAY
See also: dressing up, fantasy

Taking on a sexy new role in the bedroom allows you to sexperiment with different personalities or sex positions you wouldn't normally try, and lets you behave in a way that's incredibly liberating. If you're pretending to be Foxy Fifi the French maid you'll feel free do to things the 'real you' wouldn't dream of. You may be a nice girl at heart but role play brings out your naughty side.

> ### Cosmo tip:
> You don't have to dress up to get into a role. Just imagining yourself as someone else in your head is often enough to make you act in a totally different way.

Role-play for Beginners: Your Back-to-Basics Masterclass

Step 1: Decide on your role
Think about the types of fantasies that really turn you on. Love to be in control? You might want to be a demanding dominatrix. Have a romantic streak? Try playing the damsel in distress. Enjoy the thought of spicing up your sex life up with a one-night stand but don't want to be unfaithful? Try acting like strangers. Hot tip: sometimes playing totally against your usual personality type can be a huge turn-on, too, so, if you're normally bossy or controlling, try playing a subservient role or vice versa.

Step 2: Prepare yourself

Half the fun of playing a role is the preparation. Think about the kinds of props or outfit you might need. What would be the perfect location for your role play? What kind of hair and make-up would your character wear? What would you really like to happen when you're in character? Think about all these details and discuss them with your partner first: simply talking about acting out your fantasy will be a turn-on.

Step 3: Get into character

Don't just think about how you're going to dress: give your character a name, an accent and set of mannerisms. How does she talk, walk, sip her drink or eat? Practise feeling like the new you before you start to act her out. Once you're dressed the part, it'll feel more natural to act like the character you've become but don't forget details like body language or her signature sex moves.

Step 4: Go for it

The key to playing a successful role is to remain in character for the whole of your sex session. Whatever happens during your role-play, stick to the character you've become. Following the basic script or scenario you've prepared, act out your role until both you and your partner are satisfied.

Step 5: Revisit your role

If you want to discuss the experience or revive your sexy character, next time you're with your man ask him what his character (use the name he invented) would do now or ask him whether he'd like your character to come and join you. Just mentioning your character's name will conjure up all those sexy memories.

> **Cosmo tip:**
> Playing roles, like every aspect of sex, can get boring if you're in character all the time. Save full-on dressing up and acting-out sessions for special occasions only.

Tonight Matthew, I'm Going to Be . . .

Try these saucy scenarios for inspiration – and don't forget to add in your own sexy twists or variations on the themes . . .

Raunchy Role-play #1: Movie Star and Adoring Fan

Appeals to: Anyone who likes to feel worshipped or yearns to be famous.

What you'll need: A pair of dark glasses, an expensive-looking outfit (a fake fur coat is ideal) and champagne.

Your go-for-it guide: Don your most exclusive outfit and dark glasses and pretend you're the hottest celebrity in town. Choose your favourite star or someone you know your partner finds sexy and behave exactly as she would. You can start this role play during the day by going on a fake designer-shop spending spree. Walk in as if you owned the place and try on the most expensive item in the shop. Your lover pretends to be your biggest fan whom you stumble across by chance. Get talking (and remember you're the one in control as he's just a mere fan asking for your autograph) and end up in bed together (you can either book a room in a hotel or go back to yours). Remember: you have to be careful with this liaison as the paparazzi might spot you at any time. Your fan is your sex slave for the night but be good to him, otherwise he might try to sell your sex secrets to the papers the next morning . . .

Variations on the theme

- **Movie star and casting agent:** You'll do anything on the casting couch to get the part of your dreams . . .
- **Naughty audition:** Pretend you're a blue-movie star who's auditioning extras for her latest sextravaganza.

Raunchy Role-play #2: Doctors and Nurses

Appeals to: Anyone who likes to be examined or has a nurturing streak.

What you'll need: A nurse's outfit (Ann Summers have a great selection, or try improvising with a short white coat and stockings), a stethoscope, first-aid kit or latex gloves.

Your go-for-it-guide: It's your job to make your patient feel at ease. Start by undressing him so you can make a proper examination. Touch him all over for an initial assessment of his health, then ask him what seems to be the trouble. You'll probably discover (if he has half a brain!) that the problem seems to be something to do with his groin area. Touch him all over this area with teasing strokes, asking if anything you do makes him feel any better. You may need a closer look at his genitals and you may even need to give him some mouth-to-mouth or any special procedures that you deem medically necessary. Serious hands-on (or mouth-on) action usually needs to be prescribed. Tease his 'injured' penis in your mouth before you straddle him (still in full uniform, naturally) to complete his treatment.

Variations on the theme

- **He plays doctor:** This time you get to be the patient while your 'doctor' makes an examination all of his own.
- **Kiss of life:** Oh, dear, one of you has fallen into a coma (a fake one, obviously) and needs to be resuscitated. Do whatever you can to 'wake each other up'. (The patient has to remain as still and silent as possible while they're being 'revived'.)

> **Cosmo tip:**
> Never take on a role or dress up purely to please your partner. It'll work only if you're both turned on by it.

Raunchy Role-play #3: Prostitute and Client

Appeals to: Anyone who wants to pretend to get exactly what they pay for in bed.

What you'll need: Tarty clothes such as an extra-short skirt, high heels, stockings and suspenders plus raunchy underwear (preferably red and as rude as you like) or, if you want to be a high-class call girl, a body-skimming dress complete with no knickers.

Your go-for-it-guide: This works exceptionally well in a hotel bar. You (as the working girl) sit at the bar, order a cocktail and wait for your 'client' to approach you. (Don't make your outfit too authentic, otherwise you might be mistaken for the real thing!) Your lover then approaches you and you discuss how much you charge (prepare your answers in advance). You then go upstairs to your room but don't do a thing unless he's laid his money on the table first. Name your price for every sex act you do and get him to pay for any kinky extras along the way. Tell him you never kiss your clients. Afterwards, take your money and leave.

Variations on the theme

- **The gorgeous gigolo:** He gets to be the prostitute and you order him to perform the sex acts you really want (and can afford).
- **Pimp 'n' prostitute:** He 'owns' you and can make you do anything he wants you to. You can talk dirty to him about what you get up to with 'your clients'.

Raunchy Role-play #4: Sexy Schoolgirl and Teacher

Appeals to: The naughty little girl inside you just waiting to be taught a lesson.

What you'll need: A cute school uniform, white socks, your hair in plaits and raunchy underwear.

Your go-for-it guide: Once dressed up, walk into the bedroom coyly twiddling your hair and looking up at your lover through your not-so-innocent eyelashes. He gets to play your teacher and the subject just happens to be human biology. He has to test you on a number of questions (possibly about your knowledge of his body and his hot spots). For every question you get right he has to remove an article of clothing. For every question you get wrong, *you* have to remove something (and, if you're a really naughty girl, you'll probably get a few wrong on purpose!). He'll definitely be teaching you a lesson you won't forget in a hurry.

'Whether I'm pretending to be Ms Whiplash, a naughty nurse or even Samantha from Sex and the City, role play is a fantastic excuse to switch off my everyday personality and behave totally differently. Sometimes I don't even make it obvious I'm acting a role – I keep the fantasy in my head but my boyfriend is blown away by how assertive and confident I've become.'
Jenny, 31, call centre manager

Variations on the theme

- **The deflowered virgin:** Rather than a raunchy schoolgirl, imagine you're a virgin being touched for the very first time. He has to show you exactly what to do.
- **The stern school-marm:** This time you're the teacher and he'll get a good thrashing if he does anything wrong . . .

Other Inspirational Roles to Try . . .

1) **Sexy strangers:** Meet in a bar and pretend you're meeting for the very first time for no-strings sex.

2) **Bored housewife:** Oh dear, your boiler doesn't seem to be working. Wonder if your 'plumber' will have all the right tools.

3) **Policeman and petty criminal:** You've been stopped for speeding and will do anything not to get a ticket.

4) **High priestess and worshipper:** You are a goddess and he is one of your disciples and is totally within your power. Make him worship you in any way you want him to.

5) **Secretary and boss:** Your new male secretary is extremely attractive. His dictation skills seem to be up to scratch but what about his interpersonal skills? You'll have to find out . . .

6) **Sex toy salesman:** Turn up with a sexy box of tricks that you need to flog in order to hit your sales targets. No, of course a personal demonstration won't be too much trouble . . .

7) **Harem girl:** Imagine all the sights and sounds of the exotic East. Will you have to perform the dance of the seven veils or compete with other members of his (imaginary) harem?

> **Cosmo tip:**
> Need some more inspiration? Try reading some erotica or watching a porn film. You should find plenty of characters you can imitate.

ROMANCE

An essential aphrodisiac often overlooked by modern males (OK, and females).

> **Cosmo tip:**
> Always remember that romance and raunch go hand in hand.

SAFE(R) SEX
*See also: condoms, genito-urinary
infections, sexually transmitted infections*

Q: What is safe sex?
A: The only truly safe sex is no sex. Nada. Nothing. And realistically, if you're reading this book, that's probably not an option. Saf*er* sex is the process of minimising your risk of contracting or passing on sexually transmitted infections (STIs).

There are a few ways to practice safer sex:
1) Use condoms. When used correctly condoms reduce the likelihood of contracting or passing on sexually transmitted infections by 98 per cent. However, some infections, including herpes simplex and genital warts, can be passed on by genital contact even if you are using condoms.
2) Choose your partners carefully. You have to have unprotected sex with only one person infected with an STI to catch one. If you're not using condoms you're at risk.
3) Know the risks of the activities you engage in (see the bullet points below). Some forms of sexual activity are considered riskier than others. For example, anal sex without using a

condom is considered a very high-risk activity because the delicate walls of the back passage aren't designed to receive a penis and are therefore more likely to tear, making the transmission of infections easier. The vaginal wall is also delicate and has many blood vessels close to the surface, which is why condoms are recommended for safer sex.

4) Get tested. Often. STIs are ingenious and persistent, and some have the ability to stick around in your system for months or even years without being detected. Many have no symptoms and some (like HIV) take up to six months to show up on tests.

5) Discuss STIs with your partner. Even if one of you doesn't have any symptoms, it's best if you both get tested and treated. Telling exes can be trickier but it's recommended that if you discover you have an STI, you contact all previous sexual partners who might also have it. STI clinics can help you do this.

6) Good personal hygiene. The body is a clever organism with hundreds of finely tuned systems that are self-cleaning, self-regulating and self-protecting. But sometimes these can go out of balance and bacteria can build up, which can aggravate sensitive areas or make you more susceptible to STIs and other genital or urinary infections like thrush, cystitis and bacterial vaginosis (see **genito-urinary infections**). Washing often, peeing before and after sex and generally having a high level of personal hygiene are recommended to keep your body healthy.

Your Sexual Risk Factors

High risk
- Unprotected anal sex
- Unprotected vaginal sex

Medium risk
- Oral sex – less risky than anal or vaginal sex but not if you or your partner has an untreated STI such as herpes

Lower risk

- Kissing
- Sharing sex toys (so long as they're scrupulously clean or condom-covered)

Virtually no-risk

- Erotic massage and mutual masturbation

Zero risk

- Exchanging fantasies
- Phone sex or chatroom sex
- Total abstinence

The Oral Sex Question

Q: Can you get a sexually transmitted infection from oral sex? Is swallowing more harmful than not swallowing?

A: Oral sex is a tricky area as there's little data available regarding STI transmission from oral alone. The totally sensible do-it-by-the-book advice is that you should use a condom or a dental dam (a flat piece of latex that sits on top of the vaginal area) every time you have oral sex. In reality, not many people other than sex workers do this and even many prostitutes offer oral without a condom as one of their services. STIs *can* be passed on through oral sex but the risk is thought to be minimal unless you have sores on your mouth. If you have any cuts in or around your mouth, transmission is more likely. If you have a cold sore on your mouth avoid going south, as the virus that causes cold sores can cause genital herpes when it gets to that area. Swallowing any body fluids increases your risk slightly.

SEX FACT: *A woman having unprotected penetrative sex with a man infected with HIV is twice as likely to contract the virus as a man having penetrative sex with an HIV-positive woman.*

SAFE WORD
See also: bondage, role play, spanking

Fox, tree, banana, fimble . . . A safe-word is a neutral code word you and your partner agree on at the beginning of a sex session that means 'no' and/or 'stop immediately'. You need a safe word in many sexual situations particularly during **bondage**, **spanking** or **role play** as shouting out 'no, no, no' or pleading 'stop now' can be part of the sex play. Don't enter into any sexual power games without agreeing a safe word first, which must always be acted upon immediately if uttered.

SEMEN
See also: ejaculation, oral sex for him, penis, sperm

SEX FACT *Between the ages of sixteen and sixty the average man will ejaculate 60–100 pints of semen. Don't panic: that's not all at once. The average ejaculation contains just a teaspoon (5 ml) of liquid.*

Semen is the milky fluid propelled from the penis during ejaculation. It contains a mixture of sperm (around 10 per cent), protein, fluid from the prostate gland, fructose (which gives sperm energy), calcium, protein, zinc and enzymes that digest cervical mucus and fight off any infections. Semen protects and nourishes sperm on their arduous journey from the testicles to the vagina/outside world/condom.

SEX FACT *If he ejaculates often, the amount of semen produced gets smaller each time.*

SEX DRIVE
See under: libido

Like the stock market, your sex drive can go up or down.

SEX TOYS
See under: household objects, jewellery, toys

Pretty much anything can be used as a toy in the bedroom if you use your imagination.

SEXUALLY TRANSMITTED INFECTIONS (STIs)
See also: condoms, genito-urinary infections, safer sex

STIs in the UK are currently on the rise and, as many are symptomless, thousands of people have no idea they are infected. If you think you may have an infection or if you've had unsafe sex, you should get tested. STI testing is quick, simple and totally confidential. Either go to your GP or a special STI clinic or a GUM (genito-urinary medicine) clinic at a hospital. Staff at special clinics are trained to be non-judgemental, confidential and practical.

Cosmo tip:
Getting tested at a GUM or STI clinic at a hospital is totally confidential. Your records never leave the clinic, and so don't get passed on to anyone, not even your GP or any other part of the hospital.

Some conditions such as cystitis aren't actually passed on sexually but they can be made worse by sexual contact. See the **genito-urinary infections** section for more details.

Think You Have an STI? What To Look Out For
- Change in your normal vaginal discharge or discharge from the penis. Although vaginal discharge changes during your usual menstrual cycle, strong fishy odours, more discharge than usual or a change in colour can indicate an infection.
- Difficulty or pain when peeing.
- Itchiness or pain in the vaginal or penile area.
- Irritation or pain during intercourse.
- Mysterious lumps, bumps or blisters in and around the

genital area.
• Rashes around the genital area.
• No symptoms at all other than the knowledge that you've had unprotected sex.

STI Checklist

Here's a rundown of the most common STIs:

HIV (Human Immunodeficiency Virus)

What it is: A virus that attacks the immune system and can be passed on by exchange of body fluids.

Symptoms: Usually none but brief flu-like symptoms can occur followed by no signs of infection. Many cases are diagnosed by accident: some women find out they're HIV+ during their pregnancy health screening and blood donors are screened for HIV.

SEX FACT! *Heterosexual women are the fastest-growing group of new HIV+ cases in the UK.*

Effects: HIV causes Acquired Immune Deficiency Syndrome (AIDS). A weakened immune system causes general poor health that can be fatal.

Risks: Variable. You can contract HIV from a one-night stand but some women test negative after having a long-term relationship with an HIV+ partner. Women are much more likely to be infected by a male partner than the other way round.

SEX FACT! *Worldwide, half of all HIV infections are in people under 25.*

Testing: Anonymous testing is available at STI clinics. You'll be offered counselling before and after testing.

Treatment: Various cocktails of drugs manage the symptoms of AIDs, though side effects can be debilitating and can include vomiting and headaches.

Herpes

What it is: A virus (Herpes Simplex) that hides in the body after an initial attack. There are two strains of the virus: type 1, which infects the mouth or nose (cold sores), and type 2, which infects the genital and anal area, but the strains do cross over.

Symptoms: A burning, tingling rash and blisters on the genitals (HSV2), combined with fever and enlargement of lymph nodes in the neck. Many people don't notice these symptoms, so you may not know you have the virus.

Effects: Some people have just one attack, others have recurring bouts. If you become pregnant, your baby may be delivered by Caesarean to avoid catching it.

Risks: Highest at the beginning of an attack, even before the lesions appear. It's not known how infectious herpes is between attacks. The two strains do cross over, so it's essential to (e.g.) avoid oral sex if you have a cold sore on or around your mouth.

Testing: See your GP or go to an STI clinic.

Treatment: Antiviral tablets will relieve pain and prevent the virus from multiplying, but the virus stays with you for life once you've contracted it.

Chlamydia

What it is: The most common but treatable STI, chlamydia is caused by bacteria found in semen and vaginal fluid and passed on through sexual contact.

Symptoms: Usually none in both men and women. Some women may experience unusual vaginal discharge, pain when passing urine or lower abdominal pain. Men may experience painful swelling of the testicles.

Effects: If left untreated, can cause pelvic inflammatory disease (PID), which can then lead to infertility. Fallopian tube scarring can lead to ectopic pregnancy.

Risks: There is a 60 per cent chance of catching chlamydia from unprotected sex with someone who is already infected. An American study found that 25 per cent of eighteen-year-old girls had chlamydia after being sexually active for just one year.

'I had no idea that chlamydia had no symptoms but could cause something as serious as infertility. I'm definitely getting tested for it now.'
Rochelle, 23, student

Testing: See your GP or go to an STI clinic.

Treatment: Caught early, chlamydia can be easily treated with antibiotics. Doctors advise avoiding penetrative sex until after you've finished treatment.

SEX FACT! *Symptoms of chlamydia appear only in 20 per cent of cases. That leaves 80 per cent of people with the infection showing no symptoms at all.*

Genital warts

What it is: Warts on the genitals caused by one of the many strains of the human papilloma virus (HPV) passed on through sexual contact.

Symptoms: Some strains of HPV cause visible symptoms: warts on, inside or around the genitals. Others cause no symptoms at all.

Effects: Two or three of the one hundred strains of HPV have been linked to cervical cancer. Most are harmless.

Risks: Very infectious and passed on by any skin-to-skin contact with an affected area (so not just through penetration). Condoms do offer some protection but don't protect you entirely.

Testing: See your GP or go to an STI clinic.

Treatment: Visible warts can be treated with creams or removed but, once you have the virus, it stays in your body. Usually your immune system kicks in to suppress it.

SEX FACT! *According to a 2003 government report, cases of chlamydia have risen over 100 per cent in the last six years. Syphilis is up nearly 500 per cent and gonorrhoea is up around 90 per cent. The 16–30-year-old age group are most at risk of contracting an STI.*

Gonorrhoea

What it is: A sexually transmitted bacterial infection.

Symptoms: Many people have mild or no symptoms. Likely indicators are painful peeing and yellow, green or watery discharge from the penis or vagina. It can also infect the throat.

Effects: If left untreated gonorrhoea can cause pelvic inflammatory disease and scarring of the fallopian tubes, which can lead to ectopic pregnancy, difficulty in conceiving or infertility.

Risks: Easy to pass on via unprotected sex. Can be passed on during oral sex.

Testing: See your GP or go to an STI clinic.

Treatment: Caught early on, gonorrhoea can be treated easily with antibiotics.

Pubic lice (crabs)

What it is: Tiny lice (parasitic spider-like creatures) that live and lay eggs in pubic hair.

Symptoms: Severe itching. You can see nits (lice eggs) or crawling lice in pubic hair and other body hair (including eyebrows and eyelashes). Lice look like tiny crabs.

Effects: Unpleasant but not dangerous.

Risks: Easy to pass on through contact with infected areas (so even during non-penetrative sex).

Testing: See your GP or go to an STI clinic. Remedies are also available over the pharmacy counter, so you don't have to be tested.

Treatment: Medicated shampoo that may need to be repeated several times before it's effective.

SEX FACT *You're most likely to catch an STI when you start having sex with a new partner, but some infections may lie dormant in your body, and don't start showing symptoms for months or even years.*

Trichomonas

What it is: A tiny single-cell organism that causes trichomoniasis, an infection in the vagina (and in the urethra in men).

Symptoms: Often none for men. Women may have a smelly discharge and experience pain when peeing.

Effects: Can cause early labour if pregnant. Inflammation can make you more susceptible to other STIs.

Risks: Easy to pass on via unprotected sex.

Testing: See your GP or go to an STI clinic.

Treatment: Drugs available on prescription are extremely effective.

SEX FACT: *STIs used to be collectively known as 'Venereal Disease' or VD, after the Roman goddess of love, Venus.*

Syphilis

What it is: A bacterial infection that is fairly rare among heterosexual couples.

Symptoms: Come in three phases. Symptoms vary from sores on infected areas, to flulike symptoms, hair loss and swollen glands, to serious effects on the heart, nervous system and internal organs.

Effects: In extreme cases can cause organ failure and death.

Risks: Highly contagious during the first two stages and passed on through sex or skin contact.

Testing: See your GP or go to an STI clinic.

Treatment: A two- to three-week course of penicillin is effective during the first two stages, although the effects of third-phase (tertiary) syphilis are not easy to reverse.

SEX FACT: *In the sixteenth century the Spanish army sent out syphilis-infected prostitutes to sabotage the Italian army it was fighting against, which is one of the first recorded instances of biological warfare.*

Hepatitis A, B and C

What it is: A viral infection that causes liver damage. The three most common strains – A, B and C – are transmitted differently, not always through sexual contact.

Symptoms: Sometimes none, sometimes vomiting and diarrhoea with Hep A. Hep B and C can cause symptoms such as jaundice (yellowing skin), extreme tiredness, darker-than-usual urine and paler-than-usual faeces indicating the serious illness of jaundice.

Effects: In many cases the body's immune system fights off the virus but it can cause serious liver damage.

Risks: Hep A is usually transmitted through contaminated food, drink, anal and oral sex. Hep B and C are passed on through unprotected intercourse or via needle sharing.

'I went to a special STI clinic in a hospital. Although I was dreading the check-up, they were so quick and efficient I hardly felt anything. It turned out I had a minor infection that was cleared up almost straightaway.'
Joanne, 27, sales executive

Testing: See your GP or go to an STI clinic.

Treatment: Vaccines are available for hepatitis A and B as a preventative. These can also protect against risks from recent sexual contacts if treated early enough. Some antiviral drug treatments are available.

SEXUAL RESPONSE CYCLE
See under: arousal

Want to find out what happens when you go from ooh to oh, oh, oh to yes, yes, *yes*? See the **arousal** section for details.

SEXUAL SIGNATURE
See also: confidence

What's all this about, then?
Your sexual signature is the sex move you love the most, the one you're best at, the one that boosts your confidence, makes you feel powerful and sexy, turns you on *and* drives him wild at the same time.

Hmm – sounds interesting. Can it really do all that?
Oh, yes, so long as you find the right one. What you're looking for is a unique-to-you combination of a move you make and an attitude you have (like supreme sex-goddess confidence) while you're making that move.

So it could be my favourite sex position?
It could be, if that's the thing that makes you feel the most fabulous, but it could equally be a special oral sex technique you've found that

gets them every time or a role you take on in the bedroom, such as being a demanding diva or a submissive princess, that feels completely natural to you. Basically, anything you adore doing.

Wow – it gets better. How do I discover mine?

Start by thinking about all the times you've had really fantastic mind-blowing sex. Try to pin down exactly which aspect you loved, *why* you enjoyed it so much and what it would take to recreate that feeling. Also, think about your favourite fantasies: what really turns you on in your imagination, too.

'I really enjoy giving my boyfriend oral sex – I love the feeling of him sliding in and out of my mouth, the way he tenses his body, clutches my shoulders, touches my hair. The whole thing is such a turn-on for me that I'm convinced that's my signature move.'

Amy, 33, club promoter

So it needs to be something I feel really confident doing?

Definitely. Confidence is key to your sex signature but you'll probably find you're naturally confident with your favourite move or position, as this is what makes you so good at it. Confidence in bed is always up at the top of the turn-on tables for men.

What happens if I discover more than one?

Lucky you! You'll probably find your current partner favours one move over the others but that needn't stop you using a combination of the activities you enjoy the most.

So my sexual signature's about both of us having maximum fun?

Exactly. The better you are at some-thing, the more you enjoy it, the more into it you become and the more it turns you and, as a result of your sexpertise, him on. Simple, eh?

> **Cosmo tip:**
> If there's something he does in bed that really turns you on, pay him loads of compliments about it. It's a great way to make *his* sex signature something *you* love.

SIXTY-NINE
See also: oral sex for him, oral sex for you.

This 69 technique – where you give and receive oral sex at the same time – can be tricky to master because, if you're in the throes of passion, it's difficult to concentrate on what your tongue's doing at the other end. It's worth persevering with, though, as it's an incredibly intimate act and can be a huge turn-on for both of you. Don't make orgasm (especially simultaneous) your ultimate goal here: just lose yourself in the eroticism of it all and, if you both come together, even better!

Perfect 69 Positions

You on top
This is the most common position – and the most fun for you. He lies back on the bed while you crouch over him facing his feet. Put your hands flat on the bed, either side of his body, and slowly lean down so you reach his penis with your mouth. Next, resting on your elbows, gently lower your bottom down until your man can touch your genitals with his tongue.

Cosmo tip:
Next time you fancy some lazy oral ask for a '68'. It means 'go down on me and I'll owe you one'.

Why it works: With you on top, you have ultimate control of the speed and depth of his penis and his tongue. Try rocking your pelvis in time with the licks you're giving his penis. The blood also rushes to your nipples, so they'll be extra-sensitive.

Side by side
This works well if you're of different heights. You both lie on your sides facing each other but in opposite directions (heads to feet). Raise your top leg and let your man rest his head on your inner thigh. Move your head in towards him and take his penis in your mouth. He then reaches forwards to stimulate your clitoris and vagina with his tongue. If he's taller, he'll have to curl up to reach you.
Why it works: This is an extremely comfortable position and, as neither of you is particularly dominant here, both of you will be able

to concentrate on giving and receiving pleasure.

Him on top

He straddles you in the same way as you did in the first position (facing your feet). He then lowers his penis into your mouth and concentrates on your genitals. This position takes a lot of trust as he's effectively thrusting into your mouth. You may need to use your hand to control him.

Why it works: Your movements are restricted by his body, which means you can focus entirely on the genitals.

Cosmo tip:
Take pleasure in his pleasure: try looking at his feet while you're performing fellatio – if he's curling his toes it's a sign things are about to get explosive!

For Adventurous Girls Only: The Upside-Downer

This position is only for the truly adventurous and requires practice. He sits on the edge of the bed with his feet flat on the floor and lies backwards. Resting on your elbows, lie on top of him in the basic 69 position. He then shifts forwards so your head (and his penis) are over the edge of the bed. Get him to lift his head slightly and lock your legs behind his head with your thighs resting on his shoulders. As he supports you, holding you tightly around the waist in a hugging position, hold on to him by locking your arms underneath his knees. Then, and this is the tricky bit, get him to sit up slowly – still holding you tightly – so you're lifted upside down. The blood rushes to your head as you go down on each other, causing an amazingly stimulating – not to mention novel – sensation. Be very careful he doesn't drop you!

Cosmo tip:
Try the one-minute game: in any 69 position, you take it in turns to give pleasure for sixty seconds each until you're both ready to climax.

SIZE MATTERS?

See also: arousal, erection, penis

It's the eternal debate: does size matter?

To him: probably

Penises of porn-movie proportions plus the super-confident donkey-sized lad in the male changing rooms at school are usually the only things heterosexual males have had to compare themselves with. Let's get two things straight here: (1) porn actors aren't usually cast for their beautiful eyes: size does matter in the porn industry, so it's an unfair comparison; (2) while getting changed after a vigorous game of five-a-side, the quick glance left or right in the shower is likely to be of a flaccid rather than erect penis; proportionally, a man with a baby's arm between his legs will grow less when he becomes erect than a man with a baby sweetcorn – in other words, he's either a grower or a show-er.

To you: no

If he's at either end of the size spectrum, he's likely to be self-conscious about his manhood, so be kind to him whatever size he is. Width usually matters more to women than length and an overly large penis can be painful or uncomfortable in certain positions, so, if your partner is well endowed, be prepared to try a few new moves. If he's a tiddler he doesn't need you to point that out to him, either.

Pole Positions

For Mr Big
Go for: Any position where you're on top so you can control the speed and depth of thrusting. Make sure you're extremely well lubricated and gently insert his penis inch by inch. Use your hands to guide him in as far as is comfortable for *you*. Remember, the top third of his penis (and your vagina) is the most sensitive part, so that's the important bit.
Avoid: Doggy style or any sex from behind. This offers the deepest penetration and his penis may bang against your cervix

at the top of your vagina, causing pain and discomfort.
Turn-on twist: Try having side-on sex in front of a full-length mirror. He'll love to watch his pride and joy sliding in and out of you. It's a pretty impressive sight for you, too!

For Mr Average

Go for: Any experimental positions you haven't tried before. Mr Average won't fall out of you or thrust too deeply, so pretty much any position you both enjoy will work. Try having sex with you sitting on the edge of a table top with your legs wide open. If you can, lean back or try closing your legs for a different sensation.

Avoid: Any comparisons with ex-boyfriends who were bigger than he is. Saying 'Doggy style is so much better with you because Dave/Graham/Donkey Kong used to bash my cervix' will make him shrivel faster than a snowflake on a bonfire.

Turn-on twist: Worshipping his willy with words will really turn him on. Try phrases like 'you're so hard', 'you really fill me up', 'I want you inside me' and watch him grow.

For Mr Slim Jim

Go for: Positions where you keep your legs flat and together, as these tighten the vaginal canal. Try lying flat on your front with your legs straight while he penetrates you from behind. Squeeze your pelvic floor muscles when he's inside you to tighten your grip around him.

Avoid: Positions where you open your legs wide, which creates more space in the vaginal canal (although, if you have the opposite problem and his extra-width is causing concern, opening your legs as wide as possible is the solution).

Turn-on twist: Get him to hold down your hands in a make-believe 'can't get away' scenario. It'll get the adrenaline pumping for both of you.

For Mr Cute-but-Perfectly-Formed (a.k.a. Mr Small)

Go for: Doggy style with you kneeling in front of him offers deep penetration and he can stimulate your clitoris with his hands. Alternatively, lie on your back with your knees up against your chest: this shortens and tightens your vagina so he'll feel bigger inside you. Also, try rocking motions rather than the traditional in-and-out thrusts. That way his pelvic bone hits your clitoris, making up for lack of internal action.

Avoid: The missionary position or anything where your legs are flat rather than tipped upwards. Shallow thrusts won't really do anything for either of you.

Turn-on twist: He'll adore oral sex and, because of his slight proportions, he won't be too much to handle.

SLOW HIM DOWN
See under: delay tactics

Need to slow down his need for speed in the bedroom? See **delay tactics** for ways to make him last longer.

SPANKING
See also: bondage, fantasy, role play

Spanking is the cheeky side of bondage: it's naughty, sexy and fun. If you've been a 'very naughty girl' an occasional slap on the bottom can be extremely arousing, as it brings the blood to the surface of the skin, making you more sensitive. Although spanking can be as heavy or as light as you like, we're talking moderate pain here: enough to tantalise and titillate but not enough to cause serious damage or extreme discomfort. Fancy a little hanky spanky? Read on . . .

Spanking Safety: Before You Start

• Agree a safe word that means 'stop' with your lover. Choose something neutral like 'orange' instead of a word like 'no', which can mean the opposite in the heat of the moment.

• Avoid the kidneys (lower back), neck, joints and head when spanking to avoid doing damage to the body. Fleshy parts such as the buttocks are your best target.

• If you're using a new spanking tool (the back of a hairbrush, for example), always try it out on your own hand first. As a general rule, the shorter the instrument, the easier it is to control (so don't go for the Indiana Jones-style bull whips straight off . . .)

• Never use anything that will cause serious pain or break the skin.

• Agree your limits before you start the game. By discussing how far you want to go, you should both feel secure during your session.

SEX FACT: *The harder and narrower the implement, the more pain it delivers. Avoid canes, rules and riding crops, as these can inflict real damage. Go for something light and bendy such as your underwear or a cheque book instead.*

Spanking: Your Back-to-Basics Masterclass

What you need: The place to yourselves (spanking can be noisy!), massage oil, something to spank with – use either your hand or a light flexibe implement like a fly swat or a pair of leather gloves.

'Those big paddle hair brushes are the best spanking tools I've found: they make a great noise when you whack 'em but they don't cause that much pain (and you can buy them in a chemist without feeling embarrassed!)'

Emma, 28, decorator

Your Go-for-it Guide

1) Order your partner to kneel on all fours on the bed. This is often easier if you take on a role, say as a slave mistress, while he's your servant.

2) Position yourself behind him and start to apply massage oil to his legs and back. Using long sweeping strokes, run your

hands all over his body, being careful not to touch his bottom or his genitals.

3) Increase the pressure of your massage and, this time, run your hands over his buttocks. Warn him that if he moves or makes a sound he'll face the consequences.

4) Prepare his bottom for the pleasure/pain you're about to deliver by gently pinching and kneading it. This brings the blood to the surface, making it more sensitive to your touch. It also allows the brain to release endorphins that dull pain receptors and bring out a feeling of euphoria, enabling him to take more punishment.

5) Try a few light slaps to start with. If he moves or disobeys your command, spank him once or twice on the thighs and bottom. Tell him he's been a *very* naughty boy. Gradually build up your smacking sensations, increasing only when your lover indicates he can take more. The more he's turned on, the higher his pain threshold becomes, so he'll be able to take more punishment if he really gets into it.

SEX FACT! *According to scientific research, redheads have a lower pain threshold than blondes and brunettes due to the hormones that create red hair. They need a fifth more anaesthetic than other hair types.*

6) Next, set him some (impossible-to-answer) questions. Ask him, for example 'What number am I thinking of?' or 'How many sex positions are we going to try tonight?' or 'Do you like pain?' Every time he gets something wrong, spank him again. Even if he guesses right, change the question slightly so his answer becomes wrong. If he complains or whines that 'it's not fair', spank him again for being disobedient.

7) Occasionally let him get a question right. This time, kiss and caress his buttocks but not for long: if he moans with pleasure, slap him back into submission. (If he stays silent, slap him for not being appreciative enough: you get the picture!)

8) Vary this nice-girl/nasty-girl routine so he never knows what's coming next: a good spanking or a caring caress. When you think the game is coming to a climax, slip your hand between

his legs and touch his testicles and penis: he should be highly aroused.

9) Swap roles and start the game all over again: remember, this time he gets his revenge!

10) When you're both ready, let him enter you from behind, leaving your bottom exposed – perfect position for hanky-spanky sex.

SAFETY INFO: Never strike in anger. Sex play is fun and a controlled game, not an excuse to hurt someone.

Spanking for Very Naughty Girls: Advanced Tips

Random spanking

Don't just save a good spanking for the bedroom. While you're watching television, position yourself on the sofa so you're lying across his knees – the perfect position for him to give you a good clothes-on spanking. Sometimes just lifting your skirt up while you're doing the washing-up and having him slap you through your knickers can be arousing.

'Bad' day at work

If you're sure everyone's gone home for the day try this sexy spanking game. Have him sit at his desk (or the boss's if you dare) and pretend to be your boss. You are his humble secretary who keeps making mistakes with her typing.

> **Cosmo tip:**
> Alternate spanks with kisses or tender touches. This can feel incredibly intimate and sensitive. As spanking heightens physical sensations all over the body, don't just concentrate on the area you've been paddling: focus your kisses and caresses on other parts of the body, too.

He asks you in to explain yourself but won't take any excuses. You must be punished and he asks you to bend over the desk. He then gives you a few spanks and orders you to get it right next time. You may be ordered to perform more sexual favours before your punishment is over. If you don't have the guts to try this in the office, playing the same game at home over the dining room table can be just as fun. (Watch the saucy film *Secretary* to see the inspiration for this game.)

The tickle-me tango

Lay your man on his front, face down, and tickle his back, inner thighs and bottom with a selection of different objects – a feather, a silk scarf, a stocking, a lacy bra, rubber gloves, a string of pearls or anything that takes your fancy. Get him to guess the object. If he guesses right, reward him with a kiss. If he guesses wrong, spank him with the object. If he's clever and enjoys being spanked by a particular object, he'll consistently get that object wrong.

SEX FACT: *In the build-up to orgasm your body will be able to tolerate more pain because it releases endorphins as part of the arousal process, which block pain receptors. After orgasm, you'll be more sensitive to pain, so go easy!*

Sexual spanking

A slap on the buttocks (or across your bits) during sex can be extremely arousing. Try slapping his bottom during the missionary position (or any position where he's on top) or squeezing and slapping his buttocks and balls while you're giving him oral sex. He can try gently slapping your vulva while he licks your clitoris or spanking your bottom when you're on top. Try matching your spanking speeds to the speeds of thrusting/licking for a coordinated turn-on.

'I love having sex on all fours with my lover behind me. He spanks my bottom in time to his thrusts. It's incredibly erotic and, although I feel quite submissive, the fact that he knows he's turning me on is great for both of us!'
Jeanette, 27, designer

SPEED HIM UP
See also: delay tactics

You've been there for a while. You've had your climax. You're pretty sure there aren't any more on the way, but he's still there thrusting and pumping away as if there were no tomorrow. You're starting to feel a little uncomfortable, your mind's wandering and, quite frankly, you could do with getting some sleep.

OK, scratch the cynicism. Let's put it a nicer way: if you want to up your man's arousal levels so he has the mother of all climaxes (and fast) here's how:

Rear-entry heaven

Sex positions where he penetrates you from behind give him deep penetration, which makes many men climax quickly. Try switching to you on your hands and knees from other positions for a speedy finale. Added bonus: you can rest your body weight on your elbows if you get tired.

Talk him through it

Many men find talky dirty extremely arousing. By telling him that he's giving you immense pleasure with what he's doing, and talking him through every dirty detail, you'll be stimulating parts of his brain he never thought he had. Talk about how it feels to be thrust into, how you love to feel him deep/shallow/fast/slow etc. The idea is to talk him up into a frenzied crescendo.

Hit the spot

The male G-spot (see **G-spot – male**) is the prostate gland, which is situated inside his body under the bladder and next to the rectum. Massaging this spot either internally (via a finger up his bottom) or externally by pressing on his perineum (the patch of skin between his balls and his anus) can trigger a climax more quickly than you can say Jordan-stripped-naked.

Fiddle with his fantasies

If you've discussed his favourite fantasy, even if you're not ready to act it out, try talking him through it while you're having sex to spark his brain to an even higher state of arousal. If he wants to have sex in front of an audience, try describing how that's making you feel; if he wants another women with you, describe exactly what she'd be doing to both of you. Use the present tense to make it seem as if it were happening right here, right now, and colour the fantasy with sensual detail. The more his brain is occupied with naughty thoughts, the faster his climax will be. (You can also use this technique inside your own head with your favourite fantasies if you want to up your own arousal levels.)

SPERM
See also: penis, semen

Sperm, those determined little swimmers, make up just 10 per cent of the fluid that is ejaculated from the penis, but be warned: each millilitre of ejaculate contains between 50 and 150 million of the little blighters. Sperm are produced in the seminiferous tubules (tubes in the testicles), then transported to the seminal vesicles, a kind of holding house near the bladder, before being combined with seminal fluid and projected out of the penis during ejaculation.

SEX FACT! *According to research conducted by the University of Valencia in Spain, good-looking men have better-quality sperm than ugly men (not that this should influence your choice of partner!).*

SPIT OR SWALLOW?
See also: oral sex for him

Womankind has been debating this question from the dawn of time. Here's the final word:

- Never feel forced into swallowing. Although many men find it sexy, if it's not your thing, don't feel obliged. It's the coming-in-your-mouth part that men really like. What you do with it afterwards doesn't really matter that much.
- If you do swallow, don't pull a 'yuck' face. Imagine how you'd feel if he tasted you, then looked as if he'd just sucked a lemon.
- If you're going to spit, try to be discreet – brushing your face against the duvet or using a strategically placed glass from the side of the bed is more subtle than a manic dash to the bathroom.
- If you can't bear his semen in your mouth at all, try switching to intercourse at the crucial moment. Or massage him to a climax with your hands, against your cheek or between your breasts.

- Alternatively, using a condom throughout the whole process will circumvent the entire debate.

SEX FACT: *Although it may feel like a gallon, men usually release around a teaspoon of ejaculate only.*

STRIPPING

See also: body confidence, undressing

Learning to lose your clothes the professional way can be a turn-on for both you and him. Follow our layer-by-layer seduce-him-now guide. Getting naked has never been so much fun.

Stripping: Your Back-to-Basics Masterclass

Perfect Preparation
The outfit

Dress to impress: choose the underwear *you* feel attractive in. The key to a good performance is to feel sexy and confident. It also needs to be easy to take off, so front-fastening bras are good, or try a silky negligée you can slip off your shoulders. Next, think about clothes that won't get stuck on your head or around your hips. Think Velcro, zips, jackets and skirts that will slip down easily. Heels are a must: they lengthen your legs and make them look slimmer. A long thin scarf or old school tie is the perfect accessory for beginners – have one within reach.

The music

Again, this needs to be chosen to boost your confidence rather than entertain him. *Full Monty* classics or old show tunes are great for a showgirl performance. Sexy R&B lets you bump and grind. Pop or dance tunes tend to be too fast – make sure you choose something slow and sensual.

The rehearsal

The only way to build confidence is to practise in front of a full-length mirror. Look at the mirror as if it were your 'audience' – full eye contact throughout your performance is essential. Watch the way your body moves; see what it looks like from different angles. Enjoy the sensuality of watching yourself touch your own body (that way you'll appear much more sensual in the real thing).

Cosmo tip:
Look out for stripping classes in your local paper or online. Learning how to dance erotically is a great fitness workout and a fantastic way to boost your sexual confidence.

Your Go-for-it Guide

Once you've rehearsed your routine you're ready to go for it.

Step one: Sit your man on a chair or the bed and instruct him that he can look but not touch. Those are the house rules and, if he breaks them, the show's over.

Step two: Start by moving to the music and touching your body through your clothes, as if everything you're wearing is incredibly sensual (it helps if it is!). Undo a few buttons on your jacket and slowly slip it off your shoulders, pulling it around your body as it goes (as if there were hidden treasure inside). The idea is to handle each item of clothing as if you really didn't want it to come off, which makes you perform more slowly. Let it sensually slip down your shoulders and drop to the floor.

Step three: Do the same with your shirt or top underneath your jacket, removing it slowly and sensually. Unbutton your shirt from the bottom up so you reveal your breasts last. Undo the cuffs, then slide off one sleeve at a time. Once this is off, spend time touching your body through your underwear, feeling the fabric and teasing your man.

'I'll never forget the time Sarah stripped for me. When she appeared wearing my jacket and suspenders, I was shocked at first – she's usually self-conscious about her body but she looked gorgeous and she knew it. The mixture of surprise and domination led to the best sex we'd ever had.'
Richard, 28, publisher

Step four: Next turn round and sexily wiggle your bottom in his direction, looking over your shoulder coyly as you do this. Unzip your skirt and let it fall to the floor as you wriggle out of it. Step out of it when it's hit the floor or kick it to one side.

Step five: This is where a scarf or tie comes in handy. Put it round your neck, running it seductively between your breasts. Play with it as much as you can: turn round and rub it across your bottom, twine it round your hands, lick it, rub it backwards and forwards between your legs and over your skin. Place it round his neck if you can and pull yourself towards him. The point here is to delay taking your underwear off for as long as possible.

Step six: Once you've played long enough it's time for your bra to come off. Slip the straps coyly down over your shoulders and undo the clasp. Try holding one arm in front of your breasts (covering them up) and slowly pulling your bra from one side with the other hand.

Step seven: With your arm covering your assets, walk right up to your man and very slowly reveal your breasts to him, holding one in each hand (this creates a killer cleavage).

Step eight: When your breasts are fully revealed, back away from him. Shoes next: mules are easy to slip out of and kick to one side. If you have ankle straps, lean down sideways onto your man and unstrap them slowly while maintaining eye contact.

Step nine: If you're wearing stockings, roll them down your legs extremely slowly, pulling them off your toes (this gives you two more 'scarves' to play with).

Step ten: To remove your knickers, slide your hands underneath them at the sides (with your palms flat). Toy with him a little by pulling them down a bit and back up again, then, with flat palms, slip them down to your knees. They should fall to the floor of their own accord from there. When they hit the floor, daintily step out of them one foot at a time. You are now naked. It's up to you how long you make the look-but-don't-touch routine last.

> **Cosmo tip:**
> Fake tan, a trimmed bikini line and perfect make-up will all boost your confidence. Use bronzer or blusher on your nipples to enhance their colour.

Sizzling Tips to Sex It Up

Surprise him
Surprise your man by wearing something that wouldn't normally be in your wardrobe: if all your underwear is the sporty, white cotton type, invest in a basque or coloured lacy bra and G-string to show off the first time you strip.

Think attitude

Imagine you are your favourite sexy character, say Samantha in *Sex and the City* or Madonna in her raunchier days, and take on her attitude – walk her walk, talk her talk. Getting into a role boosts your confidence and allows you to behave in a way the 'real you' wouldn't dare to.

SEX FACT: *One in six British men goes to strip shows.*

Tie him down

If you don't trust your man to abide by the look-but-don't-touch rule, try tying him loosely to a chair. This allows you to get really up close and personal and shows that you're in control of the show. At the end of your show, strip him and lower yourself on to his erect penis while he's still tied down – it's the ultimate power trip.

'The first time I stripped for Simon, I couldn't stop laughing but it was actually the most sensual, arousing thing I've ever done. Although I was conscious of my body, judging by his reaction the last thing on his mind was my cellulite!'
Rachel, 26, receptionist

SWINGING
See also: group sex, threesomes

Also known as wife-swapping, swinging involves swapping partners with another couple or a set of like-minded people, usually at a private party. You then watch your partner have sex with someone else, both go off to different rooms with new partners or join in with other people in the same room. Swinging was made famous by 1970s key parties where partners threw all their car keys into a bowl, picked out a set at random and had sex with the owner of the keys they picked. These days there are clubs, hotels and even entire travel companies involved in the scene. The Internet has also made it much easier to seek out like-minded couples: just type in 'swingers' or 'swinging' and your home town and see what comes up, or look in the personals pages of local papers.

Swinging, like any group sex activity, shouldn't be entered into lightly, so, if you're into the idea, read the **group sex** and **threesome** sections first for things you should think about before you dangle those car keys.

SYPHILIS
See under: sexually transmitted infections

A bacterial infection still rare among heterosexual couples but on the increase.

TANTRIC SEX
See also: multiple orgasms

Hang on – isn't that what Sting does?
Oh, yes. Sting is said to be into Tantric sex, but don't let that put you off.

OK, I won't. What's it all about, then?
Tantric sex is an ancient spiritual sexual practice based on sacred Indian texts, the Tantras, which date from around the fifth century. It was originally a system of meditations practised by both Buddhists and Hindus that covered the whole of life and not just sex. These days, Tantra has evolved into a kind of spiritual sexual yoga.

Right, so lots of breathing and mangling your body into different positions, then?
It's a bit more complicated than that. Like yoga, it's about harmonising the body and soul and making them work together. Central to Tantra is the belief that the universe is made up of male and female forces, which need to be reunited within the body. Tantric sex is a way to unify these forces and experience ecstasy along the way. You do this by prolonging sexual arousal and delaying orgasm for as long as possible.

What, so you're at it for hours?

You can be and it's certainly about making time for lovemaking. Tantric sex involves learning a series of exercises and rituals that helps build spiritual connections between you and your partner. Breathing and touch techniques are essential and you need to experience both giving and receiving pleasure for their own sakes, not just as a route to orgasm.

Hmm. Doesn't it get boring?

Well, there are a lot of breathing techniques, stroking rituals and nongenital touching involved before you actually get down to the sex, which is never fast and furious. You need time, dedication and patience to master it properly but you will become highly attuned to each other. Lots of the exercises teach you to focus on enjoying the moment rather than letting your mind wander. Some couples find it's incredibly arousing and deepens the spiritual connection between them.

Not something for a one-night stand, then?

No. Mastering the correct techniques can take years, so it's only for the truly dedicated; but serious practitioners say it not only revolutionises their sex lives but changes the whole of their lives for the better.

Any other selling points?

Well, it can also help men achieve multiple orgasms and both of you experience full-body orgasms where the body and brain are flooded with orgasmic sensations that can last much longer than your everyday climax.

Ooh – that sounds like fun. How do we get started?

There are hundreds of books available on Tantric sex and, if you're really interested, one of the best ways to get into it is to go on a course. Look up Tantra on the Internet and you'll find a huge amount of info available.

Right, I'm off to breathe deeply and look into my partner's eyes for three hours

Good luck . . .

TALKING DIRTY

See also: communication, fantasy, phone sex

Talking Dirty: Your Back-to-Basics Masterclass

Step one: If you've never so much as squeaked at the point of orgasm, start off slowly with a few 'oooh's and 'ahhh's and 'that feels good's'. If he's not used to your being vocal, *anything* you say will sound great.

Step two: Sexy talk is all about vocal tone and pace. Slow your voice right down, making it much lower and quieter than normal. That way he has to lean into you to hear what you're saying. The way you breathe is also extremely important – sounding out of breath and pausing suggestively lets his imagination go wild.

Step three: Start with language you and your man use already before adding in some raunchy slang once you've built up your confidence. Be flirty and saucy, then slip in a naughty word here and there as a taste of things to come.

Step four: Now try saying something like, 'I love it when you touch me'. From there it's an easy step to becoming more descriptive with something like 'I love it when you touch my breasts . . . with soft slow strokes . . . caressing my skin . . . yes, just like that . . .' This is a fantastic way to teach your lover what you like and turn him on at the same time.

> '*Men always want to hear what a great job they're doing. I say things like "You're the best. You make me feel so hot. I need you. Don't stop." It makes them feel empowered and confident.*'
>
> Christy, 30, phone-sex-line operator

Step five: Next, ask your partner some questions about what he'd like you to do. Saying, 'Would you like it if I licked you slowly from here, to here?' sounds just as raunchy as 'I'm going to lick you from here to here'. Added bonus: you'll also find out what he really wants you to do in bed.

Step six: Try using the present tense to describe exactly what you're doing to your man (or yourself). Practise this next time you masturbate – just describe what you're doing to yourself as if you were talking to your man. It's amazing how easy it is once you get used to it. The next step is to do this in front of him – scary but very sexy . . .

Step seven: Describe what you're doing to each part of his body using language that gets dirtier and naughtier as your actions get more and more raunchy. If your language mirrors the rudeness of what you're doing, talking about it should come (ahem) more naturally.

Step eight: Once you've mastered exactly what you and your man find exciting, use your raunchy lines to talk in time with your lovemaking. Choose your words carefully, talking rhythmically and mirroring the pace of your sexy session. Bring him to the brink of orgasm before pulling the verbal trigger with a line you know he always falls for. (See the box below for some wicked inspiration.)

Four-Letter Phwoar-play: Advanced Tricks

His 'n' hers fantasy

Take turns to describe different parts of a fantasy that turns you both on. Start with something like, 'I'm in the desert and it's so hot . . .', then ask your man to take up the story. He might follow it with something like, 'It's burning up, the sweat's dripping from your breasts and your back, trickling down your body . . .' Take turns to say a sentence each to build up the fantasy from there. When you get used to this format, describe longer parts of the fantasy to each other, getting into every raunchy detail.

> **Cosmo tip:**
> If, when you start describing your fantasies, your man comes up with something you really don't like the sound of, simply take control of the talk and steer the fantasy in a different direction.

Fairytale fabrication

If you can't think of a fantasy, try telling a traditional fairy story with added rude bits. Raunching up what Prince Charming and Cinderella got up to at the ball or what happened when Little Red Riding Hood saw the big . . . *bad* . . . wolf . . . can be just as fun as a made up fantasy. Use the story to talk about things you'd really like to have done to *you*! (cunning but it works).

Lust letters

If you're still nervous, try writing an erotic lust letter to your lover. Just imagine you're together or masturbating and write down every dirty detail of what you're doing and how you're feeling. Be

Cosmo tip:
Some couples find it easier to start talking over the phone rather than face to face. Next time he's away for the night, try it and see . . .

extremely complimentary about his technique to give him an ego boost. Either send it to your lover or read it aloud next time you're together.

Wicked Words to Whisper Seductively
'I'm not wearing any knickers.'
'Mmm, I love the way you taste.'
'I need you in me.'
'You feel so big . . . so hard . . .'
'I want you in my mouth.'
'You feel sooo good inside me.'
'That feels so sexy.'
'This is my first time' (when he knows it isn't).
'You make me wet.'
'You were amazing last night.'
'I'm a dirty girl – are you dirty, too?'
'You really know how to turn me on.'
'Don't come before me, that's so good, I want more.'
'I'm coming, oh yes, I'm coming' (but only if you *are* climaxing!).

TESTICLES
See also: ball play, masturbation for him, penis

The Science Bit: What They're For

As you probably know, men have two testicles (the right one usually hangs slightly lower then the left), which are contained inside a flexible bag of skin called the scrotal sac. They produce sperm, which, along with other fluids, are ejaculated when he climaxes. To produce sperm, they need to be at a slightly lower temperature than the rest of the body which is why they're outside the body (rather than inside like the ovaries, the female equivalent). They're also an often-ignored erogenous zone: see **ball play** for foxy fondling techniques.

SEX FACT: *Each testicle produces up to 150 million sperm every 24 hours*

The Sensible Bit: How to Check Them

Men should check their testicles once a month for unusual lumps and bumps, which may be signs of testicular cancer. The bad news? Testicular cancer is the biggest cause of cancer-related death in 15–35 year old men. The good news? It's usually 100 per cent curable if caught early. As only 3 per cent of men bother to check their bits regularly, give him a helping hand by doing it for him. After he's had a bath or shower, cup his balls in the palm of your hand, leaving your fingers free to investigate the area. Feel their weight and size. Feel around for any pea-sized lumps, swellings, tenderness or unusual hardening of the surface. If you do find anything don't panic – most lumps are not cancerous. Just make sure he gets it checked out by a doctor.

SEX FACT: *Testicles rise up against his body when he's cold or about to climax.*

TESTOSTERONE
See under: hormones

Sex hormone responsible for libido levels in men and, to a lesser extent, women.

THREESOMES
See also: group sex.

If you reckon two's company and three's a climax you might want to try a threesome. Threesomes usually involve a couple inviting someone else (either male or female) to join them having sex. This can be a friend, a stranger from the Internet or a personal ad, or a sex worker. Although having sex with two women is an extremely common fantasy for many men, turning it into reality can be tricky. The same goes for women: having two men (or another woman as well as your partner) worshipping your body may feel like a great idea in your head but, in practice, actually negotiating all those breasts and penises can be harder, both physically and mentally.

SEX FACT: *Most sex therapists agree that the reality of a threesome is never as exciting as the fantasy.*

Often, the reality of the situation can throw up all sorts of complicated emotions involving jealousy, insecurity and guilt. For some couples it can be a huge turn-on. Some people try out a three-way just for the experience, often at the beginning of a relationship or as a part of a one-night stand – and that can make great future fantasy material (or a fantastic story to tell your friends). For others it's a regular part of their sex lives.

> **Cosmo tip:**
> A rocky relationship will not be enhanced by the addition of a third party. Think about your motivations carefully before you go for it.

SAFETY INFO: *Never agree to sexual experimentation such as a threesome when you're drunk or on drugs. You may feel slightly more sexually confident but it will blur your judgement.*

If you fancy a threesome, ask yourself these questions:
1) Is our relationship secure enough to handle a third party?
2) Do we both want to do this as much as each other or is one partner feeling obliged to go through with it?
3) What are the rules? Is kissing allowed? Oral sex? Penetration? Who is going to do what to whom?
4) What's going to happen afterwards – is the third party staying the night?
5) How will we handle our relationship with the third party afterwards? (Sometimes involving friends is more tricky than inviting a no-strings stranger into bed with you.)
6) Do we have enough condoms handy?
7) What lasting effects will this have on our relationship?

'My boyfriend watched me give oral sex to another woman we'd met in a club. I'd never done anything like that before but I was so into what I was doing, I hardly knew he was there. It was an amazing experience. We're happily married now but hiring the occasional female escort is a once-a-year treat for us.'
Carla, 25, receptionist.

Go through with it only after you've thought about all these questions carefully. If you just fancy the *idea* of a threesome rather than the reality, see the **group sex** section for some fantastic ideas on how to get the enjoyment of a pretend third party without actually involving real-life flesh and blood.

'I once went back to a hotel room with two men – it seemed like a laugh at the time and I don't remember much about the actual sex as I was quite drunk, but I felt quite ashamed and used afterwards. I wouldn't do it again.'
Melanie, 21, student

THRUSH
See under: genito-urinary infections

A common yeast infection sometimes triggered (although not always) by sexual contact.

TOYS
See also: household objects, masturbation for you, vibrators

Sex toys are:	Sex toys aren't:
• a great way to extend your sexual repertoire and learn about your sexual responses.	• addictive: although you might reach for your Rampant Rabbit on a regular basis, there is no research to suggest that you'll need a trip to the Priory any day soon.
• a fantastic fast route to orgasm whether you're single or coupled up.	• a man-replacement: fingers, tongues and his own long john are a different pleasure altogether.
• a form of totally safe sex (when used on your own – if you're sharing with a partner wash carefully or use a condom over your toy).	• any good at cuddling, making you laugh (although some look hysterical), asking you how your day was or telling you how great your new haircut is.

Cosmo tip:
Concerned about noise? As a general rule, the harder the vibrator, the noisier it'll be. Soft jelly vibes will be quieter (but probably less powerful) than hard plastic ones.

First-time Sex Toy Buyers' Guide

1. Think about the kind of stimulation you like and where you want to use a toy. Are you looking for clitoral stimulation (usually the easiest route to orgasm for most women), or do you want vaginal penetration or anal pleasure? (Some toys have attachments that can tickle all three, but many people find these too much of a fiddle. Often two separate toys is the answer.)

2. Think about size: if you've used a household object (like a hairbrush handle) use this as a guide to the size and shape you should go for. Alternatively, think about how many fingers feel comfortable inside you and base your choice on this.

3. If you're in a shop ask the staff: they're usually extremely knowledgeable, friendly and there to help. If you're shopping online read the catalogue info carefully to check you're buying something that suits your needs.

4. If you're in a shop, play with the toy on the inside of your wrist or the back of your neck to check the different speeds and sensations. (The skin is thin and packed with nerve endings in both these places, so it's a good substitute for more intimate areas.)

5. Don't spend loads of money the first time you buy. Yes, the 'bone' designed by Tom Dixon (a.k.a. Mr Habitat himself) may look amazing, but £199 is too much to spend on something that may spend all its time in the back of a cupboard.

6. Check battery requirements and, if buying a toy with recharge-able batteries, check charge times: sixty minutes of pleasure may require twelve hours of charging (which can be a ridiculously long time to wait!).

SEX FACT *Twenty-six per cent of women admit to using sex toys on a regular basis; 35 per cent of men admit to having experimented with a sex toy. This rises to 42 per cent of* **Cosmo** *readers' boyfriends. Hmmm, we wonder why . . .*

Toy Box Terms

Want to know what you're buying? Here's a brief rundown of the different types of toys available . . .

1) Vibrators

The most popular gadgets, vibrating toys, come in a myriad different shapes and sizes. The majority are penis-shaped or cylindrical and are designed to stimulate the clitoris, vaginal or anal area but can be used anywhere on the body. They're made of a variety of materials from hard plastic to jelly-like rubber or the more expensive silicone with a price range that's just as varied. Some are battery-operated, others are rechargeable or connected to the mains by a plug and cord. (These are often marketed as 'personal massagers' rather than vibrators, so you may not find them in sex shops.) Some are designed for internal play, others for external use only, so check what you're buying. Some, such as the notorious Rampant Rabbit, have two parts: one for vaginal stimulation, the other for clitoral action. Many have different speeds or changeable heads or attachments so you can change the pace and sensations. See the **vibrators** main section for more detailed info.

2) Dildos

Penis-shaped toys similar to vibrators but without the, er, vibrations. Also available in all shapes, sizes, materials, colours and textures.

3) Anal toys

Many toys are designed specifically for anal pleasure while others can be adapted to stimulate the sensitive nerve endings in or around the anus. Butt plugs are basically dildos with flared bases specifically designed for insertion into the anus. They're usually conical or diamond-shaped, although some are ridged or smooth. See **anal sex** for more info.

SEX FACT: *In ancient China silk used to be bound round the penis to make cock rings.*

4) Cock rings

A cock ring is a small rubber, latex, plastic or sometimes metal ring that slips round the base of the penis, strengthening his erection and allowing him to stay harder for longer. Some have fancy attachments on the outside to give you extra pleasure; others vibrate for the same reason.

 SAFETY INFO: Never use a makeshift cock ring or use one that feels painful: the tissue is delicate in this area, so look after it!

5) Nipple clamps

These are usually small clamps (like the ones you used to use in physics at school) that clip on to the nipples. There are different strengths of clamp, some vibrate, some can be connected to chains or strings that can be pulled by you or your lover, others have weights hanging from them.

'Don't knock it till you tried it, I say. My husband gave me a vibrator on our honeymoon (God knows how he got it through customs!) and, although I was a little shy at first, after a few drinks we took turns to use it on each other. All I can say is, oh-my-god! He loved it too!'

Sinead, 34, public relations

6) Bondage treats

A huge array of handcuffs, blindfolds, harnesses, bondage tape, whips, chains and masks are on sale for those who want them. Rubber, latex and leather are all popular materials. See the **bondage** section for more info.

Back to Basics: Your New Toy Masterclass

Whether you're a sex-toy virgin who's just plucked up the courage to go plastic or a veteran who's purchased a brrrrrilliant new buy, check out this step-by-step guide to sex toy success:

Step 1: When you buy a new toy, it's best to experiment with it on your own first to get used to the new sensations. Set aside some time when you won't be disturbed and get comfy.

Step 2: Start by thinking yourself into a sexy frame of mind. Conjure up your favourite fantasies, think about the parts of your body you usually love to have touched.

Step 3: Then try caressing the less sensitive parts of your body with your toy on its lowest setting. Try your belly, the tops of your hands or the tops of your thighs.

Step 4: Next, move on to more sensitive areas where your skin is thin, such as the nape of your neck, the insides of your wrists or your inner thighs. Avoid your obvious erogenous zones such as your genitals and nipples at first. Note how each new area feels, and pay as much attention to what doesn't feel so good as to what does.

Step 5: Now try placing your toy over your genitals. You might want to try it over your knickers or covered in fabric first to dull the sensation while you get used to it. Experiment with different angles and pressures. You might need extra lubrication with your toy as it can dry you out.

Step 6: If you can hold back on your climax, try different positions and speeds. Try clutching the toy between your legs while using your hands on different parts of the body. Try rubbing it up your thighs and on to your vaginal lips or try lying on top of it. Standing up and bearing down on your toy can also be fun.

Step 7: Be careful not to overdo it. Although toys can't permanently damage sensitive vaginal or clitoral tissue, too much vibration too quickly can cause an uncomfortable drying and numbing sensation.

Step 8: Let yourself go! Some women are surprised at how quickly they climax when they first use a vibrator; others take time to get used to the sensations. If you have a quick-fire climax, try using the toy on less sensitive parts of the body to build up your arousal levels for orgasm number two.

Advanced action

Step 9: Try using more than one toy at once. Some women like using a vibrator around the clitoris while inserting a dildo or second vibrator into the vagina. Others like to feel vibrations around the anal area while using a second toy on the clitoris (might take some juggling to get that one right if you're on your own).

Toy Box Safety
• Always clean your toy with soap and water after you've used it. Some toys or attachments can be washed in dishwashers but check the instructions carefully. Never immerse non-water-safe toys in water: wipe with a damp cloth instead.
• Some sexually transmitted infections can be passed on through sharing sex toys. If you're using them with a new partner, cover

them with a condom.
• Never put a toy that's been used anally back into the vagina without washing it thoroughly first: it can cause infections.
• Never insert anything in the anus that doesn't have a flared base. A non-flared toy can be sucked upwards involuntarily, which could result in a trip to casualty. Ouch!
• Remove the batteries when you're not using your toy. (But make sure you keep your batteries hidden so they don't get used for the TV remote.)

SEX FACT: *The Hitachi Magic Wand, the best-selling sex toy of all time, was originally marketed as a body massager back in the 1970s but women soon found a much more satisfying use for it. It's still recommended by sex experts the world over.*

Partner Play: Sharing Your Toys

Introducing your partner to your little vibratable friend can be tricky but the rewards are potentially endless. Follow the step-by-step process in the New Toy Masterclass above, using each step on your partner rather than on you. Take it in turns to have control of the toy at each step, using it first for body massage, then getting closer and closer to each other's genitals. Follow these dos and don'ts for a successful session:

Dos	Don'ts
Talk to him outside the bedroom first and find out how he feels about toys. He may have an extreme reaction one way or the other.	Just reach under the bed mid-romp and bring your toy into the action on the spur of the moment.
Suggest he has a little play with your toy on his own so he gets used to how it works and how it feels on his body.	*Ever* compare his size with your toy's (even in jest!). Although your toy won't be touchy on the subject, your boyfriend might be.
Reassure him that your toy is not a boyfriend replacement: it's just an occasional enhancer for both of you.	Tell him that he couldn't give you an orgasm even if he was wired to the mains and set permanently on vibrate. A crushed ego does not a good lover make.

Tips 'n' Tricks to use With Your Partner – On Him

Count down: Try using a vibrating toy over different parts of his body and get him to rate the sensations on a turn-on scale, from one to ten – with ten being total ecstasy and one being zero arousal – to find out what he does and doesn't like.

Genius genital massage: Try using a vibrator on a low setting against his perineum (the patch of skin between his balls and his anus) and his testicles – both areas are packed with nerve endings.

Male clitoral action: Hold your toy against his frenulum (the little patch of skin on the underside of the penis where the head joins the shaft) – this area is sometimes called the male clitoris because it's so sensitive. Try keeping it still, then circling it around.

> **Cosmo tip:**
> Try playing around with temperature: some women like to keep their toys in the fridge for an oh-so-cold tingle.

Tips 'n' Tricks to use With Your Partner – On You

Show off!: Try masturbating in front of your partner, showing him exactly where you like to place your toy. Next put your hands over his and guide him to the right spot. A great position for this is for him to sit behind you, reaching around your body – intimate and cuddly.

SEX FACT: *Sixty-two per cent of* Cosmo *readers own a vibrator.*

Oral fun: While he's giving you oral sex, get him to use a vibrator as well as his tongue. Try his mouth around your clitoris with a vibrator around your vaginal lips or your anal areas. Alternate the areas his mouth and the toy touch. This takes some of the pressure off his tongue and can lead to a quicker climax for you (and less work for him).

Top-tastic: Any position where you're on top is fantastic for vibrator play, as there's enough room for you to place it over your clitoris. Take turns to run your toy around your clitoris, then over his

> **Cosmo tip:**
> Vibrators or dildos made from silicone warm up to your body temperature more quickly than the plastic varieties.

belly and back again. (He can teasingly torture you by pulling it away from your clitoris if he has control.)

For info on where to buy toys see 'Useful Addresses and Contacts' on p. 347.

SEX FACT: *Vibrators are often recommended by sex therapists to women who have never had an orgasm, because they often make climaxing easier.*

TRICHOMONAS
See also: sexually transmitted infections

A tiny single-cell organism that causes trichomoniasis, a vaginal infection in woman and a urethral infection in men, which can make you more susceptible to other STIs.

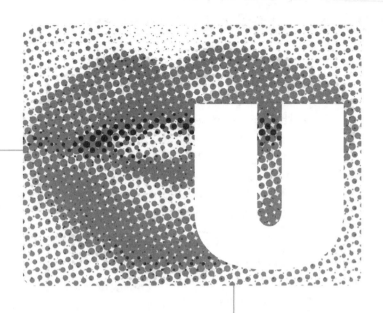

UNDERWEAR

See also: stripping

The Ten Underwear Commandments

1) Thou shalt buy lingerie for thyself, not him. The sexier and more comfortable you feel, the more confident you'll be in bed.

2) Thou shalt *never* wear grey underwear. Even if it's cool, sporty and the latest that Calvin Klein has to offer, men just don't get it.

3) Thou shalt enjoy underwear shopping as a form of foreplay or go underwear shopping together (and if he can sneak into the cubicle – well . . .!).

4) Thou shalt chuck out all emergency pants (and make him do the same).

5) Thou shalt never wear underwear that's too small: bulges never look good.

6) Thou shalt not be upset if he buys you the wrong colour/ size/type. Women's underwear is hell to buy even if you

'In my experience women wear gorgeous underwear to make themselves feel sexy rather than for men. Men just want you to take it off as soon as possible.'

Clara, 28, nurse

do know your exact bra size.

7) Thou shalt check the colour of thine underwear against thy skin-tone to see what suiteth thee. Some colours will look better than others.

8) Thou shalt leave a sexy item on in bed and touch thyself through it or get him to run his hands over it.

9) Thou shalt admit that stockings and suspenders are a huge male cliché. However, if he loves to see you in them, chances are they'll make you feel sexy too but . . .

10) Thou shalt never wear any underwear that maketh thee feel uncomfortable, embarrassed or degraded. If it doesn't boost your confidence, it's not worth the price tag.

'Wearing something raunchy under my suit at work gives me a kind of power buzz all day. I swear it makes me more assertive and decisive.'
Tracey, 36, publisher

UNDRESSING
See also: body confidence, lighting, stripping

Undressing sexily is an erotic art form and an often-ignored part of foreplay. The first step to making the most of it is to know how to tackle those tricky-to-remove items. The second is to match your peel-and-reveal routine to the mood you're in.

Here's how . . .

Tricky Togs
Use these make-things-easier tips for tricky garments to make sure they slide off sexily:
Bra bother
Bras are notoriously hard to undo, even after years of practice. Men often try the one-handed trick, which is an almost impossible feat. If he's having trouble unhooking you, for goodness' sake, give him a helping hand. Just get the clasp undone so he still gets the pleasure of actually removing your lingerie himself.

Knicker knack

The way to seductively remove your knickers (or his boxers) is to slide a hand down each side with your palms flat against your skin and shimmy them down to your knees. They should slip to the ground from there, where you can step out of them one foot at a time. This doesn't work quite so well if you're lying down, but remembering the one-foot-then-the-other rule does help.

Shirt tricks

Remember to undo all buttons, including cuffs, before you try taking this off. The sight of an open shirt is extremely erotic (on both you and him), so enjoy feeling the flesh underneath the fabric before removing it completely.

Trouser tactics

If you're taking his trousers off, it is possible (and sexy) to slide them over his feet by pulling them from the bottom, but attempt this *only* if they're loose-fitting. Getting stuck is not great for either of you. Ditto if he's removing your trews. Playing around with his thighs for as long as possible is also erotic. See **zip tricks** for more details.

Sock sins

Never *ever* leave a man in his underwear and socks. Same goes for you (so get him to remove his/your socks *before* you tackle the trousers).

Skirting issues

Skirts with elasticated waists will leave marks on your skin. Something you can unzip and let float down your body is ideal. Dresses should usually be taken over your head rather than shimmied down your body (think about how you get into it before you start a new way to get out of it!). Wraparound dresses are ideal so long as you have exquisite underwear on underneath.

Cosmo tip:
Leaving some clothes on while you have sex can be extremely arousing. Being semi-naked rather than totally in the buff can make a pleasant change and you'll be reminded of your sexy session every time you wear that item.

Undressing to Suit Your Mood

In The Mood For . . . Quickie Sex

Undressing style: fast 'n' furious: This is where you can throw all forms of decency and decorum out of the window (along with a few hastily discarded items of clothing). You're aiming to get hands on flesh as fast as you can. Enjoy the frenzied sensuality of the moment and remember that you don't have to be fully disrobed to have sex. The joy of a quickie is the delicious seediness of a skirt pulled up, a shirt ripped open and his trousers round his ankles. Enjoy this fast-paced frolic for exactly what it is.

In The Mood For . . . Emotional Intensity

Undressing style: slow, sensuous body appreciation: Constant eye contact and synchronised breathing will create the romantic connection you crave. Stand or sit in front of each other fully clothed and look deeply into each other's eyes. Slow your breathing right down and relax. Once you're breathing in time with each other, without losing eye contact, slowly let him remove one item of your clothing. Feel the sensuality of the fabric as it strokes against your body and falls to the floor and the tenderness of his fingertips as they move slowly against your skin. Now you remove an item of his clothing in the same way. Pay attention to the part of his body (or yours) that's revealed by each item. Once you're down to each other's underwear, you should both feel extremely relaxed. Gently remove each other's final garments and drink in each other's body. Finish this exercise with a full intense body-to-body hug. (You now have permission to get on with the rude stuff!)

'I love it when Mark undresses me. He's so caring and makes me feel like a total goddess. He even folds my clothes neatly! I think it's surrendering all that control to another person that's such a turn-on.'

Jill, 28, brand planner

In The Mood For . . . Total Control

Undressing style: he goes first (you stay clothed): You take control here and undress him while staying totally clothed yourself. Sit him on the bed and let him know that he's not allowed to move. As you remove each item of his clothing, kiss, caress, lick or massage the part of his body that's revealed. The idea is to concentrate on parts of his body that you wouldn't normally pay attention to: his arms, his midriff, the top of his back. Take things slowly, arousing each part of his body with your touch. When you remove his underwear, stay away from his penis for as long as possible. Stroke or lick his inner thighs, hips and buttocks. Finally, home in on his penis and lavish all your attention on it. With you still fully clothed, he'll feel slightly vulnerable, which can be arousing for both of you.

In The Mood For . . . Surrendering Control

Undressing style: passive passion: This time, *you're* the one who remains passive and he gets to undress you. Make sure he goes slowly and seductively, as you did before. He should give each part of your body full hands-and-mouth attention when it's revealed. Role play can really enhance this kind of undressing experience: imagine he's a sexy sultan and you're a nubile new member of his harem; you've never been touched by a man before so he has to teach you *everything*.

> **Cosmo tip:**
> If you're usually a whip-'em-off-quick kind of girl, hotel bedrooms are the ideal place to try something different because (1) they're usually small and compact, so you're bound to be close to each other, (2) you can usually control the lighting to make it as flattering as possible, and (3) if you're having a weekend away together, you're probably both relaxed and in the mood for romance or raunch.

UNPLEASANT SMELLS?

See also: genito-urinary infections, sexually transmitted infections

Any unusual or unpleasant smell around your genitals or his could indicate an untreated sexually transmitted infection or urinary-tract infection. See your local STI or GUM (genito-urinary medicine) clinic at your local hospital for a check-up.

Your vagina will smell subtly different at different times in your menstrual cycle. Don't be self-conscious about this: men often find the unique-to-you smell of your nether regions extremely arousing.

UNPROTECTED SEX
See also: condoms, sexually transmitted infections

Unprotected sex means any penetrative sexual activity (vaginal or anal) you have without using a condom. Having sex without a condom can cause unwanted pregnancy or the spread of sexually transmitted infections (STIs), which vary from the uncomfortable to the fatal. You can also contract some STIs without going all the way.

UPSIDE-DOWN SEX
See also: positions, x-rated positions

Want all the blood to rush to your head for a more intense, different kind of orgasm? Any position where your head is thrown backwards will create a light-headed sensation. The blood rushes to your head, making the muscles taut in the neck and head, which can heighten your orgasmic sensations.

Try these upside-down delights:
- Sit on the bed facing each other and wrap your legs around his while he penetrates you from the front (in the sexy lotus position). Now lean backwards so your head is dangling off the edge of the bed. Grinding is better than thrusting in this position, because, with your back arched, your clitoris should be exposed to his pubic bone.
- In the **reverse cowgirl** (where you're on top facing towards his feet), try lying backwards over his torso. You'll need to flex your back. His penis should then be hitting the sensitive front wall of the vagina.
- If you can do the crab yoga position (where you bend backwards arching your back with your hands and feet on the

floor), try holding this position while he gives you oral sex. It's tricky and you may not be able to hold it for long, but it creates a weirdly arousing sensation.

Advanced Upside-Down Sex: The Headstand
This one's more of a novelty than a do-it-every-day kind of trick but if you're heavily into yoga (or fancy *really* impressing a new partner) try the headstand. You need to be pretty flexible and have strong arms for this. First, with something soft under your head, go into a headstand position (where you're resting on your head and hands with your legs in the air). Now spread your legs (you may need to lean against a wall at first). He then stands between your legs, holds on to your thighs, bends forward and penetrates you. Obviously, you won't be able to move much, so he'll have to do all the thrusting. He could give you oral while you're in a headstand, too.

URINARY TRACT INFECTIONS
See under: genito-urinary infections

Some infections such as thrush, although not necessarily sexually transmitted, can be passed on by sexual contact and can affect the urinary tract.

U-SPOT
See also: A-spot, G-spot

Yup, it's another sexy spot identified by a letter of the alphabet (see **G-spot** and **A-spot** for more info on the others). The U-spot is the spot surrounding the urethral opening (the little hole above the vaginal opening that you pee out of). It's rich in nerve endings and surrounded on three sides by parts of the clitoris. (Above is the clitoral head and hood – the bits you can see – and each side of the urethra are clitoral wings underneath the skin; see **clitoris** for more details). As it's in such a sexual hot spot, it's not surprising that stimulation of the U-spot is arousing for many women.

Up your U-spot Pleasure
Use these techniques for some u-nique pleasure:
Round, round, baby
With firm pressure (the U-spot is quite small, so you need to be firm) move the pad of your finger or thumb in circular motion while you masturbate.
Up 'n' down strokes
Again, with a firm touch, brush your finger or thumb over the urethra, up on to the clitoral hood and back down again.
Oral action
Try getting him to focus the tip of his tongue on to the U-spot by opening your vaginal lips slightly and while he presses down at the top with a flat or pointy tongue.
Thrust in me
The U-spot is also stimulated during penetration. Any position where his penis brushes against the top part of the vagina on the in or out stroke will feel good (and you get the added bonus of clitoral stimulation, too). See the **CAT position** for more details, or try you on top leaning forward so you can control what he's doing.

Cosmo tip:
Not every women enjoys U-spot stimulation, so, men, please find out what she likes before you focus on it.

VAGINA

See also: arousal, clitoris, masturbation for you, oral sex for you

The Biological Stuff: Outside

Vulva: This is the correct name for the outside of the whole genital area. (And quite a nice word, really: try saying it while rolling your tongue against your teeth and thinking about sex. It's a great warm-up word if you're getting ready to talk dirty. Or even if you're bored on public transport . . .)

Pubic mound or mons pubis: The fleshy triangle above your vulva that protects your pubic bone while he's thrusting is full of spongy tissue. It's the bit that's covered in pubic hair unless you've got the guts to go for the full Hollywood (a Brazilian without the landing strip).

Clitoris: The only part of your love button that's actually visible is the clitoral head (or glans). This is the super-sensitive pea-sized nodule at the top of the vaginal area. These vary in shape and size, and are made of similar erectile tissue to that of the penis. The clitoris swells and stands erect when you become aroused and can be anything from 2–20 mm in size. See the **clitoris** section for more info.

Clitoral hood: This where the inner vaginal lips come together at the top of the vulva to form a hood over the top of the clitoral head, similar to a foreskin on a man. When you're about to climax, the clitoris often retreats under the hood (which can be frustrating for your lover, who's just spent hours locating it).

Clitoral wings: Most of the clitoris is inside your body with bulbs stretching backwards towards your pelvis and 'wings' forming an upside-down Y shape inside the tissue of your outer vaginal lips – another reason why your lips are super-sensitive.

Vaginal lips: You have two sets of vaginal lips – the inner and outer labia. They're packed with nerve endings and also made from erectile tissue that swells and deepens in colour when you're aroused.

SEX FACT: *The origin of lipstick is the fact that the vagina deepens in colour when you're sexually aroused. When you paint your lips (the ones on your face) you're mimicking this response.*

Labia majora: Your outer labia, which are covered in pubic hair on the outside. The inner surface is smooth and packed with nerve endings. When you're aroused they become engorged with blood and lift and separate – a bit like pouting! They are mostly made from fatty tissue and protect your inner lips.

Labia minora: Your inner labia, which are hairless and meet at the top of the vulva to form the clitoral hood and at the other end meet in a little fold of skin called the fourchette. Size and shape vary massively: some can hardly be seen; others hang down below the outer labia.

Vestibule: The correct term for the whole area from the clitoris to the fourchette, inside the labia minora. Many people call this the vagina. This area is kept permanently moist by mucus, which helps keep you lubricated, clean and healthy.

Urethral opening: This is the little opening just below the clitoris where pee comes from (contrary to popular belief, you don't urinate from your vagina). Some women like to be stimulated here during oral sex or masturbation. See **U-spot** for details.

Vaginal opening: The hole where his penis goes (and menstrual blood passes out of the body). Again, this area is rich with nerve endings close to the surface, particularly around the opening.

Hymen: A flap of skin across the entrance to your vagina that breaks and disappears after you've had sex for the first time (and often much earlier than this). Blood on the sheets after your wedding night from your hymen used to prove you were a virgin. This is nonsense, as the hymen is usually broken during vigorous sport or by using tampons well before you start having sex.

Perineum: The patch of skin between the bottom of the vulva and your anus. It's sensitive to the touch, and many women like this area to be stimulated during sex.

Anus: The puckered hole at the end of your rectum, which is also rich in nerve endings.

The Biological Stuff: Inside

Although this info is slightly reminiscent of a very boring sex-education class you had when you were twelve, this time it's here to help your sex life rather than make you cringe, so stick with it.

Vagina: This stretchy tube is around 7.5–10 cm (3–4 inches) long and becomes engorged with blood when you're aroused, swelling to accommodate a penis. When you're not turned on, the walls lie flat against each other. The walls of the vagina contain powerful muscles that contract rhythmically during orgasm.

SAFETY INFO: Although the vagina expands or contracts to fit pretty much anything inside, it is made from sensitive tissue that can become sore. The golden rules are: (1) Don't insert anything before you're fully aroused or that hurts and (2) Don't put anything in there you wouldn't put in your mouth.

G-spot: A highly sensitive (and highly disputed) spot on the front wall of the vagina around 3–5 cm (1–2 inches) up. In some women stimulation of this spot is highly arousing. Others feel absolutely nothing. See **G-spot** for more info.

Cervix: The neck of the uterus – located at the top of the vagina. (When you have a smear test, cells are taken from here.) It has a small hole in the middle that dilates (expands) when you're about to give birth. Sometimes it can get bruised if you're having sex with a well-endowed man.

Uterus: Also known as the womb: a pear-sized organ that expands to hold a baby when you're pregnant. The lining of the uterus sheds during your period. The wall contracts during orgasm and labour (although obviously these two sensations feel somewhat different).

SEX FACT! *The vagina is extremely resilient. When injured (for example scraped by vigorous sex or inserting a tampon) it can heal itself within 48 hours.*

Ovaries: Egg sacs at the end of your fallopian tubes either side of your uterus.

PC muscle: (pubococcygeal muscle if you want to get technical about it). A powerful muscle which forms part of the pelvic floor – the structure that runs from your pubic bone at the front to the tip of your spine at the back, forming a kind of sling around your genital area. This contracts during orgasm and you can do special exercises to strengthen it, which can increase the power of your climax. See **Kegel exercises** for info.

SEX FACT! *The outer third of the vagina contains 90 per cent of the nerve endings, so is by far the most sensitive part.*

Designer Vaginas?

The size and shape of vaginal lips varies massively from woman to woman but, because most of us don't have the check-it-out-in-the-changing-room advantage that men do, we don't have the opportunity to compare and contrast ourselves with others. Porn magazine and film vulvas are chosen for their symmetry and are often retouched to give them a bit of extra pizzazz (lip gloss, anyone?). However, some women are self-conscious about the size and shape of their inner labia – maybe they hang down lower than the outer labia or one lip is larger than the other. In a search for so-called perfection, a cosmetic-surgery procedure has been invented to correct these perceived defects and create the perfect 'designer vagina'. Hmmm . . . Although this can boost self-esteem and confidence in some women, it doesn't do *anything* to improve your sex life. As the vaginal lips are full of erectile tissue and sensitive nerve endings, do you really want any of that trimmed away? Can you imagine a man slicing bits off his erection just to make it look a little prettier? Thought not . . .

Vagina Myths

Myth one: You can be too big or too small

False: Mother Nature could've won design awards for the beauty and efficiency of the vagina. It can stretch to fit any size of man (think about it: if a baby's head can come out, even the largest lover can go in) *and* its walls also contain powerful muscles that can contract to hold on to someone who's a little on the small side. (With practice, you should even be able to hold a pencil in there while standing up, so please don't tell us he's thinner than your average HB.) However, like any muscles, these do need exercising to keep them in shape (See **Kegel exercises** for details) and after childbirth they may need some extra work (sorry).

Myth two: Too much sex = slack vagina

False: The total opposite, in fact: anything that strengthens your PC muscles will cause your vagina to tighten. Arousal and orgasm are fantastic workouts for these muscles, making them stronger, the more lovemaking you do.

Myth three: You smell bad

False: Your vagina does have its own unique smell but most men report that it's actually a turn-on rather than a

> **Cosmo tip:**
> Please don't worry about the size, shape, colour, irregularity or lopsidedness of any part of your bits. He isn't going to care what you look like.

> **Cosmo tip:**
> When you're aroused, natural lubrication is released in the vagina. If you dry out during masturbation or oral sex, try inserting a finger inside your vagina to release some of this fluid. As if by magic, you'll be all wet again.

> **Cosmo tip:**
> When he's inside you, try contracting your PC muscles (the muscles you use to stop the flow of urine when you pee). This tightens your hold on his penis and mimics contractions you have during orgasm, which can bring on your climax.

turn-off. Some women's smell changes throughout their monthly cycle but others' stays the same. Please don't feel the need to use vaginal deodorants or strongly smelling bath products to disguise your natural smell. These can upset the delicate balance of your bits so are best avoided. But be aware that if your vagina does start to produce an out-of-the-ordinary odour (a strong fishy smell or unusual discharge) this could be the sign of an infection, so get it checked out by a doctor ASAP. See **genito-urinary infections** and **sexually transmitted infections** for more info.

SEX FACT: *The vagina has an extremely efficient self-cleaning mechanism that secretes oils, protein and lubrication. These keep its delicate pH balance healthy. It's actually cleaner than your mouth, making oral sex technically more hygienic than kissing.*

'I love the way my girlfriend smells when I go down on her: it's so sexy and makes me feel like I've really turned her on.'
Malcolm, 34, marketing

Myth four: All vaginas are created equal
True: Oh, yes, your vagina is no better than my vagina or your boyfriend's ex-girlfriend's vagina but – and this is crucial – it will behave in a different way. Most women have tons of nerve endings in the clitoris but some find their vaginal lips just as wired to the nervous system. Some women love to have their clitoris flicked with a hard tongue; others can't stand it. And sometimes – yup, this is the really confusing bit – your bits behave differently at different times of the month, so, even if you're totally in the know about what you like and what you don't, your genitals may sometimes surprise you (and him).

'When you enter a woman, it just feels warm. When she tightens her muscles around you, that feels amazing – like you're really filling her up.'
John, 34, personal trainer

SEX FACT: *Vaginal secretions are usually acidic but in adolescent girls they are less acidic than in adult women, making this age group more susceptible to pregnancy and sexual infections.*

VAGINISMUS
See also: vagina, masturbation

Vaginismus is a condition in which the muscles of the vagina involuntarily go into spasm and contract when a penis (or anything else, usually: finger, tampon, vibrator) is about to enter. This makes penetration uncomfortable, painful and often virtually impossible. It can be extremely distressing for the sufferer and can cause relationship and self-confidence problems. Causes vary and sometimes include some kind of physical and/or psychological trauma. Rape, abuse, childbirth and painful penetration can all contribute to it.

SEX
FACT:
According to the Kinsey Institute for Research in Sex, Gender and Reproduction, between 2 and 9 per cent of women experience vaginismus at some point.

The good news is that treatment for vaginismus has a very high success rate. Sometimes drug therapy is used but, more commonly, treatment with a sex therapist involves counselling – to look at the root causes – plus physical 'training'. This involves learning to voluntarily contract and release your pelvis, thigh and vaginal muscles while inserting different-sized dildos, starting with something very slim and progressing from there. The treatment helps you relax and relearn the contraction response, so it's not subconscious or automatic. See a sex therapist for more info.

Please note: during early (i.e. teenage) sexual encounters, it is very common to feel tense and for penetration to feel difficult (the same goes for inserting tampons). This usually means you're not ready for penetrative sex and should wait until you are. It does not mean you have vaginismus or will feel like this every time you attempt sex in the future.

'The biggest myth about vaginismus? That only frigid women have it. So wrong. I was very interested in sex. I had no problem having orgasms through masturbation or oral sex. It's just that I couldn't stand anything inside me. In the end a gynaecologist diagnosed me with vaginismus when she was trying to do a routine examination. A course of therapy totally changed my life. If you're suffering from it, please go and see someone. It made all the difference to me.'
Pamela, 32, researcher

VASECTOMY
See under: contraception

An operation performed on a man during which the tubes connecting sperm production to the penis are severed. A form of permanent contraception.

VIAGRA
See also: arousal, erectile problems, penis

If you think all his sexual problems (or yours) will be solved by popping one little blue pill, think again. Viagra is designed for men who have serious erectile problems. These tend to be mature men, later in life, as sexual responses slow down with age, and diabetics. Viagra is not a performance enhancer or an aphrodisiac.

SEX FACT: *Worldwide, nine Viagra pills are dispensed every second.*

Viagra will
- Boost the chemicals that cause an erection and block the chemicals that are released to take an erection down (for men with serious erectile problems the down-boy chemicals outweigh the up-sir ones) – therefore making the penis hard.
- May cause side effects such as headaches, flushes and nasal congestion and, in some cases, heart problems.

Viagra won't
- Make him better in bed.
- Cure brewer's droop or the appearance of an occasional Mr Floppy.
- Improve his technique in any way.
- Improve *your* enjoyment of sex (see the box 'Viagra for Women' below).
- Work in isolation without any form of sexual desire: desire needs to be there for the drug to function.
- Cure premature-ejaculation problems (see **premature**

ejaculation for help with this).

- Up either of your libido levels.

⚠️ *SAFETY INFO: Never use any prescription drugs without consulting a doctor. Viagra can have serious side effects, so, although it's available over the Internet, this could be extremely dangerous.*

Viagra for Women?

After an eight-year study into the effects of Viagra on women, Pfizer, the makers of the drug, have decided against applying to have it licensed for female use. Although Viagra is thought to increase the blood flow to the vagina and clitoris just as it does in the penis, arousal for women just isn't that simple. For men, it seems that sexual desire always follows physical arousal (i.e. when he gets it up, he wants to get it on) but this is not necessarily the case with women (see **arousal** for details on the differences between the sexes). Trials into alternative drugs and psychological treatments for women continue.

VIBRATORS
See also: masturbation, toys

See the **toys** section for more info on how to incorporate your plastic friend into your sex life plus essential safety and buying tips. In the meantime, here's the latest on what's out there.

Cosmo tip:
Vibrators are a great short cut to a quick, easy climax but however tempting it is, don't use them all the time. Remember: variety is the spice of everyone's sex life.

'I took Viagra once just to see what would happen. It was horrible: although my penis stayed hard for hours, I felt totally disconnected from it, as if my emotions weren't involved at all, and I just had this block of wood connected to my body. My girlfriend didn't enjoy it, either – she got sore and we had to stop.'
Michael, 35, journalist

Vibrator Varieties

There are literally thousands of toys out there. All you have to do is decide your preference and price range and take your pick. Popular varieties include:

1) Penis-shaped vibrators

Your common-or-garden variety of vibrator is shaped like a penis. Some are frighteningly lifelike and come in 'realistic' colours and textures. Others are more comical glow-in-the-dark varieties, glittery versions or animal shapes. Many have several speed settings and are battery-operated; others attach to the mains. Some, such as the notrious Rampant Rabbit, have attachments that stimulate your clitoris at the same time as the vagina, and others have attachments for anal play.

2) G-spot specific toys

Vibrators with a slightly bent tip are designed to stimulate the male and female G-spot. (Yours is around 5 cm (2 inches) inside the vagina on the front wall; his is his prostate gland, felt 4 cm (1½ inches) inside the rectum, also towards the front of the body – see **G-spot** for details).

SEX FACT: *Vibrators were invented in the 1870s when male doctors used them as a cure for 'female hysteria', a common complaint thought to be relieved by the release of sexual tension. As external genital massage was not thought to be sexual, this treatment carried no sexual connotations (to the doctor at least!).*

3) Strap-on vibes

These have straps that go around your thighs or bottom (like a G-string) and have a small vibrating attachment that fits directly over the clitoris or vagina. They can be butterfly-shaped and are handy for hands-off action (i.e. you don't have to hold them in place).

4) Finger fun

Vibrating toys with various textured cases fit snugly over fingers so you can direct the vibrations exactly where you want them without having to hold a traditional 'wand'-type vibrator.

5) Underwater magic

Some vibrators are designed for use in the bath or shower. (Most aren't, so don't try your regular one in water.) Remember to use lots of lubricant if you're in the bath or shower, as water dries out your natural juices.

6) Remote-control fun

Naughty, sexy fun is to be had in the shape of a small vibrator – there are different shapes available – and a separate 'control pack' in the hands of your lover. The idea is that you wear this totally silent toy unbeknown to the people around you while your lover has his hands on the control panel.

> **Cosmo tip:**
> Most women climax from placing a vibrator over the clitoris or against the vaginal lips rather than thrusting it in and out of the vagina.

'I recently bought a vibrator, and I thought my boyfriend might be a bit insulted, so I didn't tell him. When he found it, he was really excited and called me into bed. We both use it now during sex – he loves it on his inner thighs!'
Gabrielle, 28, designer

7) Egg-stacy

Vibrating eggs or little bullet-shaped vibrators (often attached to an external battery pack) are available. They are usually inserted into the vagina. They tend to be less powerful than traditional vibrators, so aren't recommended if you're used to more powerful toys. Some eggs are remote-controllable.

8) Tongue tinglers

Vibrating tongue shapes for 'oral' sex are also available. (Remember 'Betty's Tongue' on *So Graham Norton*? It's a real toy.) Reports on the use of these gadgets are mostly disappointing, although you should get a good laugh from them.

The Female-Friendly Revolution

If you don't fancy a luminous-green, glow-in-the-dark, glittering, twisting, alien, penis-type attachment that's a scary sixteen inches long, help is now at hand. A few enlightened sex toy manufacturers have realised that not every woman on the planet needs something large and penis-shaped. As most women orgasm through clitoral stimulation, toys have now been developed that deliver this directly. Check out the ex-US-porn star Candida's 'Natural Contours' range or the Relate counsellor Julia Cole's emotional-bliss vibrators (www.emotionalbliss.com).

VIRGINITY

See also: arousal, masturbation for you, penis, penetration, vagina

SEX FACT: *The average age for losing your virginity in the UK is currently sixteen.*

Hmm . . . now where did I put that?

Chances are that, if you're reading this book, virginity was something you lost a good few years ago. Was it good for you? First sexual experiences vary from the amazing through the disappointing to the disturbing, and, although they can have an effect on how you view sex in the future, most people simply put whatever happened down to experience. If your first sexual experience was traumatic in any way and you think it has had an effect on your enjoyment of sex now, it's probably worth talking to a counsellor or sex therapist.

Ah, yes, there it is . . .

If you're reading this book and you *are* still a virgin, good sections to start with are the biological basics in **arousal**, **penis** and **vagina**. Then look again at the get-to-know-your-body stuff in the **masturbation** sections (the more you know about your own sexual responses and what gets you going, the better sex will be). For the technical how-to stuff see **penetration** and **positions,** and to get your brain engaged look up the **fantasy** section. Remember that only *you* know when the time is right and you can lose your virginity only once. Don't let anyone persuade you to do something you're not ready for.

One more time?

Playing the innocent virgin, touched for the very first time, is a fantastic role play, so, even if you lost your virginity yonks ago, it's worth revisiting the scenario to spice up your lust life. Take turns to be the innocent one or the more experienced teacher: you'll be amazed by what you can learn (and the new tricks you can teach!).

VOYEURISM

See also: exhibitionism, masturbation – mutual, stripping

Voyeurism is the art of deriving sexual pleasure by watching other people in a sexual context. Yes, that can include horrible men in dirty rain macs or Peeping Toms who like to watch women taking a bath. It can also include men who pay to watch women 'perform' through little holes in the walls of strip clubs. That's the downside.

The upside is that, between you and your man, voyeurism doesn't have to be shameful or dirty. In fact, it can be a great way to express your sexuality and enhance your relationship in some incredibly intimate ways. Here's how:

Watch and learn

By watching your man masturbate, you'll learn tons about his sexual technique, what gets him going and what rhythms, pace and style he uses on himself. You can also see how your technique differs from his and pick up tips on how to combine it with his. He gets the same benefits from watching you.

Body lotion motion

If you don't have the courage to do the whole masturbation thing in front of him, try turning your usual night-time routine into a sensual sex show for your man. After a warm relaxing bath, go into the bedroom and bring out your most luxurious body lotion. Slowly and erotically as you can, start rubbing it into your skin, paying particular attention to the more sexual areas of your body such as your breasts and buttocks. Enjoy the process and think about his eyes on your body and how, not too much later, it'll be his fingers on your skin.

Shower thrill

Put on a similar touch-yourself routine in the shower, making sure he's there to watch but keeping up the façade that you're in your own little world, unaware that he can see what you're doing. Steamed-up shower cubicles offer the impression of your body without all the details, so you might feel able to push your limits further by touching yourself incredibly intimately. Great for hotel bedrooms . . .

Mirror magic

Have sex in front of a full-length mirror and take turns to be the watcher: one of you keeps an eye on the action (as if you're unaware that the mirror's there) while the other watches the whole process in the glass. Seeing him engrossed in what he's doing while your eyes are on the reflection of you both is extremely arousing. If you swap roles, occasionally you'll catch each other's eyes in the mirror and watch the show together, which can make sexual sparks fly.

SEX FACT: *The opposite of voyeurism (enjoying watching others for sexual gratification) is exhibitionism: enjoying performing in front of others for a sexual thrill.*

Ideally, a voyeur (the watcher) will get together with an exhibitionist (the performer) and live happily every after. Alternatively, you can have a lot of fun playing around with both these roles. See **exhibitionism** for more details.

WAKE-UP SEX
See also: quickies

There's something specially sexy about a morning snuggle that turns into spontaneous raunch, and it's not just the rosy glow that accompanies you to the office. For men, sex first thing is biologically the best time of the day for it, as their testosterone levels peak in the mornings. You should also both feel rested, de-stressed and ready for action. Set your alarm an hour early and try some of these first-thing frolics.

Rise 'n' shine

Most men wake up with an erection, which isn't necessarily a sexual response: it's more mechanical and is his body's way of testing the system. You'll need to arouse his sexual senses before you get stuck in. Try gently kissing him awake round the hairline, on the lips, then down his body towards his genitals. Spend time on his inner thighs, then take his penis in your mouth for a

'Having sex in the morning gives me such a buzz all day. I have this secret smirk when I walk into the office and I'm sure everyone knows what I've been up to. Just thinking about the raunchy things we did an hour ago makes my boring mornings fly by!'
Julie, 35, systems analyst

blow-by-blow wake-up call. See **oral sex for him** for details and remember: he can use this raunchy wake-up call on you, too.

Quickie time

If you're always rushed in the mornings, make time for a super-speedy quickie. Pin him down, kiss him hard on his mouth and let him know you want him – *now*. Then jump on top of him with your knees bent, leaning forward, holding his hands above his head. Being assertive in bed will boost your confidence and make you feel more powerful and in control for the rest of the day.

Shower power

Forget fighting for the bathroom: join him in the shower instead. Sensually touch each other's body until you're awake and aroused. Then try having it standing up: use one leg to balance while you wrap the other over his hips so he penetrates you from the front. Steamy!

Breakfast star

Carry on the raunchy mood by feeding each other breakfast. Fruit, torn-up pieces of croissants dunked in coffee and soldiers dipped in a boiled egg work well for this. If anything drips, take turns to lick it off each other's body. (Probably best if you're not in your smartest work suit for this.)

WANKING
See under: masturbation

Another word for masturbation (i.e. bringing yourself to orgasm with your hand).

WARTS
See under: sexually transmitted infections

Warts in or around the genital area are caused by the HPV virus (that's HPV, not HIV), which is passed on through sexual contact.

WATER PLAY
See also: ice, outdoor sex

Water can greatly enhance your sex life in a zillion slip-slidey ways. Try these get-wet tips at home or away.

Water works

A detachable showerhead makes an excellent masturbation toy. Use it just above your clitoris so the water's pounding down on to you. Experiment with different angles and water pressures until you find something you really like.

Cosmo tip:
Make sure the water's not too hot or you'll scald the sensitive vaginal tissue.

Bathtime bliss

There's a huge array of sex toys specially designed for use in the bath, from vibrating foam balls that look like regular sponges to vibrating rubber ducks that look just like the regular varieties (no one will ever know!). Regular battery-powered toys aren't designed for use in water, so check what you're buying carefully.

Lather palaver

Take a sexy shower with your lover and lather up. Light scented candles around the bathroom, giving enough light to see each other by (but not enough to show up your wobbly bits). Without touching, strip and stand at either end of the bath with the shower running. Gently direct the shower over each other. Still without touching, start lathering up in front of him. Touch your body slowly and erotically, focusing on the areas that you like to be touched best – it's his job to watch and learn. Once you're covered in soap it's your turn to lather him up – without using your hands. Rub your body sensually against his until he's all soaped up. Rinse and repeat as often as necessary.

Tub thumping

Sex in the bath can be a squashed affair unless you get it right. Try this specially designed position: he sits with his knees up and his feet square on the bottom of the bath. Facing him, you sit on top of him (in front of his raised knees) and lower yourself on to his penis until you're sitting back, leaning against his thighs for support, with your legs either side of him. Hold his ankles for an extra twist or use your hands to caress each other. As you're on top, you should be in control of the movements.

Cosmo tip:
Water has a sneaky way of washing away your natural lubricants so you may need to use extra lube in the bath/shower/sea for things to be really comfortable. Alternatively, just stick to foreplay techniques and save intercourse for once you've both dried off.

Sex in the sea

This is a great way to have sex in front of an audience without their noticing what you're up to. Swim out to chest height, then stand in front of your man, slip your bikini bottoms to one side, wrap your legs around his hips and lower yourself on to his erection. He should then be supporting you with his arms round your bottom. The water gives you extra buoyancy so you can bounce up and down.

SAFETY INFO: Condoms and water don't mix too well, so sex in the sea/river/hotel pool is really for long-term monogamous couples only.

WET PATCH
See also: just desserts

Who sleeps in the wet patch? It's an eternal question that's plagued couples the world over for centuries. Here are some sneaky tips:

1) If you use condoms that little ol' wet patch is radically reduced (it's only your wetness that's in evidence) so the problem ceases to exist.
2) Having sex on the floor also solves the problem.
3) Sneak yourself right to the edge of the bed for the big finale – that way both of you can avoid said puddle.
4) Pretend to sleep on it yourself (lean your back just on the edge of it) then sexily pull your lover towards you while inching forward a fraction and – *voilà!* – subtly he's now in it!

OK, if none of the above work for you, the decent thing is just to take it in turns. After all, when's a little old wet patch really hurt anyone, eh?

WHIPS
See under: spanking

Implements that are sometimes used during bondage sessions for spanking.

WICKED WHISPERS
See also: phone sex, talking dirty

Psst . . . Want to know a secret? Whispering to your lover can be much more erotic than talking in your normal voice. Why? (1) Because he has to lean in to hear you, creating more body contact and instant intimacy. (2) Because when you whisper you automatically lower your voice, which immediately makes it sound sexier and more seductive. (3) Because men's ears are more sensitive to touch than women's, so having your hot breath in his ear and your mouth brushing past it as you lean in close will send shivers down his spine.

WITHDRAWAL METHOD
See also: condoms, contraception, sexually transmitted infections

An incredibly unreliable method of contraception in which the man promises faithfully to withdraw before he ejaculates. It doesn't work because (a) some pre-seminal fluid is released before ejaculation, which can make you pregnant, and (b) in the heat of the moment withdrawal can be pretty damn difficult to co-ordinate. It also offers no protect against STIs.

WORK

Sex should never feel like hard work. If it does, change position, location, routine or partner.

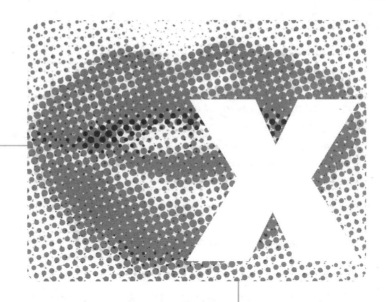

X-BOYFRIEND SEX

Sex With Your Ex – Is It Ever a Good Idea?

Yes if . . .

- Both of you fancy a bit of old-times raunch and can both handle the emotional implications.

No if . . .

- You think it means you're getting back together.
- Either of you is doing it as revenge or emotional black-mail.
- It prevents you from moving on or finding a new lover.
- It's a drunken mistake (be careful of weddings: they're a classic time for this).
- You'll feel worse in the morning.
- It's sending out the wrong messages (to either of you).

'The last person I slept with before my husband was an old flame. I'd already met my husband-to-be and it proved to me I was doing the right thing. It was definitely worth it to get him out of my system.'
Alison, 35, dental nurse

'Sleeping with my ex was the biggest mistake I made: we'd get together every few months "for old times" and the sex was great but it just meant the end of our relationship dragged on and on. I definitely wouldn't recommend it.'
David, 32, estate agent

Hmm . . . looks like the odds are stacked against sex with your ex. Of course it's always going to be tricky but sometimes, just occasionally, it can be an amazing erotic buzz. After all, you probably know each other pretty well and can reach those secret hotspots pretty easily. The bottom line is, usually it's a mistake but, if you're sure you can both handle the emotional implications, what's the harm? Just make sure condoms figure highly in your activities.

X MARKS THE SPOT
See also: zone orgasm

There are certain erogenous zones on both sexes that are pretty damn obvious and you don't need a huge red X to find them. *But . . .* if you head for the obvious every single time, sex will get dull. Try mixing up your in-bed routine so you don't take the same route every time. Try teasing different parts of each other's body, to create different X-spots. Or pretend his body and yours are treasure maps you have to navigate on which X marks the treasure at the end of your quest. Use your imagination to explore the terrain as thoroughly as possible using different touches, strokes, licks and tricks in different areas.

Try these treasure-map tricks:

* Imagine there's a river you have to follow running down your lover's back – use your tongue to trace the winding water all the way from the nape of the neck to the base of the spine. If you're in the shower or the sea, try trickling real water.
* Imagine shoulders are mountains you have to climb, and climb your fingers one at a time across his chest and over his shoulders.
* Imagine you've found a deep ravine in the hollows of his armpits, insides of his elbows or around the base of his neck. Use your tongue to explore these areas slowly and sensuously.
* Now imagine you're an explorer fighting through the jungle of

his body hair in order to get closer and closer to the treasure. Run your fingers through the hair on his body, then move on to his pubic hair, circling the X-spot on his treasure map.

- Finally, discover the treasure – and indulge his genitals in some serious hand and mouth action. Make sure he returns the favour by tracing your personal pleasure map too.

X-RATED POSITIONS
See also: penetration, positions

Limbered up? Ready for a challenge? Here is a collection of super-advanced (and extra-raunchy) sex positions only for the truly adventurous. Get stretching . . .

X-rated #1: The shoulder stand
From the basic missionary position (him on top), place your legs over his shoulders while he kneels up so you're upside down (resting your weight on your shoulders) and he's penetrating you from the front. This shortens the vaginal canal so penetration feels deeper. His body weight also gives you something to thrust against and the blood rushing to your head provides an unusually arousing sensation.

Kinky twist: maintain erotic eye contact the whole time to build sizzling intimacy between you.

X-rated #2: The summersault
Again, starting in the missionary position, try bending yourself in half so your feet are all the way over your head (and pushing against a wall if you can reach). He then penetrates you from the front, between your legs. This offers him the deepest penetration and the angle means the base of his penis should slap against your raised clitoris (he also gets a fantastic view and gets to dominate over your whole body).

Kinky twist: get him to vary the speed and depth of thrusting so you're always surprised by what he'll do next. (Hot tip: thrusting hard and fast feels great!)

X-rated #3: The wheelbarrow

OK, this one's a bit tricky and probably worth it more for novelty value than sexual satisfaction. He stands behind you and hooks your legs either over his shoulders or into his armpits (depending on how tall he is). You lean forward resting your weight on your hands (remember wheelbarrow races at primary school?). He then penetrates you from behind. There's not much movement for either of you but, as all the blood is racing to your head, your climax is likely to feel more intense.

Kinky twist: Try walking on your hands without losing contact with his penis – amusingly difficult!

X-rated #4: The handstand

Here's another athletic position if you're extra supple. Stand in front of him, jump up and wrap your legs round his waist so he's penetrating you from the front and supporting your weight by holding your thighs. Now lean backwards all the way down until your hands reach the ground (as if you were doing a handstand). Rest your palms flat on the ground while he holds on to your bottom. Again, the blood-rush to your head is extra exciting.

Kinky twist: If you think this is easy, try it when you're blindfolded: it takes a lot of co-ordination but can heighten all your senses.

X-TRA RUDE DEFINITIONS

Curious about the more extreme sexual practices out there or want to know what certain terms mean? Here's a quick list of x-tra rude activities and terms to satisfy your curiosity and, to help you to know what people are talking about when they throw a couple of words into conversation over dinner. OK, probably not over dinner . . .

Auto-erotic asphyxiation: Arousal from lack of oxygen. Extremely dangerous (people die) and strongly not recommended.
Daisy chain: Group sex activity involving a circle of people each

giving the person in front of them oral sex.

Dogging: Having sex in a car – usually in a remote car park while strangers watch you (as if they were walking their dogs).

Double-bagged: Wearing two condoms at once, just to be on the safe side. It's actually safer to wear just one, as trying to get two on can cause tears in the latex.

Double Dutch: Using two forms of contraception, usually the Pill and condoms for extra protection. A great idea.

English disease/culture: Slang term for spanking, thought to be connected to the old practice of corporal punishment in male English public schools.

Fanny: UK word for female genitals. US word for bottom (as in butt). Important to get right if you're considering a transatlantic sexual liaison.

Femoral intercourse: Where the penis slides through the vaginal lips without actually penetrating the vagina.

Frottage: Arousal from rubbing genitals against someone else without penetration (often while fully clothed).

Gang bang: When (usually) men line up to have intercourse with one women one after the other. Often refers to rape.

Golden showers: Being turned on by urine, usually in the form of being peed on.

Lucky Pierre: Someone in the middle of a sex sandwich (i.e. in between two other people).

Ménage à trois: A French term used commonly to describe a threesome.

Necrophilia: Being aroused by having sex with dead bodies.

Nocturnal emissions: Wet dreams.

Pit job: Intercourse using the armpit rather than the vagina.

Shrimping: Sucking someone's toes for sexual arousal.

Strap-on: Dildo that straps on to the body so you can penetrate your partner.

Switches: People in the **BDSM** scene who enjoy switching between dominant and submissive roles.

Top: A dominant partner (as opposed to a bottom, which is a submissive partner).

Uncut: Not circumcised.

Vanilla sex: A term used by people into extreme alternative sexual lifestyles for mild heterosexual practices (as opposed to anything especially kinky).

Water sports: Sexual activities involving urination (not to be confused with the activities your tour rep offers you on a beach holiday).

X-TREME DESIRES
See also: fantasy

Our brains can come up with some pretty weird stuff when it comes to sex. In fact, in the sexual imagination anything goes and often activities that are forbidden, taboo or disturbing are precisely the things that turn us on the most. However, there's a huge difference between fantasy and reality. Please don't feel concerned if extreme images pop into your head while you're having sex or fantasising: this does not mean you're weird, sick or disturbed. If any one of us started to act out every sexual thought that came into our heads, . we'd all appear to be totally bonkers. Extreme desires are part of sex. Some people find ways to express these desires, some people don't. It's up to you to set your own sexual boundaries, and decide how far you want to go, what really turns you on and what's best left as a fantasy. See the **fantasy** section for more details on how to deal with those extreme thoughts. (Clue: most of them are probably best left inside your head . . .)

SAFETY INFO: Extreme sexual practices and pushing your sexual boundaries often work like addictive drugs. At first you get a great buzz but then you need more and more of it (or a more extreme version of it) to get the same thrill. Be careful that you don't end up going further than you want to.

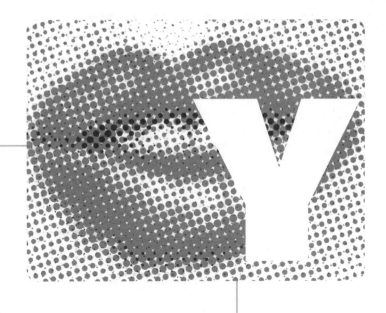

YANK
See also: breasts, masturbation for him

Meaning 1: Slang term for people from the USA.
Meaning 2: What not to do when handling male genitals or female nipples.

YELL YOUR HEAD OFF
See also: talking dirty

As every DJ worth his decks knows, sometimes it's good to *make some noise* if you want to show your appreciation. What goes on the dance floor also holds true for the bedroom. A gasp, a sigh, a squeak, a shout – they'll all let your partner know he's on to a good thing . . .

YES, YES, YES!
See also: faking

Yes rule #1: 'Yes' is a fantastically emotive word to use in bed. Use it to direct your partner (as in 'ooh, yes!') rather than using 'no' if he gets things wrong. Positive encouragement works better than criticism every time.

Yes rule #2: 'Yes' can feel incredibly powerful and affirmative. Say yes to a naughty sexual encounter. Say yes to experiencing new activities in the bedroom. Say yes to expanding your sexual horizons.

Yes rule #3: Very, very occasionally (and we mean *very* occasionally) it's OK to give the 'yes, yes, yes, *yes!*' performance of your life. See the **faking** section for details.

Yes rule #4: Never say yes when you really mean no. No obviously means no, so don't go confusing things.

YOGHURT
See also: food, genito-urinary infections

Good for: spreading on each other's body and licking off. Also a good natural remedy for thrush (see **genito-urinary infections**).

Not so good for: use in picnics on a hot day when you don't have a cool bag.

YOHIMBE
See also: aphrodisiacs, erectile problems

A natural aphrodisiac (made from the bark of the African yohimba tree), yohimbe extract and tablets can be found in health-food shops. It is used to enhance sex drive for men and has been proven to help both physical and mental **erectile problems**. (Sadly, it's not recommended for women.) Side effects can include high blood pressure and anxiety. Always check with your doctor before using any herbal or natural remedies.

YONI

See also: Tantric sex

A Sanskrit word for vagina, which, roughly translated, means 'sacred space' or 'sacred temple'. In Tantric sex, the *yoni* is respected and worshipped as a thing of beauty. The equivalent word for penis is *lingam*, which means 'wand of light' bringing a whole new meaning to the phrase 'light of my life'.

YOU

See also: communication, condoms, fantasy, masturbation for you

There's only one person who's responsible for your sexual pleasure: that's *you*.

It's up to *you* to:
- Know your body well enough to know what turns you on (see **masturbation for you**).
- Communicate what you do and don't like in bed to your lover (see **communication**).
- Constantly reinvent your bedroom antics so you don't get bored (see most of this book).
- Use your sexual imagination to make sure it doesn't shut down (see **fantasy**).
- Get as much sex as *you* need.
- Practise safe sex (see **condoms** and **contraception**).

Got that? Good.

YOU FIRST . . .
See also: orgasm

As women tend to take longer to climax than men, it makes sense to get your orgasm in first. Alternatively, taking turns to give and receive pleasure is a handy way to make sure you're both having fun.

YOUTHFUL GLOW

A happy, healthy sex life keeps you looking and feeling younger for longer. It reduces stress, lowers blood pressure and encourages cell rejuvenation so your skin looks fresher and more youthful. Go for the glow! It's a lot cheaper than anti-ageing cream.

SEX FACT: *Post-coital flushed cheeks can last up to thirty minutes after you've climaxed.*

ZIP TRICKS
See also: oral sex for him, stripping

Zips of all sorts are great for slipping up and down seductively on any part of your clothing (or his). This section concentrates on zip-up flies but, with a little imagination, these tricks could be used on any zips you like.

Zip trick #1: the show-and-tell
During a striptease, undo the zip of your trousers or skirt to reveal your sexiest underwear, then do it up again as part of the tease. Alternatively, lower it inch by inch, showing him more and more of what's underneath. (Works best if you're wearing extremely pretty/sexy new underwear.)

Zip trick #2: the man handle
In a public or semi-public place, gently slide one finger up the length of his fly while maintaining eye contact. It's a saucily seductive taste of things to come. For a finale with a flourish, once you've reached the top of his zip, suck your finger suggestively or draw it across your lips: phew! (Works best if you have long nails and an immaculate manicure.)

Zip trick #3: the back squeeze

While you're both fully clothed, stand in front of your man and reach behind you so your hands are stroking his genitals: feel his zip to gauge the right area. Next, give him a squeeze and feel his erection growing in your hand.

Zip trick #4: the tongue tease

When taking off his trousers, take your time with his flies. Since they contain his most potent erogenous zone, the longer you take to expose it, the more thrilling that exposure will be. Take down his fly an inch at a time and lick and kiss the area you've just exposed with your tongue, probing underneath the material as if you're desperate to discover what's hidden inside. Try pulling down his undies at the same to time to get direct access to his skin. Take it lick by delicious lick until he's fully exposed. He'll be gagging for oral sex by now so it's up to you whether you treat him now or make him wait even longer.

Zip trick #5: the quick-draw

If you fancy a quickie but don't have time to undress, just unzip his flies, pull out his erection, pull your knickers to one side and go for it. Extremely naughty but oh so nice! This technique is also great for oral sex too. The restrictive sensation of clothes against skin adds to the excitement.

SAFETY INFO: Be careful with zip tricks if either of you aren't wearing any underwear. They can be sexy but pubic hair or skin caught in a zip is extremely painful. Ouch!

ZODIAC SEDUCTION
See under: astro-hotspots

Your star sign doesn't just indicate your personality. Each sign is said to be ruled by a part of the body.

ZONE ORGASM
See also: fetishes, orgasm

Some people have a particularly sensitive area on the body away from the traditional erogenous zones that, when touched, kissed or licked, can cause them to climax. Some people experience orgasm when the back of their neck is caressed in a certain way, others when their fingers are sucked or the insides of their ankles are stroked. A foot fetishist may experience orgasmic sensations when putting on a special pair of shoes; a leather lover when stroking a piece of the fabric against a particular part of the body. These 'zone orgasms' are totally unique to the person they belong to and can cause no end of pleasure.

A Personalised Orgasm Prescription
If you don't have a particular zone to call your own, it is possible to create your very own orgasmic centre somewhere unique to you. The secret is to teach an area of your body that isn't normally sexually charged to send sexual messages to the brain.
• Start by arousing your usual erogenous zones (e.g. breasts, vagina or clitoris) in a way that you know gets you going. Focus your mind and really pay attention to how this stimulation feels.
• Next, start touching or stroking the area you want to sensitise at the same time as you're stroking your genitals. Try the nape of the neck, below the ears, the insides of your wrists or the areas of thin skin next to your hip bones. Anywhere where the skin is particularly thin so your nerve endings are close to the surface is a good bet.
• Continue stimulating both areas, alternating genital stimulation with your new zone. Let the pleasure waves you experience from genital touching feel as if they were coming from the new area. (Yup, your brain will start to get confused, but that's the idea.)
• At the moment of orgasm, stop genital touching but keep on touching your secondary area so your brain connects the two sensations closely together. Make sure your mind is fully engaged: think about how the stimulation *feels*, as this technique is a mind trick more than anything.

• The more you practise this technique, the less time you'll need to spend on your genitals and the more time you can focus on the new area till eventually (and it does take some time!) you need just to stimulate the new area to receive the same orgasmic feelings.

Takes Two to Tango
Try this whole process on your partner – it's much more fun with two and, as all the sensations are outside the body, the brain finds it easier to combine/confuse the two sets of messages. Try stroking his inner wrists in the same rhythm as your mouth movements while giving him oral sex. Or suck his toes while stimulating his penis with your hands. It won't be long before toe sucking alone can arouse him. Don't forget to let him do the same to you: get him to try one hand on the nape of your neck with the other on or around your clitoris. Or try any combination of body parts that takes your fancy.

'For some reason, my girlfriend loves sucking on that funny web of skin between my thumb and first finger. Because she's done it so often while we've been messing around in bed, sucking particularly hard if she's about to come, I find it really arousing now – it's like our naughty little secret!'
Ben, 29, solicitor

ZZZZZ
See also: afterplay

Q: Why do men always fall asleep after sex?

A: Not because they're lazy, uncaring or selfish. It's all down to biology. At orgasm, both men and women release the hormone oxytocin. This hormone is also released when women are breastfeeding, creating a sleep-inducing effect on the baby and a bonding sensation in the mother. Hence you fancy a cuddle while he's already snoring.

SEX FACT: *According to the Sleep Disorders Center in New York, 91 per cent of couples sleep in the same bed; 64 per cent of them admit that they sleep better with their partner than on their own. Ahhh!*

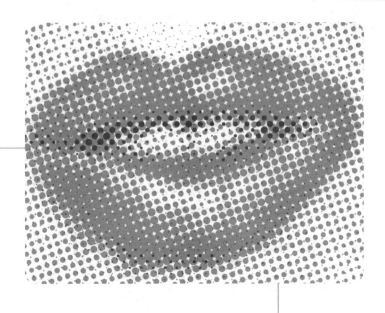

USEFUL ADDRESSES AND CONTACTS

Sexual Health and Information

British Pregnancy Advisory Service (BPAS)
Advice on pregnancy, contraception and abortion.
Phone: 08457 304 030 (Monday–Friday 8 a.m.–9 p.m., Saturday
8.30 a.m.–6 p.m. Sunday 9.30 a.m.–2.30 p.m.)
Web: www.bpas.org

Brook Advisory Service
Advice on all aspects of sexual health and contraception for people
under 25.
Phone: 0800 0185 023 (Monday–Friday 9 a.m.–5 p.m.)
Web: www.brook.org.uk

The Family Planning Association (FPA)
Free advice on all aspects of contraception, STIs and family
planning.
Phone: 0845 310 1334 (Monday–Friday 9 a.m.–6 p.m.)
Web: www.fpa.org.uk

Lesbian and Gay Switchboard Helpline
Support and information for lesbian, gay and bisexual people.
Phone: 020 7837 7324 (24 hours)
Web: www.llgs.org.uk

Marie Stopes International
Info and advice on contraception, STIs and abortion, plus clinics.
Phone: 0845 300 80 90 (Monday–Sunday 7 a.m.–10 p.m.)
Web: www.mariestopes.org.uk

Sexual Health Line (formerly National AIDS Helpline)
Advice and information on all aspects of sexual health, including HIV and AIDS.
Phone: 0800 567 123 (24 hours)
Web: www.playingsafely.co.uk

NHS Direct
Confidential advice on all health matters including sexual health.
Phone: 0845 4647 (24 hours)
Web: www.nhsdirect.nhs.uk

Positively Women
Support and advice for women with HIV and AIDS.
Phone: 020 7713 0222 (Monday–Friday 10 a.m.–4 p.m.)
Web: www.positivelywomen.org.uk

Terrence Higgins Trust Helpline
Information, support and advice on HIV and AIDS.
Phone: 0845 1221 200 (Monday–Friday 10 a.m.–10 p.m., Saturday–Sunday 12 p.m.–6 p.m.)
Web: www.tht.org.uk

Women's Health
Information on gynaecological health for women.
Phone: 0845 125 5254 (Monday–Friday 9.30 a.m.–1.30 p.m.)
Web: www.womenshealthlondon.org.uk

Shopping and Sex Toys: UK Sites

www.annsummers.com

Famous for sex parties and high street stores, the UK's biggest sex shop chain has an extensive online site for toys, parties, novelties, undies and more. www.annsummersuncut.com has even more adult products.

www.coco-de-mer.co.uk

Upmarket sex shop in London's Covent Garden (23 Monmouth Street, London WC2 9DD, 020 7836 8882) stocking gorgeous goodies from exquisite underwear to break-the-bank sex toys (some are over £1,000!).

www.emotionalbliss.com

New range of sex toys specifically designed for the female form. (Sexy pastel colours and girlie shapes rather than traditional penis substitutes.) Tasteful and informative. Also contains sex info from Relate counsellor Julia Cole.

www.gash.co.uk

Female-run and owned store for erotic toys, books and lingerie (Sheffield 0114 276 3733; London 020 7494 2323).

www.myla.com

Ultra-cool designer sex toys (to be displayed rather than hidden away) plus lux lingerie. Pricey but gorgeous (08707 455 003).

www.passion8.com

UK-owned female-friendly and female-run sex shop. Mail-order toys and treats available.

www.sh-womenstore.com

Female-friendly online sex store. Sex info and a selection of female-friendly products. Also has women-only shop in London (men are welcome in the company of a responsible female). (Sh! Women's Erotic Emporium, 39 Coronet Street, London N1 6HD, 020 7613 5458.)

Useful Sex Websites

www.clitical.com
Info, discussion forum plus how-to sex advice.

www.handbag.com/relationships/sex
General sex info plus online sexual agony aunt.

www.kamasutrafree.com
Informative sex positions site.

www.netdoctor.co.uk
Online medical information including extensive sexual health information.

www.relate.org.uk
UK relationship and sex counselling organisation.

www.safeoutdoorsex.com
Information about outdoor sex from the makers of Mates condoms.

www.sex-lexis.com
Online dictionary of sexual terms and slang.

www.sexology.org
Confidential online advice and treatment for a range of sexual difficulties.

www.tantra.org
Information on Tantric sex.

www.the-clitoris.com
Information and hands-on advice about all aspects of female sexuality.

www.world-sex-news.com
Sexual news headlines and links from around the world.

Further Reading

Cosmopolitan Sex Confessions by Natalie Dye (Robson Books). Collection of the readers' sex confessions from *Cosmo*.

Encyclopaedia of Unusual Sexual Practices by Brenda Love (Abacus Books). Weird and wonderful sex the world over.

Extended Massive Orgasms by Steve and Vera Bodansky (Vermilion). How to give and receive one-hour orgasms.

Great Sex Games by Anne Hooper (Dorling Kindersley). Pocket guide to dressing up, role play and sex games.

Guide to Getting It On by Paul Joannides (Vermilion). Positions, techniques, tips and tricks.

Hot Sex: How To Do It by Tracy Cox (Corgi). Just what it says in the title.

How To Be a Great Lover by Lou Paget (Piatkus). Lust tips from America's premier s-expert.

How To Make Great Love To a Man by Anne Hooper and Phillip Hodson (Robson Books). For women who want to excel in bed.

Kama Sutra For 21st Century Lovers by Anne Hooper (Dorling Kindersley). Updated version of the classic sex manual.

Massage Secrets for Lovers by Dr Andrew Stanway (Quadrille). Fully illustrated hands-on action.

Move Over Mrs Robinson by Wendy Salisbury and Maggi Russell (Robson Books). Guide to dating, mating and relating for women of a certain age.

My Secret Garden by Nancy Friday (Quartet Books). Women's sexual fantasies.

100 Astonishing Sex Tips (Cosmopolitan Series) by Lisa Sussman (Carlton Books). Top tips and tricks.

101 Nights of Tantric Sex by Cassandra Lorius (Thorsons). Tempting Tantra for naughty nights.

Orgasms: Over 100 Truly Explosive Tips (Cosmopolitan Series) by Lisa Sussman (Carlton Books). More orgasmic fun.

Sex Fantasies By Women for Women by Lisa Sussman (HarperCollins). Naughty sex fantasies.

Sexopedia by Anne Hooper (Dorling Kindersley). Illustrated guide to all aspects of your sex life.

Sex, Guys and Chocolate by Dr Pam Spurr (Robson Books). Guild to life's essentials.

Sinful Sex by Dr Pam Spurr (Robson Books). An unhibited guide to erotic pleasure.

Supersex by Tracy Cox (Dorling Kindersley). Illustrated sex-goddess tips and tricks.

The Ann Summers' Wild Guide To Sex and Loving by Siobhan Kelly (Ebury Press). Sex tips from the high street sex shop.

The Big O by Lou Paget (Piatkus). Orgasm tips for men and women.

The Good Girl's Guide to Bad Girl Sex by Barbara Keesling (Bantam Books). How to be a very bad girl in bed.

The Good Vibrations Guide to Sex by Cathy Winks and Ann Semans (Cleis Press). Sex guide from the founders of US sex store Good Vibrations.

The Joy of Sex by Dr Alex Comfort (Mitchell Beazley). Updated version of the classic seventies sex manual.

The Lazy Girl's Guide to Good Sex by Anita Naik (Piatkus). Be a lazy girl in bed and still have great sex.

The Multi-Orgasmic Couple by Mantak Chia (Thorsons). Taoist training for couples.

The Sex Book by Suzi Godson (Cassell Illustrated). Up-to-date guide to all aspects of sexuality.

The V Book by Dr Elizabeth Stewart and Paula Spenser (Piatkus). Vaginal health guide.

Urge: Hot Secrets For Great Sex by Dr Gabrielle Morrissey (Thorsons). Info-packed guide for great sex.